Tourism and the Experience Economy in the Digital Era

Behaviours and Platforms

Edited by Xiang Ying Mei

Routledge
Taylor & Francis Group
LONDON AND NEW YORK

Designed cover image: getty/Izzet Keribar

First published 2024
by Routledge
4 Park Square, Milton Park, Abingdon, Oxon OX14 4RN

and by Routledge
605 Third Avenue, New York, NY 10158

Routledge is an imprint of the Taylor & Francis Group, an informa business

British Library Cataloguing-in-Publication Data
A catalogue record for this book is available from the British Library

ISBN: 978-1-032-37211-2 (hbk)
ISBN: 978-1-032-37218-1 (pbk)
ISBN: 978-1-003-33592-4 (ebk)

DOI: 10.4324/9781003335924

Typeset in Times New Roman
by KnowledgeWorks Global Ltd.

Contents

Figures

Tables

Contributors

Sara Alonso-Muñoz PhD Student in Business Program at Rey Juan Carlos University. She is an Assistant Professor at Department of Business Administration (ADO), Applied Economics II, and Fundaments of Economic Analysis. Her research lines are focused on circular economy and sustainability in the tourism industry. Also, she studies supply chain management from an external capital perspective.

Pierre Benckendorff is an Associate Professor in the Tourism Cluster, Business School of the University of Queensland, Australia. He is an award-winning researcher specialising in visitor behaviour, technology-enhanced learning, and tourism. He has held several teaching and learning leadership positions at The University of Queensland and James Cook University in Australia.

Veronica Blumenthal is a senior researcher in tourism development at the Eastern Norway Research Institute at Inland Norway University of Applied Sciences. Blumenthal holds a PhD in tourism and her research interests revolve around experience design, consumer behaviour, tourism experiences, and destination development. Blumenthal has several years of international experience in the tourism industry and is an avid research communicator.

Monica A. Breiby is an Associate Professor at Inland School of Business and Social Sciences, Inland Norway University of Applied Sciences. Breiby has a PhD in nature-based tourism and aesthetic dimensions. Her main research topics are sustainable development, experience design, user behaviour, innovation processes, and destination management. Breiby is the manager of the Center for Tourism Research in Lillehammer.

Hui Min Choo is a Hospitality Business Graduate of the Singapore Institute of Technology's Class of 2021. She is currently dealing with procurements and logistics. Her research interests include digital marketing and consumer behaviour.

Saurabh Kumar Dixit, PhD, is a Professor and founding Head of the Department of Tourism and Hotel Management at North-Eastern Hill University, Shillong Meghalaya, India. His research interests include Consumer Behaviour, Gastronomic Tourism, Service Marketing, Experience Management, and Marketing in tourism contexts. He has 15 books to his credit and is an editorial board member and guest editor of many international journals.

Thor Håkon Engen graduated with a Bachelor in management and organisational development. He currently works in sales, logistics, and project management. His research interests include organisational management and service management.

Bjørnar Engh graduated with a Master of Science in Business Administration majoring in marketing management at Inland Norway University of Applied Sciences. He currently works as a business and industrial consultant at Trysil County. His research interest includes organisational management, service management, and marketing communication.

Birgitta Ericsson is a research professor at Eastern Norway Research Institute, Inland Norway University of Applied Sciences. Research topics include primarily regional economics and feasibility studies applied to issues such as second homes, cultural industries and events, tourist experiences, and tourism development in general. She is also in the operational management team for the Center for Tourism Research in Lillehammer, and affiliated projects.

Olga Gjerald, PhD, is an Associate Professor in Service Management, the University of Stavanger, Norway. She has broad research interests at the junction of leadership and service experience design and service co-creation. Her research focuses on service expectations; the mechanisms of immersion; shared leadership; managerial practices of co-creation; and service employees' basic assumptions. Gjerald is also affiliated with the UNESCO Chair on Leadership, Innovation, and Anticipation.

Rocío González-Sánchez, PhD in Business Organisation from Rey Juan Carlos University. She is an Associate Professor at the Department of Business Administration (ADO), Applied Economics II, and Fundaments of Economic Analysis. She is the author of several scientific articles in scientific journals with impact factor (JCR) and (SJR). She is currently developing lines of research related to sustainable development and new technologies in the tourism sector.

Elsie Vezemburuka Hindjou is a PhD candidate at the North-Eastern Hill University in the Department of Tourism and Hotel Management, India. She holds a Bachelor's (Honours) in Travel, Tourism and Hospitality Management, and a Master of Science in Tourism and Hospitality Management. Her research interest includes Gastronomic Tourism, Destination Branding, and Sustainable Tourism Development. She has seven years of university teaching experience.

Åse Storhaug Hole, Cand Scient., Norwegian School of Sports, MPA, University of Karlstad. She previously served as dean and director in the higher education sector. Other work experiences include teaching service innovation, organisational theory, management, and HRM and supervising master's and bachelor's theses. She is currently Professor Emerita at Inland Norway University of

Applied Sciences. Her research interest includes service innovation, service management, crisis management, and HRM.

Daria E. Jaremen – PhD, an Assistant Professor at the Faculty of Management of Wrocław University of Economics and Business, Poland. Her research interests are focused on tourism management, sustainable tourism, and tourist behaviour. She specialises in quality management and marketing research in tourism. Authors of the articles published in Tourism Economics, International Journal of Tourist Cities, Sustainability, Economies.

Deepti Jog is a faculty of marketing at the Department of Management Studies, Nalsar University, Hyderabad, India. She has a PhD from Goa Business School, Goa University. She has published research in the area of sustainability, tourism, and supply chain. Her recent research interests include tourism, tourism sustainability, and green consumption.

Ethilde Tulimuwo Kuwa is a Lecturer of Tourism Management at the Namibia University of Science and Technology. She holds a BTech degree in Tourism Management, a master's degree in Tourism and Hospitality Management, and MBA in International Business. Her research areas are eco-tourism and community-based tourism, heritage and cultural tourism, air transportation, and destination marketing. Ethilde has over 15 years of tourism and hospitality industry experience.

Terry Lantai is a PhD candidate at Inland Norway University of Applied Sciences. He is also an associate lecturer and course co-coordinator. Lantai graduated with a Bachelor of Tourism from Central Queensland University in 2004 and a Master of Science in Hotel and Hospitality Management at the University of Stavanger in 2016. His research interests include consumer behaviour, tourism management, entrepreneurship, and innovation in small businesses.

Kuan-Huei Lee is an Associate Professor in the Business, Communication, and Design Cluster at Singapore Institute of Technology. Lee received her bachelor's degree in Business Administration in Argentina, MBA from the University of Illinois at Urbana-Champaign in the US, and a PhD in Tourism Management from The University of Queensland. Her research interests include food tourism, organisation and management, and cross-cultural studies of tourist travelling behaviours.

Merethe Lerfald is a PhD-candidate at Eastern Norway Research Institute at Inland Norway University of Applied Sciences. Her field of interest is regional development and innovations in rural areas, particularly in relation to the tourism industry and the development of second homes, the regional economy, sharing economy, and research methodology.

Han Li is a PhD candidate in tourism management at the Faculty of Business, Economics, and Accountancy, University Malaysia Sabah, Malaysia. Her research explores how tourism destinations can improve the effectiveness of marketing through transmedia storytelling. Her research interests include sustainable tourism, rural tourism, small-scale tourism business development, and tourist behaviour.

Li Ling Lim is currently working as an Ambassador of Buzz of lyf one-north, who heads events and partnerships for the property. She was a Hospitality Business student from the Class of 2021 at the Singapore Institute of Technology. Her research interests include digital marketing, wellness tourism, and ecotourism.

Shasha Liu is a postdoctoral research fellow at Antai College of Economics and Management, Shanghai Jiao Tong University, China. Her research interests include decision-making, marketing, consumer behaviours, tourism technology, and tourist experiences.

Zi Bai Luo is a Professor of tourism management at the Chongqing Normal University, China. His research interests include regional tourism development and marketing, tourism planning, ecotourism, sustainable tourism, rural tourism, and tourism higher education.

Judith Mair is an Associate Professor in the Tourism Cluster, Business School of the University of Queensland, Australia. Her research interests include pro-environmental behaviour and resilience both in tourism and events; the impacts of events on community and society; consumer behaviour in events and tourism; the relationship between events and climate change; and business and major events.

Sonia Medina-Salgado, PhD in Business Administration, is currently an Associate Professor of Strategic Management at the Universidad Rey Juan Carlos. Her current research focuses mainly on social sustainability and circular economy in the tourism sector. She is the author and co-author of several book chapters and articles in scientific journals with impact factor (JCR) and (SJR) in corporate governance, sustainability, and circular economy.

Windy Kester Moe is a communication advisor at Eastern Norway Research Institute, Inland Norway University of Applied Sciences. Moe produces dissemination plans and content for websites and social media. In addition, she assists researchers with dissemination in the various phases of research projects. She has many years of experience as a reporter for various European news media.

Elżbieta Nawrocka – PhD, professor of Wrocław University of Economics and Business (Poland), at the Faculty of Management, also involved in business practice as an entrepreneur, a marketing manager, a sales office director, an expert in local development strategy, a coach at training in management, marketing, customer service. Her research interests are SE, tourist enterprise management, tourism economics, and local development.

Hogne Øian is an Associate Professor at Inland School of Business and Social Sciences, Inland Norway University of Applied Science. Øian has a PhD in social anthropology and has researched and published extensively on outdoor recreation, tourism, and in particular on nature-based tourism. His main research interests within these research fields are sustainability, the development of nature areas, planning, power relations, and equity.

Shu Jian Ong is a Hospitality Business graduate of the Singapore Institute of Technology's Class of 2021. Shu Jian received his bachelor's degree in Hospitality Business from the Singapore Institute of Technology. He is currently a Business Development Representative at EventX. His research interests include event tourism, digital marketing, and technology in tourism.

Yakup Kemal Özekici earned a PhD degree from the Tourism Management department at Gazi University and now works in the Tourism Faculty at Adıyaman University. His research interests and published articles involve the concepts of acculturation, cultural change, global culture, and restaurant management. He published articles in different journals such as the Journal of Vacation Marketing and the Journal of Hospitality and Tourism Insights.

Sofie Kjendlie Selvaag is a PhD candidate in the Ecology and Natural Resource Management program at the Norwegian University of Life Sciences. She is also a researcher at Norwegian Institute for Nature Research where she has mainly worked with visitor management in protected areas. Her main research interests include communication measures in outdoor recreation and transformations in sense of place.

Eunice Lioe Si Min obtained a bachelor's degree in Hospitality Business from the Singapore Institute of Technology in 2021. She is currently working in the e-commerce and entertainment industry. Her research interests include consumer behaviour, brand management, and marketing.

Jia Xuan Sim graduated with a bachelor's degree in Hospitality Business Management from Singapore Institute of Technology in 2021. She is currently working in the Learning and Development department at Mandarin Oriental, Singapore. Her research interest includes service quality, travel behaviour, and technology in tourism.

Kai Xin Tay is a PhD and a senior lecturer of tourism management at the Faculty of Business, Economics, and Accountancy, University Malaysia Sabah, Malaysia. Her main research interests are tourism planning, marketing in tourism, tourist behaviour, and sustainability practices.

María Torrejón-Ramos, Assistant Professor at Department of Business Administration (ADO), Applied Economics II, and Fundaments of Economics. PhD Student in Business Program at Rey Juan Carlos University. She obtained a master's degree in Tourism Marketing and a master's in Business Organisation. Her research focuses on aspects of sustainable tourism.

Lena Wistveen is a PhD candidate at Inland Norway University of Applied Sciences. She holds a bachelor's degree in history and a master's degree in science and technology studies from the Norwegian University of Science and Technology, where she also worked as a research assistant. Her research interests involve the social dimension of sustainability, nature-based tourism, socio-cultural impacts of tourism, social innovation in destinations, and co-creation of value.

Acknowledgements

The editor would like to express sincere gratitude to the authors who have contributed to the chapters of this edited book. This compendium would not have been possible without their research effort, creativity, involvement, and dedication. Deep thanks are extended to the reviewers, who have contributed with their time, knowledge, and expertise. Further thanks are extended to the Commission Editor, Faye Leerink, and Editorial Assistant, Prachi Priyanka, at Routledge as well as Ashraf Reza at KnowledgeWorks Global Ltd., for their support and guidance from the book proposal to the final publication of the manuscript. I would also like to acknowledge my family for the support and encouragement that have helped me push through the challenges and obstacles in bringing this work to fruition. Last but not least, I would like to thank my husband for his unwavering belief in me. His presence in my life has made all the difference.

Introduction

Encapsulating Experiences in the Experience Economy

Xiang Ying Mei (Editor)

The experience economy is understood as an economy, in which experiences rather than physical products or services provide economic value. The term experience economy was coined first by Pine and Gilmore in 'Welcome to the experience economy', published in Harvard Business Review in 1998, which was further expanded into a complete book with the notion that 'work is theatre and every business is a stage'. Since then, the interest and focus on staging and creating unique and memorable experiences have gained a solid foothold in both academia and relevant industries such as service and tourism, and marketing in general. Yeoman and McMahon-Beattie (2019) argue that the tourism philosophy is dominated by the experience economy. The experience economy is also where the concept of tourism experience is derived from. Experiences themselves have existed as long as human beings have existed, but it is the experience economy that truly puts the economic value in experiences. Such value can be created through memorable experiences that are tailored to tourists' needs (Pine & Gilmore, 1998). By treating work as a theatre stage where everyone involved has their roles to play, unique experiences can then be facilitated and staged (Pine & Gilmore, 1999) by using storytelling to trigger emotions and feelings. Much has changed and evolved since the term was first introduced, which was more rooted in examples primarily from the United States and a business/company viewpoint.

This section encapsulates experiences in the experience economy as an effort to set the 'scene' and direction for the rest of the edited book on how memorable experiences are facilitated while addressing how technology and digital tools come into play by facilitating such a process. It visits the development of the experience economy and highlights the discussion on tourism experiences. This is followed by considering the changes attributed to the digital era and the role played by technological development and digital tools in the 'new' experience economy. The chapter completes with a presentation of the purpose of the edited book along with a short explanation of the chapters and topics included in this compendium.

The Development of the Experience Economy

To capture the evolution of economic value from focusing on commodities to the experience economy, Pine and Gilmore provided a framework for the progression of economic value, which was later revised and reintroduced in updated publications

DOI: 10.4324/9781003335924-1

in Pine and Gilmore (2011) and Pine and Gilmore (2019). The framework illustrates the progression of economic value in four stages starting with stage 1 and commodities, *extracted* from nature such as coffee beans. Differentiation is not possible at this stage and thus prices are influenced by supply and demand. Stage 2 focuses on *making* and manufacturing physical products. Stage 3 is where services are dominated and this stage emphasises how products are *delivered* to consumers, before evolving to the experience economy and the *staging* of unique and memorable experiences in stage 4 (Pine & Gilmore, 1998). The future outlook points to a transformation in Stage 5, which is an economy where experiences are elevated from enjoyment at the time to contribute to *guiding* long-term personal transformation (Pine & Gilmore, 2011). This economy is further discussed in the concluding chapter of this edited book.

From a business point of view, the framework stresses how companies can gain a stronger competitive advantage by emphasising staging experiences rather than merely making goods and delivering services. Moreover, notions such as storytelling, the four realms of experiences, 'the sweet spot' etc. (Pine & Gilmore, 1998) are key concepts to understanding how memorable experiences are facilitated and staged. As experiences, stories have always been a part of human beings. They appeal to humans' demand for meaning in life and it is easier to remember intriguing stories that trigger emotions and feelings rather than factual information. Thus, creating unique stories through storytelling as a way to stage extraordinary experiences has become imperative in experience-based activities (Mei et al., 2020). Storytelling can be used by companies as a marketing tool to communicate to customers but it may also serve as a way where tourists can relive their experiences by telling and sharing their stories on social media. Storytelling can also be integrated into the four realms of experiences, consisting of entertainment, education, aesthetics, and escapism, which explain the type of customer experiences that are sought. Such four realms are also related to the level of participation from the customers with active participation on one end, passive participation on the opposite end on the horizontal axe, and absorption and immersion on each opposite side on the vertical axe (Oh et al., 2007). Absorption refers to the physical presence of the tourists and experiences are formed based on such presence, whereas immersion occurs when the individual lives the experience mentally (Ferrari, 2022). One cannot be active and passive at the same time nor can absorption and immersion exist simultaneously. The notion of 'the sweet spot' refers to a business providing a satisfying customer experience in all aspects (Pine & Gilmore, 1999). This is achieved when aspects of all four realms are gained. A business that can achieve this will be successful in meeting the needs of its customers. Such a view is also applicable to the tourism industry and tourism experiences (Oh et al., 2007).

Over the decades, tourism has transformed from long-travel mass tourism to short-travel small-scale experience-based tourism. Through this development, emphasis is placed on the co-creation of experiences where personal and meaningful experiences touch the tourists' emotions. Thus, in recent years, in addition to value co-creation and co-creation of tourism experience through service-dominant logic (SDL) (Mei, 2020), other concepts such as experience sharing through sharing economy and sustainable tourism experiences have become key notions in the integral experience economy research.

So What Are Tourism Experiences?

As discussed, while experiences are not something new, developing a sound definition has somewhat been challenging. Experiences are personal, interactive, and complex processes that involve emotions. It requires the active participation and immersion of the individual (Mei et al., 2020). However, as discussed in the previous section, the level of participation will vary depending on the experiences that are sought. Experiences are different from services in that they cannot be directly provided by a tourism operator, but the operator can create the conditions that allow the individual to have the best possible experience in response to the stimuli in their environment. The experience economy places great emphasis on emotions as memorable experiences can only be staged or created when emotions and feelings are involved. Like services, experiences are intangible and involve interactions between hosts and guests. The presence and actions of other individuals such as travel companions, family members and other tourists also contribute to the overall experience. This is because experiences are also considered social phenomena as they are influenced by the people that the individual is together with, in the given situation (Pine & Gilmore, 1999; Sundbo, 2020).

It is also too simplistic to think about tourism experiences as something that only occurs during the experience as experiences (and expectations) usually occur before the actual visit during the information search stage, during the visit and after when tourists return home and can reflect more on the experience. As argued, experiences have always been part of tourism, and as a service industry, the services and experiences are the central 'product' that the tourism industry offers. With the background that a destination is made up of various industries, and services, local actors make up the tourists' overall experience (Buhalis, 2000). These actors consist of taxi drivers, hoteliers and waiters, as well as services from the local attractions such as museums, theatres, beaches, amusement and parks. Close cooperation between various actors both in the public and private sectors is therefore required so that those who visit a destination have a positive and unique overall experience. Thus, it is crucial to consider tourism as part of a wider service ecosystem consisting of various stakeholders to develop the 'economy' in the experience economy. After all, the tourism industry does not exist isolated in a vacuum as development in the macro environment will also impact the development of the industry itself (Farrell & Twining-Ward, 2004). The nature of experiences and the experience economy will also naturally continue to evolve in the digital era.

The Experience Economy in the Digital Era

In the past few years, the development of technology has been fast pacing and phenomenal. The world has not turned back since the introduction of the Internet and the World Wide Web. It has revolutionised communication and information gathering leading to changes in consumer consumption and interaction. Such development has further led to the launch of smartphones and thereby social media, mobile apps, and various technological innovations such as self-service technologies (SSTs), the use of robots, augmented reality (AR) and virtual reality (VR).

Technological advancement has certainly fuelled peoples' need to seek hedonic and memorable experiences as well as the desire to showcase such experiences to the world through social media. The various stories and stream of experiences displayed on such platforms also serve as ways to satisfy tourism consumers' and especially young consumers' desire to seek recognition and acknowledgement as well as their narcissistic behaviour, which drives the need for uniqueness (Neave et al., 2020). For instance, Millennials (Gen Y) and Gen Z are both considered digital natives with distinct behaviours from previous generations (Priporas et al., 2017). While technology has not been the sole focus in previous book publications on the experience economy, the rapid advancement indicates that technology has become an integral part of the tourism industry and tourism experiences. Technology and various digital tools can certainly enable, manage and enhance tourism experiences. Digital tools within ICT (information and communication technology) can contribute to facilitating such development by easing the possibility of storytelling, sharing economy, co-creation and developing sustainable experiences.

The digital era also impacts the evolution of the experience economy leading to changes in consumer behaviour. These include (young) smart consumers who are competent and willing to participate in experience sharing (Chen et al., 2018) and hence challenge the traditional tourism consumption experiences and information sharing. However, the vast technological advancement is not without its challenges. Some tourism providers are yet to make full use of its possibilities and whilst the technology exists, the actual usage and implementation may be challenging as well its implications. Integrating technology in tourism operations may require long-term commitment, sufficient understanding of tourists' needs and behaviours and changes that need to be made in existing business models. Even though when digital tools are not directly adapted to business operations, it is necessary to understand the implications of such tools in facilitating tourism experiences. This includes for instance engagement and sharing of information, stories and experiences on social media such as online reviews, which is considered a form of electronic word-of-mouth (eWOM). It is thus important to realise that experiences are not only facilitated and created during the experience but also before and after as discussed above.

The Purpose of This Book

This edited book focuses on the 'new' experience in the experience economy or experience economy in the new technology and Internet area with topics that focus on digitalisation and new tools and platforms to frame and create unique experiences. Subsequently, it explores changes in consumer behaviour among various consumer groups. It also discusses storytelling concerning experiences in the digital era. Furthermore, it emphasises the 'economy' in the experience economy as an overarching approach to developing tourism-related industries in a service ecosystem consisting of various stakeholders. It is also important to understand the collaborative effort of various stakeholders in a destination to develop the 'economy' in the experience economy.

Contributors have provided insights on such topics in vast different economies consisting of both developed and developing regions/economies. It is assumed that different economic conditions have different growth opportunities. Therefore, different tourism activities and practices occurring in various economies are captured in this compiled compendium. While existing publications have provided significant contributions to the experience economy on an overall level, they are considered to be rather complex for students at the introductory level and tourism industry practitioners to grasp and comprehend. Much of this is attributed to the fact that they cover a range of creative industries beyond tourism industries, making much of the content difficult to relate to. Consequently, this edited book focuses exclusively on tourism-related industries due to such gaps at present by providing comprehensive discussions with their relevant cases and examples to explore the nature of the experience economy in tourism and destinations.

The edited book is divided into three parts. Part I: Understanding 'new' Tourist Behaviour with Chapter 1 focuses on Global Consumer Culture (GCC) and its repercussion on the modern tourism system. Chapter 2 explores how online reviews have changed tourist behaviour and its implication on tourism operators with the case study of The Tug Restaurant in Namibia. Chapter 3 discusses the motivations of millennials and the influence of social media in a Singaporean spa context. Following this, Chapter 4 illustrates the motives of tourists in participating in the sharing economy with Polish Uber uses as the case. Chapter 5 discusses the role of self-service technologies (SSTs) and their implications on tourist experiences. The chapter also highlights possible technology anxiety among tourists who belong to the elderly part of the population. Part II: Marketing Experiences in the Contemporary Experience Economy commences with Chapter 6 which seeks to explore value co-creation and reconsiders the nature of technology as an operand resource where the tourism ecosystem is revisited in this context. Chapter 7 explores storytelling as a marketing strategy using the case of the Love Ladder in Chongqing, China, followed by Chapter 8, which discusses user-generated content (UGC), social media and word-of-mouth and their significance in destination marketing. The last section of Part II, Chapter 9, examines the notion of immersion in virtual- and real-world experiencescape as a part of designing highly involving experiences. Part III: Technological Tools and Social Media in Conceptualising Experience Economy starts with Chapter 10 which explores Hospitality Micro Enterprises (MEs) during COVID-19 and how they integrate digital tools such as food delivery apps and mobile payment apps as part of service innovation to enhance customer experiences. Chapter 11 discusses the influence of social media in overcrowded destinations and the re-emergence of slow travel for Gen Z's using the examples of Lofoten, Norway, and Venice, Italy. Chapter 12 further investigates the role of smart tourism in developing smart tourism destinations with cases from Borneo Island. This is followed by Chapter 13 which investigates the role of Instagram in creating more sustainable tourism experiences where UGC is revisited in this context. Continuing on the discussion on sustainability, Chapter 14 disseminates the importance of a sustainable tourism experience and the role of technology using the case of the MOVELETUR project, a cross-border partnership between Spanish and Portuguese organisations to develop e-mobility on tourist routes. The edited book concludes with Chapter 15 which focuses on the future outlook of the experience economy in the tourism industry post-COVID-19 as well as evolving paradigms and trends. This chapter ends with suggestions for future research agendas.

References

Buhalis, D. (2000). Marketing the competitive destination of the future. *Tourism Management*, *21*(1), 97–116. https://doi.org/10.1016/S0261-5177(99)00095-3

Chen, T., Drennan, J., Andrews, L., & Hollebeek, L. D. (2018). User experience sharing. *European Journal of Marketing*, *52*(5/6), 1154–1184. 10.1108/EJM-05-2016-0298

Farrell, B. H., & Twining-Ward, L. (2004). Reconceptualizing tourism. *Annals of Tourism Research*, *31*(2), 274–295. https://doi.org/10.1016/j.annals.2003.12.002

Ferrari, S. (2022). Storytelling. In D. Buhalis (Ed.), *Encyclopedia of tourism management and marketing* (pp. 259–262). Edward Elgar Publishing.

Mei, X. Y. (2020). Co-creation of tourism experience through service dominant logic. In S. K. Dixit (Ed.), *The Routledge handbook of tourism experience management and marketing*. Routledge.

Mei, X. Y., Hågensen, A.-M. S., & Kristiansen, H. S. (2020). Storytelling through experiencescape: Creating unique stories and extraordinary experiences in farm tourism. *Tourism and Hospitality Research*, *20*(1), 93–104. https://doi.org/10.1177/1467358418813410

Neave, L., Tzemou, E., & Fastoso, F. (2020). Seeking attention versus seeking approval: How conspicuous consumption differs between grandiose and vulnerable narcissists. *Psychology & Marketing*, *37*(3), 418–427. https://doi.org/10.1002/mar.21308

Oh, H., Fiore, A. M., & Jeoung, M. (2007). Measuring experience economy concepts: Tourism applications. *Journal of Travel Research*, *46*(2), 119–132. https://doi.org/10.1177/0047287507304039

Pine, B. J., & Gilmore, J. H. (1998). Welcome to the experience economy. *Harvard Business Review*, *76*, 97–105.

Pine, B. J., & Gilmore, J. H. (1999). *The experience economy: Work is theatre & every business a stage*. Harvard Business Press.

Pine, B. J., & Gilmore, J. H. (2011). *The experience economy*: Updated *edition*. Harvard Business Press.

Pine, B. J., & Gilmore, J. H. (2019). *The experience economy, with a new preface by the authors: Competing for customer time, attention, and money*. Harvard Business Press.

Priporas, C.-V., Stylos, N., & Fotiadis, A. K. (2017). Generation Z consumers' expectations of interactions in smart retailing: A future agenda. Computers in Human Behavior, 77, 374–381.

Sundbo, J. (2020). Experiential dissonance. In *The Routledge handbook of tourism experience management and marketing* (pp. 238–245). Routledge.

Yeoman, I. S., & McMahon-Beattie, U. (2019). *The experience economy: Micro trends. Journal of Tourism Futures*, *5(*2), 114–119. https://doi.org/10.1108/JTF-05-2019-0042

Part I

Understanding 'New' Tourist Behaviour

1 Global Consumer Culture as a Socio-Cultural Antecedent behind Experience Economy and Its Repercussions on Modern Tourism System

Yakup Kemal Özekici

Introduction

In an ordinary economic system, offerings, commodities, goods, and services are external to the buyer. However, in the experience economy system, the experience produced offers the person engagement at different emotional, physical, intellectual, or spiritual levels (Pine & Gilmore, 1999 p. 99). The tourism system is thought to be leveraged by the democratisation of the experience economy (Oh et al., 2009). In this way, the societies' adoption of the experience economy has led to a revolutionary transformation in the production and consumption patterns of stakeholders in the tourism system, just as it has in almost all other sectors (Andreassen et al., 2017; Chang, 2018; Smidt-Jensen et al., 2009; Sundbo, 2009). More specifically, as a result of the permeation of narcissism in societies (Bučková, 2018; Westen, 1985) and the prominence of vanity and hedonism as factors influencing consumption (Gao et al., 2021), hedonic and narcissist needs of individuals are not met with leisure experience (Li & Chen, 2017; Shi et al., 2022). Beyond that, the satisfaction derived from these experiences is multiplied by sharing these experiences on social networking sites (SNSs) owing to vanity promulgation inside communities (Yao et al., 2021). This situation implies that SNS as a novel socialisation tool has brought about a new economic model, not merely a new communication style (Maschio, 2016). This issue has been discussed in extant literature (Debord, 2021), a niche branch of which posits, on the other hand, that the novel system adopted by the hospitality industry and the main components of product features within this industry are all the result of adopting a global consumer culture (GCC) (Özekici & Ünlüönen, 2019). In that context, the concepts of staged authenticity (Efthymiou, 2022; Krillova et al., 2017), commercialisation (Bao & Su, 2004), tourists seeking an authentic travel experience, and sharing this experience on SNS as a sign of superiority (Yao et al., 2021) have been regarded as intersection points among GCC, experience economy, and transformed travel experience. Thus, the modern tourism system can be regarded as an outcome of the interaction between the experience economy and GCC. The interaction between GCC and transformed tourist behaviour (Özekici & Ünlüönen, 2019), and the association between experience economy and transformed travel behaviour (Krillova et al., 2017) have been

DOI: 110.4324/9781003335924-3

examined in the literature. Nevertheless, there is a shortage of information on how the interaction among these three concepts takes place – if any at all. Therefore, the aim of this chapter is to evaluate the modern tourist behaviour and tourism system by taking GCC and the experience economy into consideration. Within the scope of tourism, it will be explained how travel has been adopted as a necessity as a result of the transformation of a survival-oriented viewpoint in societies. In addition, the travel-oriented outcomes of the paradigm difference brought to the societies by the experience economy will be explicated. Here, GCC will be examined in the context of experience economy with its transformative role in classical value components.

Experience Economy

Experience is described as 'events that engage individuals in a personal way' (Pine & Gilmore, 1999, p. 12). More specifically, economies are believed to develop in a process, the first stage of which prioritises commodities as a critical source of development. Goods and services as elements can be given an added value following commodities in later years. In previous decades, economies based on services as their leading sector were accepted to have paramount importance for development (Buera & Kaboski, 2012). Yet, the demand of societies for improved versions of the services has led to the upgrading of the latter, giving birth to the experience economy (Gilmore & Pine, 2002; Pine & Gilmore, 1988). From the consumers' standpoint, experience refers to encountering and consuming a memorable event in an enjoyable manner (Oh et al., 2009). That is, consumers now seek ways of storing unique experiences rather than owning a product, in this way increasing the attractiveness of having leisure. In terms of touristic activities, tourist experiences are believed to take place in four manners in proportion to the level of perceived experience at a given destination (Mehmetoglu & Engen, 2011). These are passive participation, active participation, absorption, and immersion. Accordingly, the more a tourist experience approaches an immersion level, the most likely he or she participates and involves in that touristic activity (Oh et al., 2009, pp. 120–121; Pine & Gilmore, 1999, p. 31).

Acculturation to the Global Consumer Culture (GCC)

The consumption culture is the mindset of emphasising an identity by displaying a purchased product (Baudrillard, 1998; Wearing et al., 2013). The worldwide penetration of this culture is based on the idea, which presupposes that mass consumption is a necessity for the survival of the mass production-oriented system. To operationalise the idea, the production mechanism of the industry has been transformed into a more monotonous pattern, and the free time and payment of workers have been increased as a consequence (Featherstone, 2007). Acculturation to GCC (AGCC) represents the intersection of two separate literature on these two concepts. For one, GCC is defined as a social order in which life relations, which become meaningful with symbolic and materialistic resources, are determined by the market (Arnould & Thompson, 2005, p. 869). This culture refers to prioritising consumption activities (Mady et al., 2011). Within AGCC, of which acculturation represents the second branch of the literature refers to an identity-oriented process of predisposing individuals to accept the value components of the GCC (Al-Issa & Dens, 2021). In this sense, the common point between these two concepts manifests itself as the positive attitude towards consuming the goods and services that symbolise GCC (Oswald, 1999, p. 303). GCC and acculturation have been addressed together by previous studies in the available literature (Berry, 2008; Jensen et al., 2011). Yet, the operationalisation of AGCC by means of such a merger was fulfilled by Cleveland and Laroche (2007)'s model.

AGCC as an Antecedent of Experience Economy

There are particular issues that reveal how the acculturation process of communities to the GCC paves the way for the diffusion of the experience economy. The first and most noteworthy point that makes GCC essential is the preliminary role of identity in consumption preferences. This is because consumption is regarded as a symbol for individuals to demonstrate their identities (Geertz, 1973; Giddens & Sutton, 2014). In this regard, the transformed structure of demand within societies – due to the fact that the present economic system transcended from extracting commodities to staging experiences (Pine & Gilmore, 1999) – stems from a shift in people's expectations. Put differently, as Featherstone (2007) argues, a majority of the people in communities within which a consuming culture is infused are focused on consuming rather than creating values or products; these are all signs and lifestyles based on consumption. Indeed, the popular ideas adopted by the Y and Z generations that defend 'living the moment or carpe diem' rather than 'saving for tomorrow' (Bryx et al., 2021) can be considered responsible for the predispositions of communities to demand having experiences (Bauman, 2001). The conversion refers to an identity-oriented change in societies (Czarnecka et al., 2020). A society in which the motivation is to prioritise consuming transforms the individuals' identities. Such identity transformation involves the altering of conventional symbols and lifestyles (Bauman, 2000; Giddens, 1991). Supported by media and marketing as agents of GCC (Appadurai, 1990; Berry, 2008; Wearing et al., 2013), this transformation process yielded narcissism and individualism to promulgate into communities, thereby prioritising consumption and joy (as opposed to production), rather than becoming altruistic, and craving ownership, especially for Y and Z generations (Bryx et al., 2021; UBS Insights, 2020) and western societies (Bauman, 2000). Hence, consuming particular objects and experiencing certain settings (e.g., visiting destinations) featured by GCC agents may induce narcissist tendencies and a sense of wanting to be superior. Consistent consumption and featuring individualistic specifications are infused by means of fulfilling self-actualisation (Baudrillard, 1998; Featherstone, 2007; Wearing et al., 2013). Along this path and within the context of the 21st century, SNSs are seen to play the most prominent role in this transformation process and the infusion of both GCC and the idea of enjoying life across the globe (Dey et al., 2020; Kızılcık & Taştan, 2019; Ozer, 2019). In support of this notion, Dutot and Lichy (2019) found that SNS and social influence enhance the GCC concept even further. Therefore, consumption is favoured over production with an increased sense of wanting to experience as it serves as a motivation to enjoy life or the moment.

Consequences of Spreading AGCC

The inducing role of GCC on societies is reflected in different ways across communities. For instance, the exposure of some Muslim communities to the global market has resulted in a consuming culture to further spread inside the community through media and marketing channels. As a result, for some individuals, veiling by women, practised with the motivation to hide one's hair from men's views, has been recoded into a consuming activity that mediates the meeting experience patterns (Elaziz & Kurt, 2017). What is more, Muslim minorities are observed to celebrate birthday parties and the new year (Khan et al., 2018). Organisations have become widespread owing to demands for such activities across societies (Pine & Gilmore, 2013). In the ongoing process, democratised leisure activities across the globe and modern tourism systems are thought to be the outcomes of such permeation.

Modern Tourism System and Tourist Behaviour in Association with the GCC

The transformative effect of acculturating into the GCC on leading communities towards individualism has become a leading factor that lays the ground for the experience economy to blossom. This is how the process functions: The consumer culture permeates through mass media, marketing, and advertisement. The development of technology has led to the replacement of mass media with the SNS. Through SNS, commercial culture is adopted. In this context, individualism (Maschio, 2016) and narcissist value components are entrenched in the identity of societies (Bučková, 2018; Westen, 1985). This is made possible by consumers sharing content via Web 2.0, through which the social milieu is encouraged to create and share content demonstrating that the individual is unique and superior to her/his counterparts. As a result, the content increases in the form of retweets and likings, and the sense of self-importance is elevated, thus increasing the individual's narcissism level (Andreassen et al., 2017). This process has resulted in a changed consumption pattern. The relevant pattern includes having memorable experiences as well as publicising these experiences on SNS (Gao et al., 2021; Yao et al., 2021). Obviously, there are some tourism system-oriented consequences as well upon the meeting of the GCC and experience economy. The first of these consequences involves tourist motivation.

Tourist Motivation

As highlighted in Figure 1.1, the joint point that settles the relation between GCC and experience economy in the context of the tourism system is tourist motivation since the latter is key to determining the experience type and degree (Oh et al., 2009; Prentice et al., 1998). In turn, the demanded experience volume determines the production and design of destination settings (Driver et al., 1987). Consequently, such design

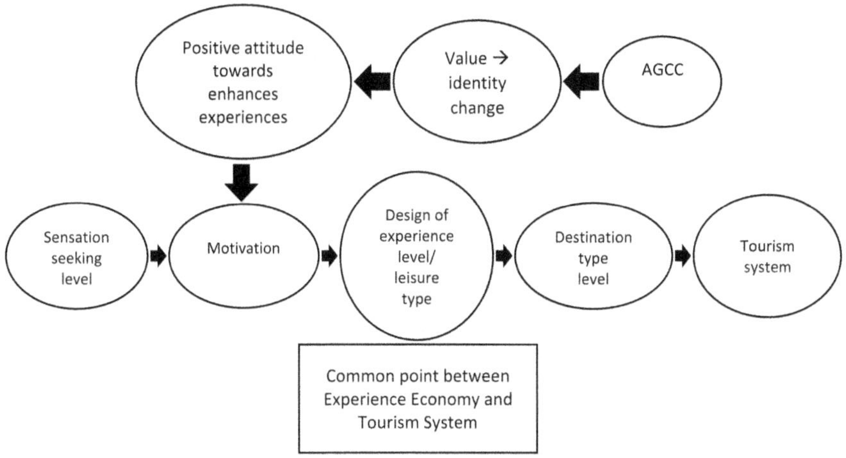

Figure 1.1 Tourist motivation as a junction point in the relation of the AGCC and experience economy

Source: Author's own work

determines the way the entire tourism system is formed. Activity motivation plays a determinative role in the relationship between experience economy and AGCC since such an activity is conducted to experience and immerse in a given setting. Tourists employ this setting and its component atmosphere to further their level of experience (Richards, 2001). The determinative point is the sensation-seeking level of tourists as it explains why they prefer a certain type of motivation over others. This is because, in the realms that make up the experience, as the experience level increases, so does the level of immersion by the individual. The most advanced level of these realms reflected in activity is escapism. This is based on which the individual participates in the holiday with the motivation to get away from the daily routine. Thus, the level of immersion increases with active participation. In contrast, entertainment is known to be the lowest in terms of experience-oriented activity types among passive participation and absorption realms. In this context, as the experience level increases, so does the immersion level and the extent to which the tourist affects the activity mechanism (Mehmetoglu & Engen, 2011; Oh et al., 2009; Wearing et al., 2013). According to the tourist typology of Cohen (1972), the increasing level of sensation-seeking from organised mass tourists to drifters determines the type of activities and the motivation of tourists. At this point, the permeation of acculturation into GCC features becomes a central point because AGCC affects the transformation of the value components of identities and redesigns the leisure motivation structure of communities in terms of leisure preference. Next, such redesigned values recode identity and determine both the attitude and the behaviour towards any object (Stern, 2000; Tajfel, 1974). Consequently, they redesign leisure motivation (Campbell, 2007).

- Thought point: How do you think your leisure motivation is shaped by the social milieu? Consider how you make your holiday decisions and consider the posts of your milieu on SNS platforms and delineate them.

Transforming the Role of the AGCC on Tourist Motivation

The producing role of consumer culture in designing leisure motivations has been addressed in the literature (Dimanche & Samdahl, 1994). The producing mechanism is believed to work on the relation sequence as follows: Adopting GCC results in a conversion within the value components of individuals (Debord, 2021) – those moving away from the collective value components as a result of adopting the value components of the consuming culture, which encourages consumption and prioritises the 'self'. Next, individuals might not make careful budget planning for later initiatives (Czarnecka et al., 2020) and rather prefer to use (all) their resources to have present experiences, such as luxury consumption, which is regarded as a component of identity (Al-Issa & Dens, 2021). This is because the 'self' is positioned at the centre due to the permeation of hedonism, narcissism (Bučková, 2018; Westen, 1985), and vanity (Yao et al., 2021). As a result, the main motivation for consumption is turned into satisfying the 'self'. In this manner, individuals tend to experience memorable leisure activities as much as their budget affords. Along this line, sharing relevant experiences on SNS platforms amplifies the role of relevant factors and strengthens them. This refers to a mutual relation among personality-oriented factors (narcissism, hedonism), cultural factors (AGCC), and technological advancements (SNS). As a result, a tourism system is redesigned by GCC promulgating within societies through modernisation, 'McDisneynisation', commoditisation, homogenisation, and infusion into urban culture (Özekici & Ünlüönen, 2019, p. 509). A novel tourism system, as such, can provide staged experience, memorable acts (Oh et al., 2009; Sternberg, 1997), and attractive sharing contexts. Transformations in the demand structure also led to the transformation of tourism supply mechanisms (Cohen et al., 2014). The tourism system can be regarded as a point where the experience economy mentality is embedded prevalently. Entertainment constitutes an archaic part of the tourism system, and it has been prevalent as an outcome of the experience economy (Pine & Gilmore, 1999). Almost all activities at destinations are designed to materialise experiences in emotional, cognitive, or perceptual contexts, laying the foundations of tourism in accordance. Yet, the interrelation among the experience economy, AGCC, and the conditions under which the current tourism system operates has other implications as well.

Further Spread of GCC – Cases and Examples

Recreation Coupled with Gastronomy and Culinary Arts

A reflection of the interrelation among these three concepts is clearly visible within the tourism sector; to begin with, the conversion of certain parts of the conventional tourism system as a result of a further spread of GCC and experience economy has made recreation gain even more notoriety than before. As a matter of fact, it has been emphasised in the literature that the recreation sector is seen as even more important by tourists (Elaziz & Kurt, 2017). For example, the experience derived from animation activities contributes to tourist satisfaction even in hotels with certain restrictions, such as halal or religiously acceptable measures (Kalaycı, 2022). In this sense, the necessity of transcending to the next level of meeting consumer experience expectancy with the available products is evident in gastronomy and culinary arts. As themed restaurants are seen as places where experience overtakes food consumption (Pine & Gilmore, 1999), the demand for a higher level of experience better paves the way for gastronomy. This sector, by definition, includes the ultimate satisfaction of visual senses in comparison to conventional food presentation views, and the reason for its further emergence is the probability of recall. The reason behind this is that providing an experience with visual and auditory senses along with the sense of taste enables that experience to be registered in the memory more strongly (Dolcos & Cabeza, 2002; Oh et al., 2009). As such, gastronomy as a field has been integrated with visual arts (Hegarty & O'Mahony, 2001) and engineering (Aguilera, 2017) to provide an aesthetic experience and cater for more senses than taste. Next, an aesthetic experience includes enjoying the scenery and the surrounding beauty and atmosphere in a setting. In this respect, the subject of experiencing the atmosphere and service environment in restaurants places an individual in a position to choose to immerse in a given experience as opposed to passive participation (Oh et al., 2009; Pine & Gilmore, 1999; Sulek & Hensley, 2004). The emergence of themed restaurants is an indicator of the spread of the experience economy model because of the motivation to share the experience in these restaurants on social media platforms.

Adopting GCC as an identity results in the transformation of both value and consumption tendencies of Muslim communities. Being concrete evidence as a reflection of the issue regarding the role of cultural transformation towards demanding experience-oriented service, a wide range of themed halal restaurants and cafes can be given. In Singapore for instance, cafes themed of New York City (named Overrice), serving artisanal cakes (The Fabulous Baker Boy), or western style fusion (Citrus By The Pool, Good Bites) gained popularity. All these cafes operate in halal concept in terms of ingredients which are permissible to eat based on Islamic rules (Lee, 2022). However, although edible materials and characteristics are in accordance with Islamic principles, style and atmosphere, as well as experience sensed within the place evoke western metropole cities. This heightens the centre of GCC (Featherstone, 2007) by being far away from cultural values of local culture.

Staged Authenticity in Experiences

Individuals participate in leisure activities to experience an authentic atmosphere by escaping the lifestyle established in cities, where almost every point, norm, and value components are standardised (MacLeod, 2004). However, they try to meet these needs with a standardised leisure choice, the conditions of which as well as what will happen at each stage of the leisure activity are predetermined (Özekici & Ünlüönen, 2019). These travel-oriented demand patterns of societies have revealed staged authenticity in destinations (MacCannell, 1973). Staged authenticity is the result of operationalising the calculability and predictability criteria, which are included in the McDonalidisation principles used in the spread of GCC within the tourism system (Özekici & Ünlüönen, 2019; Yolal, 2016). Furthermore, it can be said that authenticity is developed as a result of the experience economy. Indeed, Pine and Gilmore (1999) suggested that businesses should move towards producing 'staged' products that offer a memorable experience from a product-oriented perspective (Oh et al., 2009). Accordingly, localities are redesigned as they are envisioned in the minds of tourists to meet the experience-seeking motivation.

Masai tours are one of the most distinct examples that represent a staged authenticity issue. Masai is an indigenous tribe in Africa. Kenya and Northern Tanzania are known as their habitat, and they are believed to sustain a lifestyle persisting for centuries without any transformation. As seen from online marketing activities (Tripadvisor, 2023), a regular tourist experiences a tribe lifestyle when taking a trip towards Masai tribe. However, various parts of these experiences are actually designed consciously to get tourist immersed (Blinston, 2015). Although modern Masai people transformed their life standards such as adopting technology or changing dressing style, what village homes visitors observe during trips are products of tourism system, designed to elevate the experience level of tourist immersion and not resided in fact (Blinston, 2015; Stainton, 2020). Also, Masai warrior dancing equipped with spears is staged by a local private organisation to meet the expectations of tourists formed as a result of marketing activities during pre-trip period (Bruner, 2001).

New Generational Tourist Behaviour

The interrelation referred to earlier also includes the deviation of tourist behaviour (Pearce, 2011) at destinations. It has been emphasised in the literature that tourist behaviour can even be abnormal (Uriely et al., 2011). This is also a clue to the impact of the consuming culture on the tourism system along with the experience economy. This is because, as a result of the expanding narcissism with the consuming culture and adopting value components such as vanity and materialism (Bučková, 2018; Westen, 1985; Yao et al., 2021), the individual can demand consuming patterns that she/he cannot perform in the milieu (Uriely et al., 2011). However, according to social control theory, the social prohibition created by the milieu prevents the emergence of these behaviours (Gelles, 1983). Therefore, the escape motivation developed as a component of the experience economy may emerge as a result of adopting the consuming culture. Supporting the relevant idea, previous studies have linked the rising deviant leisure behaviours with consumer culture (McDonald et al., 2008 cited in Wearing et al., 2013). The augmentation may lead the new generational tourist behaviour to be regarded as normal (Uriely et al., 2011). Thereafter, this behaviour may be accepted as a part of norms within the tourism system at particular destinations (Özekici & Ünlüönen, 2022). Similar results have been obtained for deviant tourist behaviours at some destinations (Uriely et al., 2011).

Eastern Mediterranean countries such as Tunisia, Egypt, and Lebanon have succeeded to create the image as mass tourism destinations, which rose with the image studies that started at the end of the 1970s. At the end of the 1980s, with the abandonment of the Keynesian Fordism understanding, the consuming pattern and demand structure of societies changed. Individuals tended increasingly to prefer experience-based leisure activities. Thus, a trend towards alternative tourism types emerged. The situation degenerated the tourism system of countries of interests based on mass tourism and contribution of tourism revenue to this economy was shrunk as a result of leisure services with lower prices to keep competitive power (Hazbun, 2008). This situation in turn brought about culture tourism to be highly demanded and heritage sites presented within the country were redesigned to supply touristic services. However, numerous tourists with the motivation to experience the setting engendered an unexpected result. Culture tourism centred on the monuments was observed to be abused by those who aimed to immortalising their experience in an immoral way. Ancient Egyptian monuments are one of the most distinct examples for this. Some visitors are believed to carve their names on these monuments (Egyptianstreets, 2014). For instance, a Chinese tourist was seen to carve his name on 3500-year-old Luxor temple. Also, a Danish tourist has climbed the Great Pyramid of Giza to entertain and to be photographed at the point (Fang, 2022).

The Emergence of Alternative Tourism Types

Individuals who think that they can prove their originality and uniqueness in society by adopting certain consumption patterns are mainly the reason behind mass production, which is the legacy of the industrial revolution (Ewen, 2001; Wearing et al., 2013). This situation may have triggered the development of alternative tourism types as well as the realisation of a tailor-made marketing process. As a result, alternative tourism types, such as film tourism, are preferred by tourists to immerse in certain emotions experienced while watching a film in a deeper manner (Beeton, 2005). In line with this, owing to the GCC permeating, the desire to have leisure experiences by Islamic communities has blossomed (Elaziz & Kurt, 2017), leading to the redesigning of mass tourism there in accordance with Islamic principles and halal tourism.

Turkish film series were observed to be prevalently preferred in Middle-Eastern countries. The series such as Ertuğrul Resurrection elevated image of Türkiye as well as Turkish destinations which in turn boosted a number of Middle-Eastern tourists over 200 per cent in a particularly short period (Akarsu et al., 2015; Busby et al., 2013). Albeit impacted from Turkish TV series, these tourists predominantly choose to experience atmosphere of the destination in accordance with their standards in terms of not only for facilities but also for values, norms, and religion practices. Turkish hospitality industry has had a considerable development for mass tourism which was structured to serve European tourists. This demand from the Middle East has re-structured the working process of stakeholders in alignment with expectations and service standards specific to Middle-Eastern tourists. Thus, accommodations with halal concepts spread along Turkish destinations. However, operators of these establishments have based their operation procedures on mass tourism principles. This includes offering open buffet, staying obliged to schedule of leisure, and designing recreation program (Elaziz & Kurt, 2017) similar to their other classic all-inclusive hotels. In recent years, the number of accommodation establishments with halal concepts in Türkiye has amplified with a such effect that Turkish halal tourism industry is regarded best from Muslim tourist perspective over the world (Comcec, 2016, p. 107).

In sum, as seen in Figure 1.2, at the heart of the experience, economy lies the motivation to live a memorable experience. In this respect, SNS platforms play a catalysing role in the permeation of GCC across the globe. Content creation and sharing on these platforms are encouraged to augment social and financial resources, which in turn form a spillover effect for the social milieu of the individual and manipulate their demand patterns (Stephen, 2016). Supporting this notion, Yao et al. (2021) found in an experiment that the perceived awareness of travel experience contents appearing on SNS platforms can urge decision-making to travel for social milieu. Thus, it can be predicted that the more of a community adopts GCC, the more individuals tend to allocate resources for experiencing leisure, to change their demand pattern for travel and leisure experiences, and to share such experiences on SNS platforms to fulfil self-actualisation and to increase social capital.

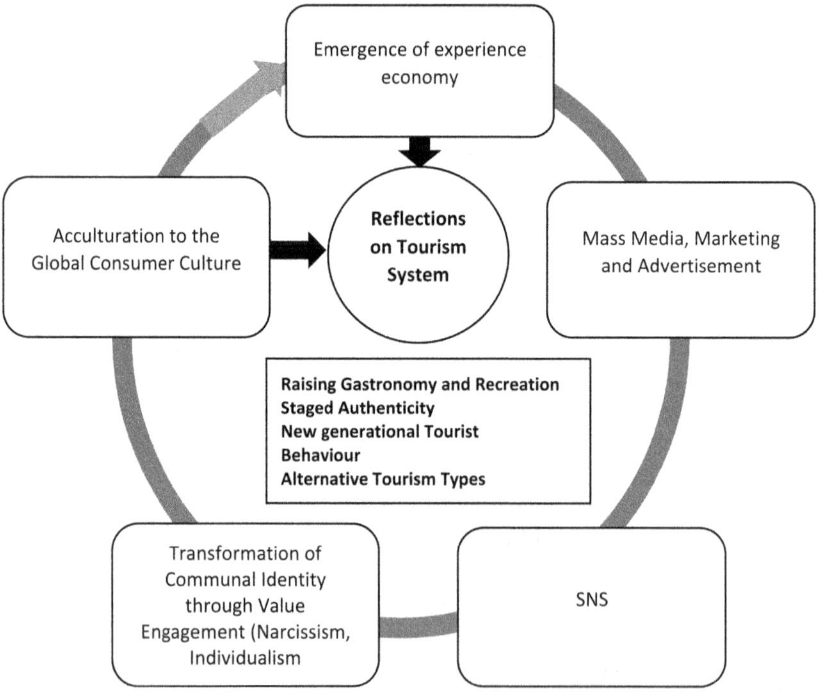

Figure 1.2 Process of the emergence of the experience economy and its reflections on the tourism system

Source: Author's own work

In turn, this tendency may predispose them to adopt a 'carpe diem' approach to life and to have as much experience as possible. Thus, it can be pointed out that the GCC-SNS relation may lead to a further spreading of an experience economy system and transform the present tourism system.

- Thought point: Do you think that other than the experiences mentioned in this chapter, AGCC enables other alternative leisure experiences to be demanded by individuals? Please explain through resorting to your memory and past experiences.

Conclusion

This chapter discussed how a permeated GCC today has enabled the experience economy to emerge, democratised the tourism system across the world, and helped design a modern tourism system. In this context, a belief has been instilled within communities that self-actualisation can be achieved through the creation of a specific self-identity. This identity has the characteristics of consuming the most spectacular brands and having experiences that attract attention and admiration. In this process, first of all, instead of collectivism, individualistic values are infused through mass media as SNSs are widely used. Thus, value components such as narcissism, individualism, and hedonism are integrated into the identity of societies by means of instilling that consuming certain products and experiencing certain activities enable individuals to make a name for themselves in different circles (Ewen, 2001; Wearing et al., 2013). In this way, the idea of filling leisure time with a consumption-oriented lifestyle has become the new motto of societies (Baudrillard, 1998; Bauman, 2000; Featherstone, 2007; Giddens, 1991). The necessity of making mass production sustainable for this purpose is the core antecedent behind the causation sequence. SNS tools play a role in spreading the consumer culture around the world. In the past, shopping malls were seen as hubs of the consuming culture; today, it is visible that SNSs have replaced shopping malls as hubs (Wearing et al., 2013).

Living the moment, or 'carpe diem' and enjoyment have turned into the consumption motivation adopted by the new generation. However, the SNSs created by the developing technology have been adopted as a platform where individuals can show themselves at any time. As a result, living the memorable experience and publicising it have become important motivations. This, beyond the change of mass marketing, has led to the redesigning of mass tourism, the restructuring of the classic service scape, the formation of alternative tourism types, and the repositioning of the well-known service systems with an experience-oriented approach. Although the profound impact of the interrelation between GCC and experience economy has been hypothesised in the world of phenomenology, the examination of experience economy within the scope of tourist experience is still at its conceptual level. It is a fact of today that the cases in question have not been empirically examined (Oh et al., 2009). For this reason, future research will take the developing experience economy literature a step further by examining the experience economy within the scope of tourism and on the basis of sociology theories. In addition, the role that the GCC plays in the travel budget planning behaviour (Czarnecka et al., 2020) remains unaddressed especially for the behavioural patterns of Muslim tourists, making it another direction for future studies.

Further Questions

- How can the tourism system be further developed by considering the effects of AGCC and experience economy?
- How can the effects of AGCC and experience economy further impact the modern tourism system?
- What can be other research agendas involving concepts of identity, consuming culture, acculturation, and experience economy?

Further Readings

Bauman, Z. (2013). *Liquid modernity*. John Wiley & Sons.
Debord, G. (2021). *Society of the spectacle*. Bread and Circuses Publishing, Cambridge.
Quadri-Felitti, D., & Fiore, A. M. (2012). Experience economy constructs as a framework for understanding wine tourism. *Journal of Vacation Marketing, 18*(1), 3–15. https://doi.org/10.1177/1356766711432
Semrad, K. J., & Rivera, M. (2018). Advancing the 5E's in festival experience for the Gen Y framework in the context of eWOM. *Journal of Destination Marketing & Management, 7*, 58–67. https://doi.org/10.1016/j.jdmm.2016.08.003

References

Aguilera, J. M. (2017). The emergence of gastronomic engineering. *Innovative Food Science & Emerging Technologies, 41*, 277–283. https://doi.org/10.1016/j.ifset.2017.03.017
Akarsu, T., Pantea, F., Charles, D., & Melewar, T. C. (2015). *The changing destination image of Turkey through the effect of Turkish television series* [Conference session]. Conference Proceedings of the 5th International Colloquium on Place Brand Management: Governance and branding of destinations: Relationships and impacts for successful brands. International Colloquium on Place Brand Management. Italy, pp. 52–53.
Al-Issa, N., & Dens, N. (2021). How do religiosity and acculturation to the global consumer culture drive the perceived value of luxury? A study in Kuwait. *Journal of Islamic Marketing*, Vol (Ahead of print). https://doi.org/10.1108/JIMA-03-2021-0080
Andreassen, C. S., Pallesen, S., & Griffiths, M. D. (2017). The relationship between addictive use of social media, narcissism, and self-esteem: Findings from a large national survey. *Addictive Behaviors, 64*, 287–293. https://doi.org/10.1016/j.addbeh.2016.03.006
Appadurai, A. (1990). Disjuncture and difference in the global economy. *Theory, Culture & Society, 7*(2/3), 295–310. https://doi.org/10.1177/026327690007002017
Arnould, E. J., & Thompson, C. J. (2005). Consumer culture theory (CCT): Twenty years of research. *Journal of Consumer Research, 31*(4), 868–882. https://doi.org/10.1086/426626
Bao, J., & Su, X. (2004). Studies on tourism commercialization in historic towns. *Acta Geographica Sinica, 59*(3), 427–436. https://doi.org/10.11821/xb200403013
Baudrillard, J. (1998). *The consumer society: Myths & structures* (C. Turner, Trans.). Sage.
Bauman, Z. (2000). *Liquid modernity*. Polity Press.

Bauman, Z. (2001). Consuming life. *Journal of Consumer Culture, 1*(1), 9–29. https://doi.org/10.1177/146954050100100 1

Beeton, S. (2005). *Film-induced tourism.* Channel View Publications.

Berry, J. W. (2008). Globalisation and acculturation. *International Journal of Intercultural Relations, 32*(4), 328–336. https://doi.org/10.1016/j.ijintrel.2008.04.001

Blinston, L. K. (2015). *Staging "authenticity" in cultural tourism of the Maasai* [Bachelor's thesis, Utrecht University, Utrecht].

Bruner, E. M. (2001). The Masai and the Lion King: Authenticity, nationalism, and globalization in African tourism. *American Ethnologist, 28*(4), 881–908. https://doi.org/10.1525/ae.2001.28.4.881

Bryx, M., Sobieraj, J., Metelski, D., & Rudzka, I. (2021). Buying vs. renting a home in view of young adults in Poland. *Land, 10*(11), 1–31. https://doi.org/10.3390/land10111183

Bučková, Z. (2018). The culture of narcissism in the postmodern society. *Marketing Identity, 6*(1/2), 37–49.

Buera, F. J., & Kaboski, J. P. (2012). The rise of the service economy. *American Economic Review, 102*(6), 2540–2569. https://doi.org/10.1257/aer.102.6.2540

Busby, G., Ergul, M., & Eng, J. (2013). Film tourism and the lead actor: An exploratory study of the influence on destination image and branding. *Anatolia, 24*(3), 395–404. https://doi.org/10.1080/13032917.2013.783874

Campbell, J. (2007). *Adolescent identity development: The relationship with leisure lifestyle and motivation* [Unpublished dissertation, University of Waterloo].

Chang, S. (2018). Experience economy in hospitality and tourism: Gain and loss values for service and experience. *Tourism Management, 64*, 55–63. https://doi.org/10.1016/j.tourman.2017.08.004

Cleveland, M., & Laroche, M. (2007). Acculturation to the global consumer culture: Scale development and research paradigm. *Journal of Business Research, 60*(3), 249–259. https://doi.org/10.1016/j.jbusres.2006.11.006

Cohen, E. (1972). Toward a sociology of international tourism. *Social Research, 39*(1), 164–182.

Cohen, S. A., Prayag, G., & Moital, M. (2014). Consumer behavior in tourism: Concepts, influences and opportunities. *Current Issues in Tourism, 17*(10), 872–909. https://doi.org/10.1080/13683500.2013.850064

Comcec. (2016). *Muslim friendly tourism: Developing and marketing MFT products and services in the OIC member countries.* Standing Committee for Economic and Commercial Cooperation of the Organization of Islamic Cooperation (COMCEC) Coordination Office, 28.

Czarnecka, B., Schivinski, B., & Keles, S. (2020). How values of individualism and collectivism influence impulsive buying and money budgeting: The mediating role of acculturation to global consumer culture. *Journal of Consumer Behavior, 19*(5), 505–522. https://doi.org/10.1002/cb.1833.

Debord, G. (2021). *The society of the spectacle.* Unredacted Word.

Dey, B. L., Yen, D., & Samuel, L. (2020). Digital consumer culture and digital acculturation. *International Journal of Information Management, 51*, 102057. https://doi.org/10.1016/j.ijinfomgt.2019.102057

Dimanche, F., & Samdahl, D. (1994). Leisure as symbolic consumption: A conceptualization and prospectus for future research. *Leisure Sciences, 16*(2), 119–129.

Dolcos, F., & Cabeza, R. (2002). Event-related potentials of emotional memory: Encoding pleasant, unpleasant, and neutral pictures. *Cognitive, Affective, & Behavioral Neuroscience, 2*(3), 252–263.

Driver, B. L., Brown, P. J., Stankey, G. H., & Gregoire, T. G. (1987). The ROS planning system: Evolution, basic concepts, and research needed. *Leisure Sciences*, *9*(3), 201–212. https://doi.org/10.1080/01490408709512160

Dutot, V., & Lichy, J. (2019). The role of social media in accelerating the process of acculturation to the global consumer culture: An empirical analysis. *International Journal of Technology and Human Interaction (IJTHI*, *15*(1), 65–84. https://doi.org/10.4018/IJTHI.2019010105

Efthymiou, L. (2022). Staged authenticity. In *Encyclopedia of tourism management and marketing* (pp. 1–3). Edward Elgar Publishing. https://doi.org/10.4337/9781800377486.staged.authenticity

Egyptianstreets. (2014). *Graffiti defaces 2000 year old monuments in Luxor*. Retrieved January 21, 2023, from https://egyptianstreets.com/2014/01/20/graffiti-defaces-2000-year-old-monuments-in-luxor/

Elaziz, M. F., & Kurt, A. (2017). Religiosity, consumerism and halal tourism: A study of seaside tourism organizations in Turkey. *Tourism: An International Interdisciplinary Journal*, *65*(1), 115–128.

Ewen, S. (2001). *Captains of consciousness: Advertising and the social roots of consumer culture* (Rev ed.). Basic Books.

Fang, C. (2022). *Tourists behaving badly around the world*. Retrieved January 22, 2023, from https://blog.cheapism.com/worst-tourists/

Featherstone, M. (2007). *Consumer culture and postmodernism* (2nd ed.). Sage. https://doi.org/10.4135/9781446212424

Gao, L., Mei, Y., Yang, X., Zhao, C., & Li, D. (2021). Vanity and food waste: Empirical evidence from China. *Journal of Consumer Affair*, *55*(4), 1211–1225. https://doi.org/10.1111/joca.12369

Geertz, C. (1973). *The interpretation of cultures* (Vol. 5019). Basic books.

Gelles, R. J. (1983). An exchange/social control theory. In D. Finkelhor, R. J. Gelles, G. T. Hotaling, & M. A. Straus (Eds.), *The dark side of families: Current family violence research* (pp. 151–165). Sage Publications.

Giddens, A. (1991). *Modernity and self-identity: Self and society in the late modern age*. Stanford University Press.

Giddens, A., & Sutton, P. W. (2014). *Essential concepts in sociology*. John Wiley & Sons.

Gilmore, H. J., & Pine, B. J. (2002). *The experience IS the marketing*. Brown Herron Publishing.

Hazbun, W. (2008). *Beaches, ruins, resorts. the politics of tourism in the Arab world*. University of Minnesota Press.

Hegarty, J. A., & O'Mahony, G. B. (2001). Gastronomy: A phenomenon of cultural expressionism and an aesthetic for living. *International Journal of Hospitality Management*, *20*(1), 3–13. https://doi.org/10.1016/S0278-4319(00)00028-1

Jensen, L. A., Arnett, J. J., & McKenzie, J. (2011). Globalization and cultural identity. In S. Schwartz, K. Luyckx, & V. Vignoles (Eds.), *Handbook of identity theory and research* (pp. 285–301). Springer. https://doi.org/10.1007/978-1-4419-7988-9_13

Kalaycı, C. (2022). *Helal konseptli otellerde sunulan animasyon hizmetlerinin müşteri memnuniyetine etkisi* [Unpublished dissertation, Kastamonu University].

Khan, A., Lindridge, A., & Pusaksrikit, T. (2018). Why some South Asian Muslims celebrate Christmas: Introducing 'acculturation trade-offs'. *Journal of Business Research*, *82*, 290–299. https://doi.org/10.1016/j.jbusres.2017.07.023

Kızılcık, O., & Taştan, H. (2019). Mağara Turizminin Motivasyon Faktörlerinin Belirlenmesi: Karaca Mağarasi Örneği. *Çukurova Üniversitesi Sosyal Bilimler Enstitüsü Dergisi*, *28*(3), 240–251. https://doi.org/10.35379/cusosbil.648466

Krillova, K., Lehto, X. Y., & Cai, L. (2017). Existential authenticity and anxiety as outcomes: The tourist in the experience economy. *International Journal of Tourism Research*, *19*(1), 13–26. https://doi.org/10.1002/jtr.2080

Lee, M. (2022). *17 Stylish halal & Muslim-owned cafes in Singapore to check out*. Retrieved January 17, 2023, from https://www.womensweekly.com.sg/gallery/food/stylish-halal-cafes-in-singapore/

Li, T., & Chen, Y. (2017). The destructive power of money and vanity in deviant tourist behavior. *Tourism Management*, *61*, 152–160. https://doi.org/10.1016/j.tourman.2017.02.001

MacCannell, D. (1973). Staged authenticity: Arrangements of social space in tourist settings. *American Journal of Sociology*, *79*(3), 589–603.

MacLeod, D. V. L. (2004). *Tourism, globalization and cultural change: An island community perspective*. Channel View Publications. https://doi.org/10.21832/9781873150733

Mady, T., Cherrier, H., Lee, D., & Rahman, K. (2011). Can sentiment toward advertising explain materialism and vanity in the globalization era? Evidence from Dubai. *Journal of Global Marketing*, *24*(5), 453–472. https://doi.org/10.1080/08911762.2011.634328

Maschio, T. J. (2016). Culture, desire and consumer culture in America in the new age of social media. *Qualitative Market Research: An International Journal*, *19*(4), 416–425. https://doi.org/10.1108/QMR-04-2016-0038

Mehmetoglu, M., & Engen, M. (2011). Pine and Gilmore's concept of experience economy and its dimensions: An empirical examination in tourism. *Journal of Quality Assurance in Hospitality & Tourism*, *12*(4), 237–255. https://doi.org/10.1080/1528008X.2011.541847

Oh, H., Fiore, A. M., & Jeoung, M. (2007). Measuring experience economy concepts: Tourism applications. *Journal of Travel Research*, *46*(2), 119–132. https://doi.org/10.1177/0047287507304039

Oswald, L. R. (1999). Culture swapping: Consumption and the ethnogenesis of middle-class Haitian immigrants. *Journal of Consumer Research*, *25*(4), 303–318. https://doi.org/10.1086/209541

Özekici, Y. K., & Ünlüönen, K. (2019). Bir Küresel Tüketim Kültürü Aracı: Turizm. *Sosyal, Beşeri ve İdari Bilimler Dergisi*, *2*(7), 508–524. https://doi.org/10.26677/TR1010.2019.196

Özekici, Y. K., & Ünlüönen, K. (2022). Problematic customer behaviors and their triggers: The perspective of restaurant employees. *Journal of Hospitality and Tourism Insights*, *5*(3), 663–686. https://doi.org/10.1108/JHTI-12-2020-0244

Ozer, S. (2019). Towards a psychology of cultural globalisation: A sense of self in a changing world. *Psychology and Developing Societies*, *31*(1), 162–186. https://doi.org/10.1177/0971333618819279

Pearce, P. L. (2011). *Tourist behavior and the contemporary world*. Channel View Publications.

Pine, B. J., & Gilmore, J. H. (1988). Welcome to the experience economy. *Harvard Business Review*, July-August, 1–21.

Pine, B. J., II, & Gilmore, J. H. (1999). *The experience economy: Work is theatre & every business a stage*. Harvard Business School Press.

Pine, B. J., & Gilmore, J. H. (2013). The experience economy: Past, present and future. In J. Sunbo & F. Sorensen (Eds.), *Handbook on the experience economy* (pp. 21–44). Edward Elgar Publishing.

Prentice, R. C., Witt, S. F., & Hamer, C. (1998). Tourism as experience: The case of heritage parks. *Annals of Tourism Research*, *25*(1), 1–24. https://doi.org/10.1016/S0160-7383(98)00084-X

Richards, G. (2001). The experience industry and the creation of attractions. In G. Richards (Ed.), *Cultural attractions and European tourism* (pp. 55–69). CABI Publishing. https://doi.org/10.1079/9780851994406.005

Shi, D., Yi, B., Shi, F., & Satta, S. (2022). Motivation configuration of bluxury tourism behavior: An FsQCA application. *Cornell Hospitality Quarterly*, *63*(1), 33–47. https://doi.org/10.1177/19389655211014472

Smidt-Jensen, S., Skytt, C. B., & Winther, L. (2009). The geography of the experience economy in Denmark: Employment change and location dynamics in attendance-based experience industries. *European Planning Studies*, *17*(6), 847–862. https://doi.org/10.1080/09654310902793994

Stainton, H. (2020). *The truth about your tour to the Maasi tribe*. Retrieved January 20, 2023, from https://tourismteacher.com/maasai-tribe-tour

Stephen, A. T. (2016). The role of digital and social media marketing in consumer behavior. *Current Opinión in Psychology*, *10*, 17–21. https://doi.org/10.1016/j.copsyc.2015.10.016

Stern, P. (2000). Toward a coherent theory of environmentally significant behavior. *Journal of Social Issues*, *56*(3), 407–424. https://doi.org/10.1111/0022-4537.00175

Sternberg, E. (1997). The iconography of the tourism experience. *Annals of Tourism Research*, *24*(4), 951–969. https://doi.org/10.1016/S0160-7383(97)00053-4

Sulek, J. M., & Hensley, R. L. (2004). The relative importance of food, atmosphere, and fairness of wait: The case of a full-service restaurant. *Cornell Hotel and Restaurant Administration Quarterly*, *45*(3), 235–247. https://doi.org/10.1177/0010880404265

Sundbo, J. (2009). Innovation in the experience economy: A taxonomy of innovation organizations. *The Service Industries Journal*, *29*(4), 431–455. https://doi.org/10.1080/02642060802283139

Tajfel, H. (1974). Social identity and intergroup behaviour. *Social Science Information*, *13*(2), 65–93. https://doi.org/10.1177/053901847401300204

Tripadvisor. (2023). *Masai village tour*. Retrieved January 19, 2023, from https://www.tripadvisor.com/AttractionProductReview-g297913-d18845279-Masai_Village_Tour-Arusha_Arusha_Region.html

UBS Insights. (2020 September 16). *What does the future of happiness look like?*. Retrieved June 1, 2022, from https://www.ubs.com/global/en/wealth-management/insights/chief-investment-office/investment-opportunities/investing-in-the-future/2020/future-of-humans-happiness.html

Uriely, N., Ram, Y., & Malach-Pines, A. (2011). Psychoanalytic sociology of deviant tourist behavior. *Annals of Tourism Research*, *38*(3), 1051–1069. https://doi.org/10.1016/j.annals.2011.01.014

Wearing, S. L., McDonald, M., & Wearing, M. (2013). Consumer culture, the mobilization of the narcissistic self and adolescent deviant leisure. *Leisure Studies*, *32*(4), 367–381. https://doi.org/10.1080/02614367.2012.668557

Westen, D. (1985). *Self and society: Narcissism, collectivism, and the development of morals*. Cambridge University Press.

Yao, Y., Jia, G., & Hou, Y. (2021). Impulsive travel intention induced by sharing conspicuous travel experience on social media: A moderated mediation analysis. *Journal of Hospitality and Tourism Management*, *49*, 431–438. https://doi.org/10.1016/j.jhtm.2021.10.012

Yolal, M. (2016). Authenticity, commodification, and McDonaldization of tourism experiences in the context of cultural tourism. In M. Sotiriadis & D. Gursoy (Eds.), *The handbook of managing and marketing tourism experiences* (pp. 217–233). Emerald Group Publishing Limited.

2 Online Reviews, a Restaurant's Foe or Pal?

The Tug Restaurant, Swakopmund

Elsie Vezemburuka Hindjou, Ethilde Tulimuwo Kuwa, and Saurabh Kumar Dixit

Introduction

The 21st century has witnessed the significant influence of the Internet on consumer behaviour, affecting awareness of products, purchase behaviour, opinions, and evaluation of products (Mangold & Faulds, 2009). The Internet and social media growth have become of great interest to both the marketer and the consumer (Rosario et al., 2016). This has revolutionised how people acquire and share information and how consumers communicate and socialise (Salleh et al., 2016). The Internet advancement resulted in various virtual platforms such as social media. Wang et al. (2020, p. 1) defined *social media* as 'an online social networking platform' that attracts billions of users worldwide and represents a virtual place where people 'connect and communicate with others'.

Consequently, social media enables consumers to share their purchasing experiences through electronic word of mouth (eWOM) to create a reliable source for other consumers (Gretzel & Yoo, 2013; Tran, 2015;). Online reviews, a form of eWOM, are a source of information influencing consumer decision-making (Dixit, 2017; van Lohuizen & Trujillo-Barrera, 2020; Zhao et al., 2019), about where to dine, and retrieving valuable information from other customers regarding a particular restaurant. Therefore, online reviews are vital for consumers seeking reliable information about a service or product. Online review platforms have transformed the usual interaction from traditional-offline communication to online-instant communication (Clow & Baack, 2018). It is noted that the main sources of restaurant image are promotion and advertising, opinion of others/WOM (friends, family, and travellers), and media (TV, magazines, newspapers, books, the Internet, and travel guides); (Dixit, 2017; Govers et al., 2007). Consequently, the restaurant environment has become more complex due to the multitude of these intermediaries. As such, restaurants are faced with the challenge of shared food opinions in a constant consumer experience co-creation process (Dossena et al., 2021). Thus, the need to study online reviews vis-a-vis restaurants is relevant.

The primary objective of this chapter was to examine online reviews as an antecedent for restaurant promotion. The chapter discusses the significance of online reviews for restaurants as well as the significance of online reviews' credibility. Additionally, the chapter explores the dining experience in relation to eWOM.

DOI: 10.4324/9781003335924-4

It examines whether online reviews are a foe or a pal of the restaurant by analysing the consumer buying decision as a result of positive reviews.

Online Reviews

The Significance of Online Reviews

The innovative service of social media platforms has various benefits, such as enabling customers to look for information about a restaurant of choice anytime and anywhere using technological devices. The previous sentiment is shared by Göral and Tokay (2015), who state that online reviews are an essential reference when making inferences and evaluations. Customers generally ask family and friends, and if they cannot find answers, they turn to online reviews whose primary goal is to reduce the risk associated with a service or product (Göral & Tokay, 2015). Furthermore, when browsing the review platforms during the buying decision-making process, the customer can choose a restaurant that suits their selection criteria (Parikh et al., 2017). In other words, they control the information they seek since virtual platforms are user-driven and non-linear (O'Connor, 2008). In addition to *risk reduction*, Parikh et al. (2017) indicate other reasons why customers seek online reviews, including

- *Search time reduction*: when presented with a plethora of options and information, consumers find it challenging to sort through them. Thus, building a review platform lowers search costs and aids customers in swiftly and simply finding information about restaurants.
- *Buyer's remorse:* consulting reviews lessen the likelihood that a customer will regret forking over a substantial chunk of money for a dining-out experience.
- *Group influence:* this is significant because, even if a person has not eaten at a particular restaurant, their perceptions and actions may be influenced by what their peers say about it.

Therefore, online reviews are more important than ever and significantly influence customer eating-out decisions (Tucker et al., 2017). Despite its significant impact, little research has been done on eWOM in the context of restaurants (van Lohuizen & Trujillo-Barrera, 2020). Studies on online restaurant reviews are now relevant, given that a typical visitor spends about a third of their travel expenses on food-related purchases (Chaney & Ryan, 2012; Dixit, 2019; Economic Research Service [ERS/USDA], 2019).

Additionally, online reviews as a source of information are considered more convincing to people who seek this same product or service and help to reduce the intangibility factor (Zhang et al., 2010). The nature of restaurant offerings, that is, the inability to examine prior to purchase, means that the potential customers' need to rely on the opinions of those who purchased before them will continue to grow. Because of the intangibility nature of the restaurant services, customers feel that they are risky to purchase; thus, consumers tend to depend on interpersonal reviews on eWOM (Lewis & Chambers, 2000; Ruiz-Mafe et al., 2020). Huifeng et al. (2020) state that consumers view online reviews as more credible sources; as opposed to information provided by the firm, which might be viewed with scepticism and possible disbelief (Park & Nicolau, 2015). Hence, online reviews are seen as more independent and unbiased (Meuter et al., 2013). Consequently, customers become less dependent on the producers' information (Tang, 2017). As such, opinions shared on e-platforms are valuable because they allow consumers to share and discuss their experiences with other consumers who have the same interests (Vásquez & Chik, 2015). Consequently, customers are more than ever bound to encounter a mixture of positive and negative opinions about the same product or service (He & Bond, 2015). That is to say, different opinions about a similar restaurant due to dissimilar or similar tastes and preferences could be observed too.

Customers today are more active online than ever; before, during, and after interactions with service providers, such as restaurants, create large masses of information about their activities and experiences (Berthon et al., 2015; Wuenderlich et al., 2015). Furthermore, the management of the online image is crucial in attracting tourists, especially international visitors, who tend not to have any previous experience in the region (Lund et al., 2018). Therefore, online reviews continue to be an important e-tool that restaurants can use to identify the satisfaction determinants and make improvements and investments which could bring them a competitive advantage.

- Thought point: Can you think of a time when you posted about your dining experience online? What did it feel like? In what context was your review (positive or negative)? What factors about your dining experience prompted you to post about it?

The Importance of the Credibility of Online Reviews

The credibility of online reviews is a critical factor for the customer. Credibility is viewed as the extent to which one perceives information provided as unbiased, believable, accurate, or factual (Qiu et al., 2012). When an individual perceives online reviews as highly informative and credible, he/she will consider those opinions in their purchasing decision (Cheung et al., 2008). However, given the lack of empirical research on how consumers assess the reliability of online reviews, credibility is one crucial element of online reviews, as a lack of it affects the reliability of that platform (Thomas et al., 2019). In the same vein, Thomas et al. (2019) indicate that consumer online purchase intentions are motivated by factors that are based on completeness, argument quality and the qualities of online reviews, peripheral cues, product and service ratings, website reputation, and accuracy. The findings above reinforce that customer perceived value is a significant determinant of customer satisfaction, and customer satisfaction, once published on social media, is a significant predictor of the restaurant's image and buying decision.

Furthermore, online reviews influence restaurant branding, reputation, acquisition, and retention programs (Rosario et al., 2016). However, at times the credibility of online reviews is questioned, mainly because some firms offer incentives to consumers for writing positive online reviews. Paid reviews, however, reduce the availability of objective information and damage the credibility of the reviews (Pentina et al., 2018). Restaurants that are customer-oriented will focus on providing memorable experiences and encourage customers to share their genuine opinions, providing them with an opportunity to improve. In contrast, those concerned about high customer influx will continue to offer incentives for positive reviews, with some creating fake reviews and defaming their competitors. Consequently, these restaurants rob themselves of an opportunity to improve and perhaps a chance to build loyalty. Similarly, such restaurants affect the business of their competitors. Despite the growing suspicion about online review manipulation, the need to seek out information is an essential mentality for potential customers globally (Tang, 2017). Therefore, the need to understand the effects of online reviews; and to manage digital platforms in the experience economy persists.

- Thought point: Can you think of a time when you referred to online reviews to choose a dining location? What did it feel like reading the different reviews on your intended dining location? Did you finally make a decision based on the reviews you read? Which factors in the reviews made you think they were credible?

The Dining Experience vis-à-vis eWOM

Scholars have studied online reviews concerning restaurants from different perspectives; review valence (van Lohuizen & Trujillo-Barrera, 2020), restaurant review website attributes (Brewer, 2017), online reviews' effects on visit intentions (Aureliano-Silva et al., 2021; Park et al., 2021), drivers of eWOM (Liu et al., 2018), and on the economic value of online reviews (Chunhua et al., 2015). Additionally, several meta-studies (Rosario et al., 2016; van Lohuizen & Trujillo-Barrera, 2020; You et al., 2015) have confirmed that consumer review valence and volume on a product have positive impacts on sales. However, despite the extensive research on online reviews and their significance in the tourism and hospitality industry, research on the impact of online reviews on the dining experience remains fragmented. Consumers go to express their satisfaction through content that they post online on travel-promoting sites, tourist blogs, and videos (Gunasekar et al., 2021), similarly their dissatisfaction too. The sentiment above is supported by Li et al. (2020) and Teviana et al. (2017) who argue that tourists' satisfaction encourages them to be loyal to a destination by making them re-visit and recommend it to others. Satisfactory restaurant experiences may trigger positive eWOM (Zhao et al., 2012), whereas dissatisfactory dining experiences may trigger adverse reviews. Consequently, by reading restaurant reviews, consumers learn about previous diners' overall eating experiences, including the calibre of the cuisine and service (Gunden, 2017). Hence, customer satisfaction has an overriding role in restaurant sustainability (Kim et al., 2009) and restaurants must monitor and improve customer satisfaction through excellent dining experiences so much so because restaurant experience is significantly related to customer satisfaction (Choo et al., 2016).

Consumers once they have a positive experience with the restaurant, they feel that writing positively about the company gives the company something in return while sharing their positive experience. Additionally, customers believe that sharing their contentment or discontentment with others will aid others in their buying decision-making. However, the level of novelty and authenticity sought by each diner is, in fact, disparate. Accordingly, the development of food experiences should start with the needs of the individual to result in diner satisfaction, a memorable visit, and a positive recommendation.

- Thought point: Can you think of a time when you went dining out? What were the specific needs you wanted satisfied? Were those needs satisfied as a result of your dining experience? Did the experience prompt you to recommend or not recommend the restaurant?

Case Study of The Tug Restaurant in Namibia

The Tug is a restaurant with a locally sourced and richly diverse menu situated at A. Schad Promenade, Molen Road Jetty Area in Swakopmund (a coastal tourism hub), in the Erongo region, Namibia. The Tug prides itself in selecting only top grades of export fish and meat together with fruit and vegetables specifically hydroponically grown for them in the Swakopmund Desert. The restaurant was designed and built around the original oil-fired Daniel Hugo Tugboat (where it gets its name from). Not only is it located on the shoreline of Swakopmund with unforgettable panoramic views of the Atlantic Ocean but has also welcomed over 3 million guests in the last 27 years. The Tug is rated 4.5/5 on TripAdvisor and has the highest number of reviews in Swakopmund, 3138, at the time of this study (August 2022). This study adopted netnography in the form of non-participant observation and is based on online reviews published on the travel site TripAdvisor (www.tripadvisor.com) in regard to The Tug Restaurant. This approach was taken to avoid influencing the reviews in any way, for the reviews to be as natural as possible (Kozinets, 2010). Furthermore, the passive netnographic approach applied in this study supports a high personal and social distance between researchers and bloggers (Arsal et al., 2010). Kozinets (2010, p. 89) offers six criteria when selecting sites for netnographic research: they should be 'relevant, active, interactive, substantial, heterogeneous, and data-rich'. TripAdvisor, one of the largest travel community sites providing customer-to-customer communication, was chosen because it offers a large range of communities and options to specify search criteria.

The first step in this study was to select the databases from which to retrieve data. The data retrieved from TripAdvisor was conducted on 23rd to 25th July 2022, so the researcher became acquainted with the background of the case and starts to form initial impressions around the reviews, it was then repeated on 6th August 2022, to include new reviews and to have a greater pool of reviews. Second, keywords for data screening were identified. The keywords used to identify the reviews were; Recommend, A Must, and Worth a Visit; a total of 332 reviews containing the keywords were retrieved and analysed.

Online Reviews as an Antecedent for Restaurant Promotion

Of the 332 reviews, 18 (5%) did not recommend the restaurant as a result of a bad experience; however, 314 (95%) were positive marketing of the restaurant, the results are presented in Figure 2.1.

The reviews revealed that diners with higher levels of satisfaction with The Tug are willing to give more positive recommendations. In other words, they would be promoting the restaurant in their online reviews. It is evident that the level of satisfaction experienced influences the recommendation or non-recommendation of an establishment. Below are a few narratives expressing positive promotion of The Tug:

> [....] Our table had a picture of both seafood and beef, with all the meals being delicious. Would highly recommend a visit for anyone visiting Swakopmund.
>
> [....] The food overall was excellent. Would definitely recommend the Tug if you want good food and a wonderful dining experience.
>
> [....] provided excellent service with a good knowledge of wines and attention to detail. We enjoyed a delicious meal while enjoying the sun setting into the sea. Highly recommend this restaurant.
>
> Recommended by our guesthouse owner and well worth a visit. It is very popular so booking before you arrive in Swakopmund is advisable. Food very good.

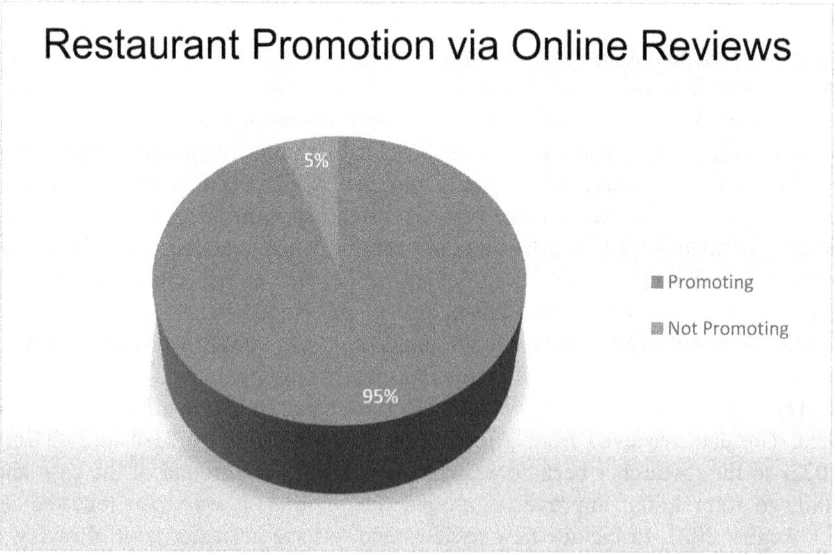

Figure 2.1 Restaurant promotion

Source: Authors' own work

[....] We had Kingklip with vegetables and rice and the Springbok Medaillons and after tasting it, we have to say: the hype is more than well deserved! The service was good and this was one of the best meals we had in Namibia and if you are in Swakopmund, The Tug is a MUST!

[....]Good selection of wines with availability of buy by the glass or bottle. Service was excellent as well. I suggest it as a must do if you are in Swakopmund.

The word cloud above (Figure 2.2) shows phrases that were used to describe visitors' experiences at The Tug. A positive recommendation is a result of a good experience with a given restaurant; according to the positive reviews, The Tug has done well to create positive experiences for its clientele. The following phrases were used to express recommendations for The Tug; highly recommend, worth a visit, definitely recommend, and cannot recommend enough; used to promote the restaurant.

The findings show that only 5% of the reviews were posted as negative marketing regarding The Tug Restaurant. Studies indicate that reading negative reviews has a more significant impact on attitude towards the product than positive reviews in comparison to neutral reviews or no reviews (Floh et al., 2013), decreasing the restaurant's potential and future sales. The above narrative was not the case with The Tug; the study found a high number of positive reviews and recommendations that continue to be posted on TripAdvisor even after the negative few. The study also found that when the positive promotion outweighs the negative promotion, the adverse effects are minimal, as more promotion continued to pour in, in the

Figure 2.2 Word cloud: Visitors' experiences

Source: Authors' own work

case of The Tug. Nonetheless, below are the few narratives that represent negative marketing of The Tug:

> Paid a fortune to dine in the restaurant, ordered the goat cheese and the big platter of seafood to share, and got sick before I made it out of the restaurant. [....] The service was terribly slow, and for African prices the food was extremely expensive. Definitely, I don't recommend. [...] bad food and service - avoid!
>
> What can I say except this is probably one of the most disappointing restaurant experiences to date in Namibia. [....] Waited ages for the bill, I took charge in the end... No charge for any of the mains but a terrible night and it spoiled our evening out. Tourist trap is too polite, charging over-the-top high-end prices for an extremely poor experience. I should have learnt from my first experience and never returned. Not recommend. For the same price, you can eat at the Ocean Cellar which is top-notch.
>
> We were very excited for this place, craving some fish. We ordered the seafood extravaganza, overall very bready taste to the fish. Service was excellent and the view was nice. So 3 out of... Wouldn't recommend to friends.
>
> Good views of the ocean from the restaurant/bar. Was there for lunch. Calamari was nothing special, the tarter sauce with it was awful, honestly. It tasted somewhat sour and smelled off. [....] I would not recommend eating there, at least not the calamari.

The reviews revealed that incredible experiences leading to satisfaction would prompt the customer to share their experiences via online reviews and recommend The Tug. This will enhance the restaurant's image as a place that offers excellent experiences. However, poor service or service failure and poor or lousy food quality will result in dissatisfaction, which will prompt various responses, including complaining, negative word-of-mouth, and decisions not to repurchase.

Online Reviews' Influence on Buying Decisions

Recommendations from friends, relatives, acquaintances, and even total strangers (eWOM) have become one of the main factors that mitigate perceived risk when deciding to travel. Although food tourism-related activities are products of experience and cannot be evaluated prior to their consumption, consumers tend to rely more on the recommendations and views of others. eWOM communication has been shown as the most influential and predominant information resource in developing a restaurant's image. The narratives below show that positive local food experiences play a role in influencing buying decisions:

> The views of the ocean and sunset are really nice. The food we ordered was tasty but somehow I expected something even more awesome (based on reviews). Wine list is very good. All in all, it was an enjoyable dinner.

> We booked a table online before arriving in Swakopmund based on the reviews and the menu. We had a lovely table in what I guess was the old tug bridge/captains area with a view over the town rather than the sea but not a problem. We were served quickly and efficiently. Food was excellent and very well-priced. [....]
>
> We booked The Tug based on reviews we read on TA. We were very lucky to get a reservation and as it was a Saturday we were thrilled to get an intimate window table where we could watch the waves crash upon the jetty. Taking on our waiter's recommendation we opted for The Tug platter. It was delicious and we were able to try fish we had never heard of such as angel fish and kingklip. It was simply delicious... so fresh, no gimmicks just good food. [....]
>
> We booked a table for dinner at The Tug based on TripAdvisor reviews. The oysters to begin with were huge and so fresh. We had the seafood platter for main course, it says it serves 1 on the menu, but more like 1.5 or even 2. It was delicious, especially the mussels cooked in a sauce, the calamari was melted in your mouth and the prawns were equally good. [....]
>
> We went to The Tug based on TripAdvisor reviews and were sorely disappointed. OK we live in SF where the seafood is outstanding, but we expected no less from this restaurant. Food: The food is mediocre at best. [....] The food was not up to expectations at all. [....] Overall we wished we had eaten somewhere else. This must be a very popular place with the locals, with little attention paid to tourists. Very disappointing!!
>
> [....] The lunch menu was more extensive than I expected, and reasonably priced considering the quality of food, creative location, service, and atmosphere. At the recommendation of other reviewers, I had the catch of the day and was not disappointed.[....]

eWoM is considered one of the most important sources of information at the point of purchase due to the inability to examine tourism products before purchase. According to Litvin et al. (2008), WOM has a powerful impact on customers' actions. Therefore, this study deemed it necessary to determine if online reviews are a pal or foe, in that how they influence buying decisions. Though the study found that only a handful of diners indicated that their buying decision was due to previous positive reviews posted, the narratives above indicate that positive recommendations indeed impact The Tug's customers' purchase decisions. It should also be noted that both positive and negative online reviews leverage customers' decision-making processes (Yang et al., 2018). Furthermore, the study also found that other diners go there based on recommendations from their tour guides, friends, and accommodation hosts. This shows how powerful the impact of WOM is on buying decisions. Additionally, customers who base their buying decision on positive reviews come with great expectations compared to those who do not; this leaves the restaurant with a colossal responsibility of living up to those expectations if not exceeding them.

Conclusion

Customer satisfaction plays a crucial role as consumers are prone to share their experiences or encounters based on their interactions with the product or service provider. As indicated previously, the need to understand the impact of online reviews is a part of managing digital platforms in the experience economy. The case study in this chapter shows that positive reviews influence service and product buying decisions. Visitors to The Tug share their food and food-related experiences via eWOM, and eWOM acts as a marketing tool for the restaurant (Prawannarat, 2017). As a result, consumers who are intrigued by positive reviews have more expectations than those not. Thus, dining establishments should maximise this opportunity by providing unique and memorable experiences that visitors cannot stop talking about and will act as a basis for potential customers' buying decisions. Restaurant owners and managers must also be aware that user-generated eWOM messages are a rich data source that influences potential customers' buying intentions. Therefore, understanding and improving those elements impacting customer satisfaction can increase their business.

The findings recommend that organisation owners such as restaurants aim for a holistic understanding of service dimensions that create memorable experiences for diners; this is critical to increasing diners' satisfaction (Dixit, 2020; Pizam & Tasci, 2019). Furthermore, managers must take actions to foster credible reviews such as offering awards and/or privileged status to those indicating factors influencing their buying intentions/decisions such as friends, tour-guide, hosts, previous reviews, and family.

While the study has its implications, it has its limitations as well. First, the data examined herein includes one case study; however, different conclusions might be derived for different restaurants. Thus, comparing different types of restaurant reviews would be interesting. The present study makes several proposals for future research. Second, the study has its findings based on reviews with the identified keywords only (recommend, a must, worth a visit); reviews using other phrases (such as: eat there; don't bother going there) to promote or not promote the restaurant were not included, as such the results cannot be generalised. Therefore, future studies should collect empirical data and online reviews to strengthen the findings. Lastly, the question of how customers assess the reliability of online reviews remains unanswered. Hence, future research can address this issue by conducting a cross-sectional survey of diners to study the above.

Further Questions

- How can online reviews be further used as effective marketing tools for restaurants to boost revenues and sustainable operations?
- How can negative online reviews be handled and whether openly addressing negative reviews can benefit restaurants?

- Which key elements of the dining experience influence customer satisfaction or dissatisfaction?
- What further measures should restaurants consider to encourage diners' online interaction and credible reviews?

Further Readings

Gunden N. (2017). *How online reviews influence consumer restaurant selection* [Master dissertation, University of South Florida]. https://digitalcommons.usf.edu/etd/6707/

Jeong, E., & Jang, S. (2011). Restaurant experiences triggering positive electronic word-of-mouth (eWoM) motivations. *International Journal of Hospitality Management, 30*(2), 356–366.

Riesco, J. L. (2010). *Restaurant marketing strategies*. Riesco Consulting Inc.

Susskind, A. M., & Maynard, M. (2019). *The next frontier of restaurant management: Harnessing data to improve guest service and enhance the employee experience (Eds)*. Cornell University Press.

References

Arsal, I., Woosnam, K. M., Baldwin, E. D., & Backman, S. J. (2010). Residents as travel destination information providers: An online community perspective. *Journal of Travel Research, 49*, 400–413. http://dx.doi.org/10.1177/0047287509346856

Aureliano-Silva, L., Leung, X., & Spers, E. E. (2021). The effect of online reviews on restaurant visit intentions: Applying signaling and involvement theories. *Journal of Hospitality and Tourism Technology*. https://doi.org/10.1108/JHTT-06-2020-0143.

Berthon, P., Pitt, L., Kietzmann, J., & McCarthy, I. P. (2015). CGIP: Managing consumer-generated intellectual property. *California Management Review, 57*(4), 43–62.

Brewer, P. (2017). *The impact of restaurant review website attributes on consumers' internal states and behavioral responses* [Doctoral dissertation, University of Tennessee]. https://trace.tennessee.edu/utk_graddiss/4860

Chaney, S., & Ryan, C. (2012). Analysing the evolution of Singapore's world gourmet summit: An example of gastronomic tourism. *International Journal of Hospitality Management, 31*(2), 309–318. https://doi.org/10.1016/j.ijhm.2011.04.002

Cheung, M. K., Lee, M. K. O., & Rabjohn, N. (2008). The impact of electronic word-of-mouth: The adoption of online opinions in online customer communities. *Internet Research, 18*(3), 229–247.

Choo, T. C., Jamil, B., Aryty, A., & Daud, A. (2016). Electronic word of mouth (eWOM) on restaurants in Sarawak. *Geografia OnlineTM Malaysia Journal of Society and Space, 12*(13), 39–49.

Chunhua, W., Ha, C., Chan, T. Y., & Xianghua, L. (2015). The economic value of online reviews. *Marketing Science, 34*(5), 739–754.

Clow, K. E., & Baack, D. (2018). *Integrated advertising, promotion, and marketing communications*. Pearson Education Limited.

Dixit, S. K. (2017). *The Routledge handbook of consumer behaviour in hospitality and tourism*. Routledge.

Dixit, S. K. (2019). *The Routledge handbook of gastronomic tourism*. Routledge.

Dixit, S. K. (2020). *The Routledge handbook of tourism experience management and marketing*. Routledge.

Dossena, C., Mochi, F., Bissola, R., & Imperatori, B. (2021). Restaurants and social media: Rethinking organizational capabilities and individual competencies. *Journal of Tourism Futures*, *7*(1), 20–39. https://doi.org/10.1108/JTF-06-2019-0050

Economic Research Service (ERS/USDA). (2019). *Food dollar series*. Retrieved August 21, 2022, from: https://www.ers.usda.gov/data-products/food-dollar-series/

Floh, A., Koller, M., & Zauner, A. (2013). Taking a deeper look at online reviews: The asymmetric effect of valence intensity on shopping behaviour. *Journal of Marketing Management*, *29*, 646–670.

Göral, R., & Tokay, S. (2015). Online customer reviews on restaurants and expert opinions: An integrated approach. *European Journal Interdisciplinary*, *2*(1), 9–19.

Govers, R., Go, F. M., & Kumar, K. (2007). Promoting tourism destination image. *Journal of Travel Research*, *46*(1), 15–23. https://doi.org//abs/10.1177/0047287507302374

Gretzel, U., & Yoo, K. H. (2013). Premises and promises of social media marketing in tourism. In S. McCabe (Ed.), *The Routledge handbook of tourism marketing* (pp. 491–504). Routledge.

Gunasekar, S., Das, P., Dixit, S. K., Mandal, S., & Mehta, S. R. (2021). Wine-experienscape and tourist satisfaction: Through the Lens of online reviews. *Journal of Foodservice Business Research*. https://doi.org/10.1080/15378020.2021.2006039

He, S. X., & Bond, S. D. (2015). Why is the crowd divided? Attribution for dispersion in online word of mouth. *Journal of Consumer Research*, *41*(6), 1509–1527.

Huifeng, P., Ha, H., & Lee, J. (2020). Perceived risks and restaurant visit intentions in China: Do online customer reviews matter? *Journal of Hospitality and Tourism Management*, *43*, 179–189.

Kim, W. G., Ng, C. Y. N., & Kim, Y. S. (2009). Influence of institutional DINESERV on customer satisfaction, return intention, and word-of-mouth. *International Journal of Hospitality Management*, *28*(1), 10–17. https://doi.org/10.1016/j.ijhm.2008.03.005

Kozinets, R. V. (2010). *Netnography: Doing ethnographic research online*. Sage Publications.

Lewis, R. C., & Chambers, R. E. (2000). *Marketing leadership in hospitality*. John Wiley.

Li, H., Liu, Y., Tan, C., & Hu, F. (2020). Comprehending customer satisfaction with hotels: Data analysis of consumer-generated reviews. *International Journal of Contemporary Hospitality Management*, *32*(5), 1713–1735. https://doi.org/10.1108/IJCHM-06-2019-0581

Litvin, S. W., Goldsmith, R. E., & Pan, B. (2008). Electronic word-of-mouth in hospitality and tourism management. *Tourism Management*, *29*(3), 458–468. https://doi.org/10.1016/j.tourman.2007.05.011

Liu, A. X., Steenkamp, J., & Zhang, M. (2018). Agglomeration as a driver of the volume of electronic word of mouth in the restaurant industry. *Journal of Marketing Research*, *55*(4), 507–523.

Lund, N. F., Cohen, S. A., & Scarles, C. (2018). The power of social media storytelling in destination branding. *Journal of Destination Marketing & Management*, *8*, 271–280.

Mangold, W. G., & Faulds, D. J. (2009). Social media: The new hybrid element of the promotion mix. *Business Horizons*, *52*(4), 357–365.

Meuter, M., McCabe, D. B., & Curran, J. M. (2013). Electronic word-of-mouth versus interpersonal word-of-mouth: Are all forms of word-of-mouth equally influential? *Services Marketing Quarterly*, *34*, 240–256. http://www.tandfonline.com/doi/abs/10.1080/15332969.2013.798201

O'Connor, P. (2008). User-generated content and travel: A case study on tripadvisor.com. In Information and Communication Technologies in Tourism 2008: Proceedings of the International Conference in Innsbruck, Austria, 2008, edited by P. O'Connor, Höpken Wolfram, Gretzel Ulrike. Vienna, Austria: Springer, pp. 47–58.

Parikh, A. A., Behnke, C., Almanza, B., Nelson, D., & Vorvoreanu, M. (2017). Comparative content analysis of professional, semi-professional, and user-generated restaurant reviews. *Journal of Foodservice Business Research, 20*(5), 497–511. https://doi.org/10.1080/15378020.2016.1219170

Park, S., & Nicolau, J. L. (2015). Asymmetric effects of online consumer reviews. *Annals of Tourism Research*, 50, 67–83.

Park, C. W., Sutherland, I., & Lee, S. K. (2021). Effects of online reviews, trust, and picture-superiority on intention to purchase restaurant services. *Journal of Hospitality and Tourism Management, 47*, 228–236.

Pentina, I., Bailey, A. A., & Zhang, L. (2018). Exploring effects of source similarity, message valence, and receiver regulatory focus on Yelp review persuasiveness and purchase intentions. *Journal of Marketing Communications, 24*, 125–145.

Pizam, A., & Tasci, A. D. A. (2019). Experienscape: Expanding the concept of servicescape with a multi-stakeholder and multi-disciplinary approach. *International Journal of Hospitality Management, 76*, 25–37. https://doi.org/10.1016/j.ijhm.2018.06.010

Prawannarat, B. (2017). *The impact of restaurant review website attributes on consumers' internal states and behavioral responses* [Doctoral dissertation, University of Tennessee]. https://trace.tennessee.edu/utk_graddiss/4860

Qiu, L., Pang, J., & Lim, K. H. (2012). Effects of conflicting aggregated rating on eWoM review credibility and diagnosticity: The moderating role of review Valence. *Decision Support Systems*, 54, 631–643, https://linkinghub.elsevier.com/retrieve/pii/S0167923612002357

Rosario, A. B., Sotgiu, F., De Valck, K., & Bijmolt, T. H. (2016). The effect of electronic word of mouth on sales: A meta-analytic review of platform, product, and metric factors. *Journal of Marketing Research, 53*, 297–318.

Ruiz-Mafe, C., Bigné-Alcañiz, E., & Currás-Pérez, R. (2020). The effect of emotions, eWoM quality and online review sequence on consumer intention to follow advice obtained from digital services. *Journal Of Service Management, 31*(3), 465–487.

Salleh, S., Hashim, N. H., & Murphy, J. (2016). The role of information quality, visual appeal and information facilitation in restaurant selection intention. In A. Inversini, & R. Schegg (Eds.), *Information and Communication Technologies in Tourism 2016* (pp. 87–97). Springer. https://doi.org/10.1007/978-3-319-28231-2_7

Tang, L. (2017). Mine your customers or mine your business: The moderating role of culture in online word-of-mouth reviews. *Journal of International Marketing, 25*(2), 88–110.

Teviana, T., Ginting, P., Lubis, A. N., & Gultom, P. (2017). Antecedents of tourism destination image and customer satisfaction in tourism industry. *European Research Studies Journal, 20*(3A), 435–445.

Thomas, M. J., Wirtz, B. W., & Weyer, J. C. (2019). Determinants of online review credibility and its impact on Consumers' purchase intention. *Journal of Electronic Commerce Research, 20*(1), 1–20.

Tran, K. P. (2015). The influence of social media on establishing a restaurant's image and reputation: Case study of The Kafe Village restaurant. Retrieved June 4, 2022, from: http://www.theseus.fi/handle/10024/102024

Tucker, K., Radetich, N., & Jantsch, J. (2017). *Social media marketing for restaurants*. Duct Tape Publishing.

van Lohuizen, A. W., & Trujillo-Barrera, A. (2020). The influence of online reviews on restaurants: The roles of review valence, platform, and credibility. *Journal of Agricultural and Food Industrial Organization*. https://doi.org/10.1515/jafio-2018-0020

Vásquez, C., & Chik, A. (2015). "I am not a foodie…": Culinary capital in online reviews of Michelin restaurants. *Food and Foodways*, *23*(4), 231–250.

Wang, W., Liang, Q., Mahto, R. V., Deng, W., & Zhang, S. X. (2020). Entrepreneurial entry: The role of social media. *Technological Forecasting and Social Change*, *161*, 120337. https://doi.org/10.1016/j.techfore.2020.120337

Wuenderlich, N. V., Heinonen, K., Ostrom, A. L., Patrício, L., Sousa, R., Voss, C., & Lemmink, G. A. M. (2015). Futurizing smart service: Implications for service researchers and managers. *Journal of Services Marketing*, *29*(6/7), 442–447.

Yang, Y., Park, S., & Hu, X. (2018). Electronic word of mouth and hotel performance: A meta-analysis. *Tourism Management*, *67*, 248–260. https://doi.org/10.1016/j.tourman.2018.01.015

You, Y., Vadakkepatt, G., & Joshi, A. (2015). A meta-analysis of electronic word-of mouth elasticity. *Journal of Marketing*, *79*, 19–39.

Zhang, Z., Ye, Q., Law, R., & Li, Y. (2010). The impact of e-word-of-mouth on the online popularity of restaurants: A comparison of consumer reviews and editor reviews. *International Journal of Hospitality Management*, *29*(4), 694–700.

Zhao, L., Lu, Y., Zhang, L., & Chau, P. Y. K. (2012). Assessing the effects of service quality and justice on customer satisfaction and the continuance intention of mobile value-added services; an empirical test of a multidimensional model. *Decision Support System*, *52*, 645–656.

Zhao, Y., Xu, X., & Wang, M. (2019). Predicting overall customer satisfaction: Big data evidence from hotel online textual reviews. *International Journal of Hospitality Management*, *76*(A), 111–121. https://doi.org/10.1016/j.ijhm.2018.03.017

3 The Motivation of Singapore Millennials in Spa Tourism and the Influence of Social Media

Kuan-Huei Lee, Hui Min Choo, Li Ling Lim, Eunice Lioe Si Min, Shu Jian Ong, and Jia Xuan Sim

Introduction

Health tourism has been an age-old practice since the time of the Greek, Egyptian, and Roman civilisations. People back then travelled for various reasons such as to collect spa waters, for pilgrimage to a sacred site for soothing purposes, and to benefit from warm thermal baths (Cormany, 2017). Today, health tourism is being developed and promoted as a high-value tourism product by numerous countries to expand their tourism base. Hence, this explains the increasing attention that health tourism has received as a distinct tourism niche in the literature. As a fascinating city, Singapore spa-goers are also increasing in numbers. There is a growing interest in self-care retreats and spas have become more convenient for visitors to relax and recharge, even on lunch breaks (Ng, 2010). The spa industry plays an important role in Singapore's health and wellness sector and is valued at S$140 million each year. Spa-goers are seeking a particular experience either for recreation or health related, and many of them are visiting spas after searching on social media.

The chapter aims to understand the push and pull motivating factors of Singapore millennial spa-goers to engage in local hotel spa services and the influence of social media. It intends to provide useful insights for researchers and practitioners in Singapore's spa industry and assist hotel spa managers in developing innovative product offerings to capture this next wave of consumer demand. The study can assist the industry to learn more about the experience of spa-goers and create better products/services to attract new customers and retain existing ones.

Health, Wellness, and Spa Tourism

What Is Health Tourism?

With respect to the definition of health tourism, there are different forms such as medical tourism and wellness tourism. Some authors contended that health tourism is an umbrella term for other sub-sectors, including spa, wellness, and medical tourism. Medical and wellness tourism indiscriminately alluded to health-related tourism on occasion. However, Smith and Puczkó (2009) define health tourism as a wider concept which includes wellness tourism, medical tourism, and medical wellness tourism. Despite health tourism being interchangeably used with medical

DOI: 10.4324/9781003335924-5

tourism by numerous governments, a distinction should be made between the two concepts. Goeldner (1989) defines health tourism as (1) staying away from home, (2) health as the most important motive, and (3) done in a leisure setting. Another extensively quoted definition of health tourism was that of Müeller and Kaufmann (2001, p. 7) as

> the sum of all the relationships and phenomena resulting from a change of location and residence by people in order to promote, stabilize and, as appropriate, restore physical, mental and social well-being while using health services and for whom the place where they are staying is neither their principle nor permanent place of residence or work.

Sub-Sectors of Health Tourism

There is also disagreement regarding the internal boundaries of health tourism. For instance, there is no consensus in the literature regarding the relationship among health, medical, and wellness tourism. Several studies (Botterill et al., 2013; Connell, 2006; Hall, 2011) have regarded health and medical tourism as distinct entities, while other studies (Smith & Puczkó, 2009) have applied a similar approach regarding health and wellness tourism. The United Nations' International Recommendations for Tourism Statistics (UNWTO, 2010) proposed to separate health and medical tourism. 'Health and medical care' are a broad category and comprise 'receiving services from hospitals, clinics, convalescent homes and, more generally, health and social institutions, visiting thalassotherapy and health and spa resorts and other specialized places to receive medical treatments when they are based on medical advice, including cosmetic surgeries using medical facilities and services' (UNWTO, 2010, p. 25). Although thalassotherapy and spa treatments are usually closely associated with wellness, the UNWTO did not explicitly recognise this category.

The five segments of the health tourism market linked to different categories of health-related tourism are as follows (Goeldner, 1989):

1 Sun and fun activities (leisure tourism).
2 Engaging in healthy activities, though health is not the main motive (outdoor recreation, adventure tourism, sports tourism, and wellness tourism).
3 Health is the primary motive for travel (e.g. a sea cruise or travel to a different climate) (health tourism and wellness tourism).
4 Travel for sauna, massage, and other health activities (spa tourism and wellness tourism).
5 Medical treatment (medical tourism and dental tourism).

While the above classification is helpful in distinguishing elements of the demand for health and spa tourism, it does not recognise the importance that those health products and spas play in destination marketing and promotion, or as a part of tourism development strategies. Another definition for health tourism is 'a commercial phenomenon of industrial society which involves a person travelling overnight away from the normal home environment for the express benefit of maintaining or improving health, and the supply and promotion of facilities and destinations which seek to provide such benefits' (Hall, 2003, p. 274).

What Is Wellness Tourism?

Müeller and Kaufmann (2001, p. 7) contend that wellness tourism is a subcategory of health tourism and defined it as 'a state of health featuring the harmony of body, mind, and spirit, with self-responsibility, physical fitness/beauty care, healthy nutrition/diet, relaxation (need for destressing)/meditation, mental activity/education and environmental sensitivity/social contacts as fundamental elements'. Kaspar (1995) suggested that people who seek wellness tourism are travelling to places outside their homes to do activities that can enhance their mind, body, or social well-being. This special-interest tourism requires travellers to make deliberate and purposeful contributions to their well-being. Müeller and Kaufmann (2001) also explain that this group of travellers reside in a wellness hotel. It is a specialised accommodation that provides professional health information and individual care and extensive service packages that encompass aspects such as physical fitness, beauty care, healthy nutrition, relaxation, meditation, mental activity, and education. In some countries, Chen et al. (2013) note that there are wellness hotels that combine therapies and spas as their product offerings. These properties hire licensed medical staff to reside in the hotel and provide guests with therapies, including Chinese herbal medicine, acupuncture, and body shaping.

Different Types of Spas

The International Spa Association (ISPA) defines spas as an organisation that aims to enhance a person's overall well-being through a variety of professional services that support the growth and renewal of mind, body, and spirit. Table 3.1 has classified the types of spas into eight categories, depending on the treatment and facilities available. They are club spas, cruise ship spas, day spas, hotel spas, medical spas, mineral spring spas, and resort spas.

Cohen and Bodeker (2010) share that the range of spa treatments depends on the type of spa (e.g. hotel, day, destination, and club), guests, and their lifestyles. Spa menus were found to offer similar product offerings and can be broken down as follows: body treatments, massages in intervals of 25, 50, and 80 minutes; and facials in intervals of 50 and 80 minutes.

- Thought point: Can you differentiate health, wellness, and spa tourism? What are the different types of spas?

Table 3.1 Types of spas

Day	'A day spa offers a variety of spa services, including facial and body treatments on a day-use-only basis'.
Hotel/Resort	'A hotel/resort spa offers a spa, fitness and wellness service as well as spa cuisine menu choices and overnight accommodation within a resort or hotel'.
Destination	'A destination spa is not part of another resort or hotel. The destination spa's primary purpose is to guide individual spa-goers to healthy lifestyles. Historically an extended stay, this transformation can be accomplished by a comprehensive program that includes spa services, physical fitness activities, wellness education, healthful cuisine, and special interest programming'.
Medical	'A spa in which full-time, on-site licensed health care professionals provide comprehensive medical and wellness care in an environment that integrates spa services, as well as traditional, complementary and/ or alternative therapies and treatments. The facility operates within the scope of practice of its staff, which can include both aesthetic/ cosmetic and prevention/ wellness procedures and services'.
Club	'A facility whose primary purpose is fitness and that offers a variety of professional administered spa services on a day-use basis. A hotel, gym or fitness club that has a sauna, steam or whirlpool bath is not a spa unless it explicitly offers spa products and services as an added benefit'.
Mineral Spring	'A spa offering an on-site source of natural mineral, thermal or seawater used in hydrotherapy treatments'.
Cruise Ship	'A spa aboard a cruise ship providing professionally administered spa services, fitness and wellness components/and spa cuisine menu choices'.
Cosmetic	'A spa that primarily offers aesthetics/cosmetic and prevention/wellness procedures and services such as facials, peels, waxing and other non-invasive procedures that are within the scope of practice of its staff but do not require on-site medical supervision'.

Source: Adapted from Hashemi et al. (2015, p. 3).

Understanding Spa-Goers

Who Can Be Called Spa-Goers?

Spa-goers are classified as people who seek spa experiences and are used interchangeably with the term 'spa visitor' across studies. As more people are searching for hotels that offer spa services (Mak et al., 2009), the tourism industry strives to enhance people's quality of life by offering wellness-related products and services to address these needs (Chen et al., 2008). The global spa industry is experiencing rapid growth over the years, particularly in Asia, Global Wellness Institute (2018) notes that the growing phenomenon is driven by the rising concern about maintaining one's appearance and prevention of health issues. Mak et al. (2009) identify that 'relaxation and relief', 'escape', 'self-reward and indulgence', and 'health and beauty' were significant motivating factors for Hong Kong spa-goers. This differs from the European spa-goers who perceive spa experience as curing a disease or for healing purposes (Douglas, 2001). On the other hand, American spa-goers perceive it as an experience for self-reward.

The difference in perception is largely influenced by cultural and social backgrounds. In view of this, Mak et al. (2009) explain that the perception of European spa-goers might be associated with the practice of patronising spas as part of their public insurance program (Alén et al., 2006), whereas spa is not subsidised for America's public insurance programme. This may explain the disparity in perceptions of the spa experience. Having examined Hong Kong millennials' behavioural intentions towards hotel spas, Lam and Gao (2019) found that 'price' was the most important factor, followed by 'therapists'. Furthermore, 'price', 'location', 'product', and 'promotion' are factors that would greatly impact their booking intention. Similarly, Guillet and Kucukusta (2019) agree that spa attributes such as therapists' qualifications, price, and treatment would significantly influence a spa-goer's booking intention. On the other hand, Trihas and Konstantarou (2016) reveal that European spa-goers are motivated by relaxation, enhancing physical health, and beauty treatments. Factors such as cleanliness and maintenance of the spa, staff knowledge, hygiene, behaviour, courtesy, and quality of service would influence their decision-making in selecting a spa.

Tsai et al. (2012) assert that there was a shift in the demographics of spa-goers within the last two decades. Initially, baby boomers dominated the spa industry as women aged above 50 years old recognised the healing properties of spas. However, spas have also appealed to women who are aged below 40 years old due to their busy lifestyles. There was an emerging market for younger spa-goers (Panchal, 2012) and modern spas were attracting more Generations X and Y in recent years. In general, the percentage of female spa-goers was larger in size than males. Nonetheless, more males were visiting spas for relaxation purposes and personal grooming. Male and female spa-goers were motivated by different factors when visiting a spa. For instance, 'escape' motivates male respondents to visit a spa more than females (Mak et al., 2009).

Motivation of Spa-Goers

Motivation is associated with the internal forces that incite and steer one's behaviour, influencing the individual's psychological or biological needs and wants (Kim et al., 2017). Wellness travel embraces psychological and physiological facets because travel is expected to satisfy different levels of needs, such as psychological (e.g. intrinsic, personal, and interpersonal rewards) and physiological needs (e.g. health and fitness).

Maslow's hierarchy of needs is a widely accepted concept to explain people's motivations. People are motivated to achieve certain needs and they will strive to achieve these needs to avoid dissatisfaction. The needs are organised hierarchically, from basic to complex needs (Table 3.2). To progress to the higher level

Table 3.2 Maslow's hierarchy of needs

Need category	*Description*
Self-actualisation	Self-actualisation needs are about developing one's self, which is the need for personal growth, developing and achieving one's potential to be the best they can be. This is the highest level of needs that an individual can achieve.
Esteem	Esteem needs are about having the need for personal esteem, such as positive self-esteem and self-evaluation and having confidence. It is also about feelings of accomplishment, the need for validation from others, respect, recognition, status, and reputation.
Social	Social needs are the need for love, intimacy, friendship, and belonging. These needs are achieved through relationships with families, friends, and romantic partners.
Safety	Safety needs are psychological needs such as needs for having stability, a safe and secure environment, and a stable financial situation.
Physiological	Physiological needs are the most basic needs and requirements that humans need in order to survive, such as having water, food, shelter, sleep, and air.

Source: Adapted from Desmet and Fokkinga (2020, p. 9).

needs, one must first fulfil their needs at the lower level. The five stages of needs are physiological, safety, social, self-esteem, and self-actualisation.

Push and Pull Model

The concept of 'push and pull' motivational factors is widely adopted to understand the concept of motivation. The push factors encompass internal motives and intrinsic motivators. These factors are personal needs and wants that stem from physiological, social, or psychological needs. It also stems from an individual's attitude, such as perceptions, learning, and motivation. The seven socio-psychological motives (push) are exploration, escape from a mundane environment and evaluation of self, prestige, relaxation, regression, enhancement of kinship relationships, and social interaction. Spas should take into consideration these socio-psychological motives of spa-goers before focusing on their spa features and facilities (pull). As such, the examination of push motives should be examined temporally before pull motives. Following Azman and Chan (2012), the push factor for spa-goers is to achieve their self-satisfying goal of being able to escape reality, relax and pamper themselves, and reward themselves after work. Another push factor would be self-fulfilment to take a break and recover from the busyness of life. In contrast, the pull factors encompass external motives or extrinsic factors. These are external environmental factors connected to external, situational, or cognitive aspects, and the spa attributes such as tangible resources and the marketing image that the spa conveys, which attracts spa-goers to the spa. The pull factors include the attributes of a spa such as having a peaceful environment and atmosphere, good service, availability, a wide range of treatments and professionalism.

- Thought point: What is motivation? Can you recall different needs in Maslow's Hierarchical of Needs and apply them to a different activity setting?

The Millennial Generation and Social Media

Researchers have interchangeably used terms such as the 'digital generation' and 'Generation Y' to refer to millennials (Benckendorff et al., 2009). The demographic profile of the millennials varied across studies, such as between 1980 and 2000 (Godelnik, 2017); 1980 and 1995 (Monaco, 2018); or 1979 and 1994 (Santos et al., 2016). For this study, the researchers defined the demographic of millennials to be between 1980 and 2000.

Millennial Characteristics and Behaviours

Millennials are distinguished as individuals who are diverse, tech-savvy, environmentally conscious, appreciate the work-life balance, and care about social responsibility (Richards & Morrill, 2020). As this market segment is consistently looking for new experiences, it is important for industries to provide experiences to cater to them (Sofronov, 2018). Millennials are considered to be more educated than the previous generations and widely exposed to the Internet (Aceron et al., 2018). Hence, fast and complimentary Internet is also important to them (Gotardi et al., 2015).

As millennials rely heavily on the Internet for information (Valentine & Powers, 2013), it highlights the significance of marketers to focus on online marketing to entice this market. Being digital natives, they tend to source online information (e.g. reviews) before deciding on their travel plans (Richards & Morrill, 2020). Moreover, they enjoy sharing their experiences on their social media platforms to connect with people in their social circle.

Additionally, their purchasing behaviour revolves around personalisation, convenience, and a plethora of offerings that are made available (Sweeney, 2006). Several studies have found that millennials preferred original and honest advertising messages (Aceron et al., 2018), which showcase storytelling, creativity, and sophistication (Veiga et al., 2017). Apart from advertising, millennials rely on electronic word-of-mouth (WOM) (e-WOM) and recommendations from family or friends (Mangold & Smith, 2012), which are considered credible sources to them. Singapore millennials are tech-savvy and sophisticated as they rely on both online and traditional methods when planning their travel itinerary. Eighty-three per cent of millennials stated that they preferred using mobile applications and online sources (e.g. Tripadvisor, Agoda, Zuji, Skyscanner, and Kayak) for their research.

Case Study: Singapore Millennian Spa-Goers

How Was the Study Conducted?

The study adopted a qualitative approach using online in-depth interviews via Zoom during May 2021, with 13 millennials who had visited or had the intention to visit a spa. Physical interviews were not possible due to restrictions during the pandemic. Each interview was carried out to gain insights into their motivations in seeking spa experiences and their spa consumption patterns in Singapore.

Demographic Characteristics

A total of 13 different interview sessions were conducted over Zoom and respondents were labelled by respondent codes (R1–R13), respectively (Table 3.3). The respondents were all females and aged between 24 and 26 years old. Eight respondents were employed in full-time positions, while the remaining were students. Most of the respondents had made prior spa visits, with only three respondents who had not been to any spa before. Of the ten respondents with a past spa experience, facials, and body massages were the most common type of spa treatment. In addition to body massages, two respondents had completed body treatments.

Table 3.3 Qualitative interviewees' responses

Respondent code	*Age*	*Gender*	*Occupation*	*Prior spa visit experience*	*Spa treatments done*
R1	25	Female	Employed full-time	Yes	Facials, body massages
R2	26	Female	Student	Yes	Body massages, body treatments
R3	25	Female	Employed full-time	Yes	Facials, body massages
R4	25	Female	Student	Yes	Facials, body massages
R5	25	Female	Employed full-time	Yes	Body massages
R6	25	Female	Employed full-time	Yes	Facials, body massages
R7	24	Female	Employed full-time	Yes	Facials
R8	25	Female	Employed full-time	No	NIL
R9	24	Female	Student	Yes	Facials
R10	24	Female	Student	No	NIL
R11	24	Female	Student	No	NIL
R12	25	Female	Employed full-time	Yes	Body massages, body treatments
R13	25	Female	Employed full-time	Yes	Facials

Source: Authors' own work.

Themes Developed from the Findings

Themes and sub-themes were extracted through analysis of the interview transcripts and key themes were established, namely 'push factors for spa visits', 'pull factors for spa visits', and 'variables deterring hotel spa visits'.

Theme 1. Push Factors for Spa Visits

- Relaxation
- Social Bonding
- Health
- WOM and Social Media

Theme 2. Pull Factors for Spa Visits

- Affordability
- Environment
- Professionalism

Theme 3. Variables Deterring Hotel Spa Visits

- Costs
- Alternatives

Push Factors for Spa Visits (Theme 1)

Relaxation: Most respondents expressed that the spa was a way for them to gain relaxation in their lives. Despite some of the respondents having no prior spa experiences, they associated the spa as a setting that provided services for them to unwind from their busy schedules.

> It feels comfortable and relaxing. I get to reward myself and feel refreshed after a long week of work.
>
> (R6)

> The first thing that comes to my mind about a spa is relaxation. So it helps me to relax after a long and tiring day of work, be it school work or part-time jobs.
>
> (R11)

> Spa is a place to relax my body and mind from the hustle and bustle of work and life. It is where we would usually get our massages and relax ourselves.
>
> (R13)

Social Bonding: Several respondents revealed that they have enjoyed going to a spa with their loved ones (i.e. family and friends), as they viewed the spa as a social engagement and bonding activity. Thus, they were more likely to visit the spa alongside their loved ones rather than visiting spas alone.

> Friends and family who encourage me to go to the spa. It is a form of a social thing and trying different spas will be more interesting. I would prefer more family packages. The spa must be family-friendly.
>
> (R5)

> The second consideration to motivate me to go to a spa would be whether there are people to go with me to the spa, be it family or friends.
>
> (R11)

Health: A handful of respondents indicated that a spa is a place for them to enhance their personal wellness. They viewed the spa as a type of service that would provide pain relief and improve their bodily functions such as blood circulation and skin complexion.

> The health benefits that it can bring to me. Health benefits – better blood circulation, helps with your headaches. Improvement of the skin complexion and tone.
>
> (R1)

> I enjoy treating myself to a spa treatment as it gives me energy. Facials make my skin feel soft and massages help me to relieve body aches and pains.
>
> (R6)

> I would say that spa is about wellness. It is a service that people buy to enjoy and do things for their physical well-being and mental well-being.
>
> (R10)

WOM and Social Media: Some respondents expressed that referrals from their families and friends would motivate them to visit a spa. They would be inclined to visit a spa if they received WOM recommendations from their families and friends, who had past positive experiences with the recommended spa establishments. Referrals also included online reviews and social media platforms. The experience in the spa is spread rapidly by technology to the world. People can use social media and the Internet to check online reviews to obtain eWOM.

> We googled and found the top 10 spas in Korea.
>
> (R2)

> I would look at online reviews and if there are 3 to 4 bad reviews on how dirty the place is, I would avoid the place, regardless of how good the deal is.
>
> (R3)

> If my friends visit someplace and they said that it was really good and helped to solve their skincare issues, then I will be willing to give it a try.
>
> (R10)

Pull Factors for Spa Visits (Theme 2)

Affordability: All respondents stood on the common ground that they would be motivated to visit a spa if the spa offerings were affordably priced. As the respondents had limited financial capabilities, they were attracted to value-for-money spa offerings and would be willing to spend between $50 and $250 per spa visit.

> And pricing is important too. The pricing is very affordable. I think a good price is $10 a person, you can enjoy a full day there .... The price should also match the facilities and the cleanliness.
>
> (R2)

> I would say for someone like me who wants to buy things that are value-for-money, I believe that the lowest price will probably be around $100. I'm willing to pay around $100 and up to $250.
>
> (R11)

Environment: Several respondents highlighted that the top factors that they looked out for were the cleanliness and hygiene of a spa. They also avoided going to crowded spas and preferred spas that provided them with a peaceful and quiet environment.

> It was very clean, and the service was top-notch. Fuss-free. The mannerisms and customer service makes me feel respected.
>
> (R3)

> The atmosphere is very important. The spa must make me feel relaxed. It must be peaceful, clean, and quiet. I should allow myself to disconnect from the outside world, rather than stress me even more. It must be clean, and the staff should be skilful and friendly.
>
> (R6)

Professionalism: A handful of respondents revealed that they would be attracted to visit spas by the professional services that these settings offer. They felt that the staff working at spas were professionally trained with the necessary knowledge and skills to address their specific needs. For instance, spa professionals were able to recommend suitable facial and body treatments in consideration of their skin conditions rather than solely hard selling. Additionally, the spa professionals could properly tackle issues, which the respondents were unable to resolve on their own.

> In terms of service, it is very important .... I prefer staff to greet me, and no hard selling of products. I want a peaceful experience.
>
> (R1)

> I think since they are professionals, they probably have expertise in handling any skincare issues or anything that I cannot fix on my own.
>
> (R10)

> I think the body treatments are the ones that require more knowledge and skills, and these knowledge and skills are only known and learnt by the professionals working at a spa.
>
> (R11)

Variables Deterring Hotel Spa Visits (Theme 3)

Costs: For respondents who had not been to a hotel spa before, most of them indicated that the cost factors involved in spa treatments had deterred them from visiting. As they were studying or had just entered the workforce, these respondents viewed spas as a costly experience with respect to their present limited financial means. Therefore, spa was not a necessity for them.

> I think financially wise because we are only 20-ish, it is not like we are full-timers that are working so these are costs, financial issues.
>
> (R9)

> I think that it is because their packages are usually a bit pricey. I mean at this age, I do not see a need for it yet.
>
> (R10)

Alternatives: Some of the respondents mentioned that they had held back on spending for a spa visit, particularly in the hotel spa setting, because they were currently engaged in alternative services provided by non-hotel spa operators. These non-hotel spa operators included day spas such as local beauty and spa centres that are conveniently located in the respondents' neighbourhoods. Additionally, they would take part in other wellness activities for their personal well-being instead of going to the spa.

> And I have facial services outside, so it is not necessary that I have to visit a hotel or a specific spa centre to get these things done.
>
> (R9)

> I do not see the need to engage in a spa for my well-being, I can do other activities.
>
> (R10)

From the qualitative outcomes, participants found going to the spa to be relaxing, bonding with family or friends, and beneficial to health. They also read reviews from social media or received some form of WOM from close circle members. As millennials, price is a major concern followed by the cleanliness of the environment, and professionalism in spa skills and service. In line with the significance of Singapore's spa industry and the emerging market of millennial spa-goers, the researchers explored the push- and pull-motivating factors. Interviewees stated that 'costs' was the main concerning factor that deterred them from visiting.

Discussion and Implications

An increasing consumer desire for healthy lifestyles and experiential travel has led to the exponential growth of wellness tourism in Asia and globally, with millennial spa-goers on the rise. As Singapore's spa industry played an important role in the health and wellness sector, this chapter aimed to explore the motivating factors of Singapore millennial spa-goers in engaging a local hotel spa. With these findings, relevant stakeholders in the spa and hotel industries could better entice this emerging market segment. Due to a growing purchasing power and interest in travelling, millennials were found to be the future of tourism. Not only are they digital natives and experience-driven, but also the researchers identified their buying behaviour to be centred on personalisation, convenience, and the availability of a variety of offerings. Millennials tend to rely on and regard e-WOM and recommendations from family or friends as credible sources. Due to their price consciousness, millennials seek the best deals when planning their trips and tend to share them with their family and friends. Furthermore, they regarded travelling as an opportunity to escape, gain new experiences, and socialise with their family and friends. The experience of spa-goers can be quickly shared through different social media platforms, people are checking for online reviews of previous spa-goers before engaging in the service.

Conclusion

The spa industry has become important in a country such as Singapore. In line with such demand, spa experience as part of the experience economy is significant to understand particularly among consumer groups such as the millennials. As such groups are also considerably influenced by WOM and social media, it is necessary to take such digital tools into consideration when developing spa-related products and experiences. Based on the findings, the following recommendations aim to optimise the competitiveness and viability of Singapore's spa industry in the long run. As shared by the interview respondents, they were willing to pay between \$50 and \$250 per spa visit. The spa package could be a collaboration with popular attractions, high tea buffets, or manicure services. These spa packages could be promoted through online shopping platforms, social media pages, and the hotel spa website, as millennials are digital natives and like to seek out the best online promotions. Hotel spas may introduce marketing campaigns that support millennial spa-goers to bond with their loved ones. With reference to the qualitative findings, it was found that 'social bonding' would motivate millennials to be involved in spas. Hotel spas could introduce a 'refer-a-friend' campaign, in which the spa-goer could receive benefits by referring a friend to visit a hotel spa together, such as having a complementary treatment of their choice, with terms and conditions applied. In addition, their friend could receive a discounted rate on their first visit. This will allow the spa-goer to bond with their friends and help to enhance the brand awareness of the hotel spa since millennials enjoy posting their experiences and reviews on social media platforms.

Should the ongoing pandemic situation improve, the researchers would recommend future researchers conduct physical interviews. As continuous research would be needed to monitor the changing preferences of spa-goers, future researchers could investigate other motivating factors for spa involvement such as the spa and hotel attributes and conduct a larger sample using a quantitative research method. Additionally, further studies could conduct interviews with spa industry practitioners to understand the perspective of spa providers.

Further Questions

- Would people's motivation to seek spa and spa experiences be different in a different city or country?
- How would social media influence consumers' decision-making in different study contexts or even different among consumer groups (e.g. baby boomers, Gen Y, and Gen Z)?
- How can spa experience providers take advantage of social media and other digital and technological tools to develop better spa experiences and attract spa goers?

Further Readings

Azman, I., & Chan, J. K. L. (2012). International health and spa tourists' motivational factors in Sabah, Malaysia: The push and pull factors. *Journal of Tourism, Hospitality & Culinary Arts*, *4*(3), 87–104.

Hashemi, S. M., Jusoh, J., Kiumarsi, S., & Mohammadi, S. (2015). Influence factors of spa and wellness tourism on revisit intention: The mediating role of international tourist motivation and tourist satisfaction. *International Journal of Research*, *3*(7), 1–11.

Trihas, N., & Konstantarou, A. (2016). Spa-goers' characteristics, motivations, preferences and perceptions. *Journal of Tourism, Culture and Territorial Development*, *7*(14), 106–127.

References

Aceron, R. M., del Mundo, L. C., Restar, A. S. N., & Villanueva, D. M. (2018). Travel and tour preferences of millennials. *Journal of Economics and Management Sciences*, *1*(2). https://doi.org/10.30560/jems.v1n2p141

Alén, M. E., Fraiz, J. A., & Rufín, R. (2006). Analysis of health spa customers' expectations and perceptions: The case of Spanish establishments. *Polytechnical Studies Review*, *3*(5/6), 245–262.

Azman, I., & Chan, J. K. L. (2012). International health and spa tourists' motivational factors in Sabah, Malaysia: The push and pull factors. *Journal of Tourism, Hospitality & Culinary Arts*, *4*(3), 87–104.

Benckendorff, P., Moscardo, G., & Pendergast, D. (2009). Tourism and generation Y. In *Tourism and Generation Y*. https://doi.org/10.1016/j.tourman.2010.05.010

Botterill, D., Pennings, G., & Mainil, T. (2013), *Medical tourism and transnational health care* (pp. 1–9). Palgrave-MacMillan.

Chen, K. H., Chang, F. H., & Kenny, C. W. (2013). Investigating the wellness tourism factors in hot spring hotel customer service. *International Journal of Contemporary Hospitality Management*, *25*(7). https://doi.org/10.1108/IJCHM-06-2012-0086

Chen, J. S., Prebensen, N., & Huan, T. C. (2008). Determining the motivation of wellness travelers. *Anatolia*, *19*(1). https://doi.org/10.1080/13032917.2008.9687056

Cohen, M., & Bodeker, G. (2010). Understanding the global spa industry: Spa management. In *Understanding the Global Spa Industry*. https://doi.org/10.4324/9780080879161

Connell, J. (2006). Medical tourism: Sea, sun, sand and… surgery. *Tourism Management*, *27*(6), 1093–1100. https://doi.org/10.1016/j.tourman.2005.11.005

Cormany, D. (2017). Introduction to the phenomenon of "medical tourism". In *Medical tourism and wellness* (pp. 19–44). Apple Academic Press.

Desmet, P., & Fokkinga, S. (2020). Beyond Maslow's pyramid: Introducing a typology of thirteen fundamental needs for human-centered design. *Multimodal Technologies and Interaction*, *4*(3), 38. https://doi.org/10.3390/mti4030038

Douglas N. (2001). Travelling for health: Spa and health resorts. In N. Douglas, & R. Dierrett (Eds.), *Special interest tourism: Context and cases* (pp. 261– 268). John Wiley & Sons.

Global Wellness Institute. (2018). *Global wellness tourism economy*. https://globalwellnessinstitute.org/wp-content/uploads/2018/11/GWI_GlobalWellnessTourismEconomyReport.pdf

Godelnik, R. (2017). Millennials and the sharing economy: Lessons from a 'buy nothing new, share everything month' project. *Environmental Innovation and Societal Transitions*, *23*, 40–52. https://doi.org/10.1016/j.eist.2017.02.002

Goeldner, C. (1989). 39th congress AIEST: English workshop summary. *Revue de Tourisme*, *44*(4), 6–7.

Gotardi, L., Senn, Y., Cholakova, E., Liebrich, A., & Wozniak, T. (2015). How do millennial travellers use their mobile devices in a city destination? – Empirical evidence from Switzerland. *E-Review of Tourism Research, ENTER 2015*(July).

Guillet, B. D., & Kucukusta, D. (2019). Analyzing attributes of the spa service experience: Perceptions of spa-goers traveling to Hong Kong. *Journal of China Tourism Research*, *15*(1), 66–83. https://doi.org/10.1080/19388160.2018.1516585

Hall, C. M. (2003). *Health and spa tourism*. In S. Hudson (Ed.), *International sports & adventure tourism* (pp. 273–292). Haworth Press.

Hall, C. M. (2011). Health and medical tourism: A kill or cure for global public health? *Tourism Review*, *66*(1-2), 4–15. https://doi.org/10.1108/16605371111127198

Hashemi, S. M., Jusoh, J., Kiumarsi, S., & Mohammadi, S. (2015). Influence factors of spa and wellness tourism on revisit intention: The mediating role of international tourist motivation and tourist satisfaction. *International Journal of Research*, *3*(7), 1–11.

Kaspar, C. (1995). Gesundheitstourismus im trend. *Jahrbuch der Schweizer Tourismuswirtschaft*, *96*, 53–61.

Kim, E., Chiang, L. (Luke), & Tang, L. (Rebecca). (2017). Investigating wellness tourists' motivation, engagement, and loyalty: In search of the missing link. *Journal of Travel and Tourism Marketing*, *34*(7). https://doi.org/10.1080/10548408.2016.1261756

Lam, L. Y. J., & Gao, Y. (2019). Hong Kong millennials' intention to visit local hotel spas. *Journal of China Tourism Research, 16*(4). https://doi.org/10.1080/19388160.2019.1597800

Mak, A. H. N., Wong, K. K. F., & Chang, R. C. Y. (2009). Health or self-indulgence? The motivations and characteristics of spa-goers. *International Journal of Tourism Research, 11*(2). https://doi.org/10.1002/jtr.703

Mangold, W. G., & Smith, K. T. (2012). Selling to millennials with online reviews. *Business Horizons, 55*(2). https://doi.org/10.1016/j.bushor.2011.11.001

Monaco, S. (2018). Tourism and the new generations: Emerging trends and social implications in Italy. *Journal of Tourism Futures, 4*(1). https://doi.org/10.1108/JTF-12-2017-0053

Müeller, H., & Kaufmann, E. L. (2001). Wellness tourism: Market analysis of a special health tourism segment and implications for the hotel industry. *Journal of Vacation Marketing, 7*(1), 5–17. https://doi.org/10.1177/135676670100700l

Ng, J. (2010). *ASIA: Singapore*. https://globalwellnesssummit.com/wp-content/uploads/Industry-Briefing-Papers/PDFs/Singapore-2010-Jennifer-Ng.pdf

Panchal, J. H. (2012). *The Asian spa: A study of tourist motivations, "flow" and the benefits of spa experiences*. https://researchonline.jcu.edu.au/26967/1/26967_Panchal_2012_thesis.pdf

Richards, G., & Morrill, W. (2020). Motivations of global millennial travelers. *Revista Brasileira de Pesquisa Em Turismo [Brazilian Journal of Tourism Research], 14*(1), 126–139.

Santos, M. C., Veiga, C., & Águas, P. (2016). Tourism services: Facing the challenge of new tourist profiles. *Worldwide Hospitality and Tourism Themes, 8*(6), 654–669.

Smith, M. K., & Puczkó, L. (2009). *Health and wellness tourism*. Elsevier.

Sofronov, B. (2018). Millennials: A new trend for the tourism industry. *Annals of Spiru Haret University. Economic Series, 18*(3), 109–122.

Sweeney, R. (2006). Millennial behaviors and demographics. *Newark: New Jersey Institute of Technology. Accessed On, 12*(3), 4–5.

Trihas, N., & Konstantarou, A. (2016). Spa-goers' characteristics, motivations, preferences and perceptions. *Journal of Tourism, Culture and Territorial Development, 7*(14), 106–127.

Tsai, H., Suh, E., & Fong, C. (2012). Understanding male hotel spa-goers in Hong Kong. *Journal of Hospitality Marketing and Management, 21*(3), 247–269. https://doi.org/10.1080/19368623.2012.624295

UNWTO. (2010). *International recommendations for tourism statistics 2008*. https://unstats.un.org/unsd/publication/seriesm/seriesm_83rev1e.pdf

Valentine, D. B., & Powers, T. L. (2013). Generation Y values and lifestyle segments. *Journal of Consumer Marketing, 30*(7), 596–606. https://doi.org/10.1108/JCM-07-2013-0650

Veiga, C., Santos, M. C., Águas, P., & Santos, J. (2017). Are millennials transforming global tourism? Challenges for destinations and companies. *Worldwide Hospitality and Tourism Themes, 9*(6), 603–616. 10.1108/WHATT-09-2017-0047

4 Motives of Tourists for Participating in the Sharing Economy from the Perspective of the Experience Economy

A Case Study of Polish Uber Users

Daria E. Jaremen and Elżbieta Nawrocka

Introduction

The answer to the question of why people undertake travel as tourists and why they choose a given option for satisfying their tourist needs, e.g. destination, accommodation or transport, has remained an unchanging area of interest both for researchers and the tourist industry for many years. This is because knowledge of such motivations allows the providers of tourist services to better understand tourists' decisions and to prepare an offer more suited to their needs. In this way, they can better satisfy their clients, as well as gain a competitive advantage by employing marketing instruments that activate motivation, thus directing the behaviour of buyers. The result of understanding the motives that provide direction and an aim to the behaviour of tourists is the appearance of new offers, the opening up of new destinations and changes in standards of service.

In the context of considerations into the motivations for tourist travel, certain experience categories hold a key position (Eide et al., 2017). The term 'experience' (from the Greek: εμπειρία, the Latin: experientia) is used by many authors without a clear formulation of a definition for the term (Sundbo & Sørensen, 2013). Experience is usually accepted to be the sum of information (knowledge) and skills gained on the basis of observation and one's own life experiences, which can be released by stimuli that have an effect on the human senses. This means something that happens within people's minds. Experience is determined by both external stimuli processed by human consciousness and the needs, and personal strategies of the individual (cf. Giddens, 1991).

The sharing economy (SE) is a dynamically developing phenomenon driven on the one hand by the development of ICT (Botsman & Rogers, 2010), and on the other hand by entrepreneurial consumers. The SE is mainly developing in service industries, and in particular, as indicated by Sigala (2017) is changing tourism, taking a significant place in the accommodation and passenger transport sectors. Today, it is rare to meet a tourist who has not heard of the Airbnb or Uber platforms. Uber, which was launched in 2009, provided 6.9 billion journeys in total in the last year before the pandemic. In comparison, the figure for 2017 was 3.8 billion. Even the pandemic years did not put Uber users off (almost 5 billion journeys in 2020, and 6.3 billion in 2021).

DOI: 10.4324/9781003335924-6

With the development of the SE, a new type of tourist appeared – the SE platform user. As indicated by data published by Airbnb, many of its users would not have undertaken a tourist trip if they had not been able to make use of cheap accommodation. A similar conclusion can be supposed with regard to Uber. There are many people who do not use taxis but are happy to use the similar offer provided by Uber drivers. It can therefore be presumed that the SE tourist-user has specific motives for making their choices.

- Thought point: So what experiences does a tourist purchasing tourist services via SE platforms expect?

The aim of the chapter is to conceptualise the motives for tourists' choice of services offered via SE platforms, and their operationalisation using a specific example. Defining key choice factors required an integrated approach and a combination of theoretical perspectives: the concept of motivation, SE and the experience economy. The chapter presents the motivations for using the services of Uber – the largest platform connecting drivers and passengers. The chapter discusses as follows:

- the theory of tourist motivation,
- the essence of the SE,
- the characteristics of the new tourists using SE platforms,
- and their experiences related to making use of car-sharing services.

The theoretical considerations are accompanied by a case study of Polish tourists – users of Uber.

Motives for Participation in Tourism: The Appearance of a New Tourist?

Since the 1970s, researchers have continually studied the motives behind tourists' decision-making, more so as these motives change dynamically. New motives appear, their structure changes (mutual relations), and their number, as with a number of needs, is unlimited.

- Thought point: What motivates you to travel and influences your tourist decisions?

Fodness (1994) saw motives as the driving force behind any and all choices made by tourists. Among the various factors determining the behaviour of tourists (cultural, demographic and economic factors), motives play a key role as they are the direct cause for taking action. The tourist motive triggers an action to achieve the aim of satisfying tourist needs. The specific behaviour is most often determined not by one but by many motives (polymotivational), between which a specific hierarchy is defined (some motives are more important than others). Travel can be undertaken, for example, not only to celebrate one's wedding anniversary, but also to fulfil one's dreams of seeing Rome.

- Thought point: Why is it worth knowing about models of motivation?

Research conducted in the field of tourist motivation has led to the development of concepts to explain the essence, typology and mechanisms of tourist motives. Among studies often cited in the literature are as follows:

1 Plog's (1974) allocentricity and psychocentricity model links motives for participating in tourism to an individual's personality placed on a continuum, whose poles were defined as the allocentric and psychocentric type. Psychocentric is a 'self-limiting, nervous and unadventurous' tourist, preferring 'familiarity' in their holiday travels. Allocentric tourist is open, self-confident and wants to see and do new things, and discover 'the world around them'.
2 Dann's (1977) model takes into account '*push*' and '*pull*' motivations for tourist travel. The first includes 'anomie' (the wish to escape from everyday reality) and 'ego-enhancement' (bolstering one's own status through travel), which are internal in character and induce the individual to undertake tourist travel. The second, meanwhile, is external factors attracting a tourist to a given destination.
3 Crompton's (1979) model. Among seven '*push*' (sociopsychological) factors Crompton lists: escape from a perceived mundane environment, exploration, evaluation of self, relaxation, prestige, regression, enhancement of kinship relationships and facilitation of social interaction. Among the '*pull*' factors are novelty and learning.
4 Iso-Ahola's (1982) 'escape-seeking' model proposes a dichotomous division of mutually non-exclusive '*push*' motivations, including the discovery motivation and escape from routine. Both these groups are considered in two dimensions: personal and interpersonal.
5 Pearce's (1988) travel career ladder, based on Maslow's theory of motivation, underlines the existence of a hierarchy of tourist motivations, which begins with the need to relax, followed by security, relations, self-assessment and fulfilment.
6 Pearce and Lee's (2005) travel career patterns model is a development of the previous model. It organises motives into three levels: the core level (the need to escape, and rest), the middle level (experiencing novelties, contact with the local community, authenticity) and the external level (the need to build relations). The authors of the model underline that with a tourist's increasing experience, the middle level grows considerably.

The source literature also describes other tourist motivation typologies, including:

- 3S – *Sea, Sun, Sand* (Knowles & Curtis, 1999),
- 7S – 3S plus, *Safari, Surfing, Shopping, Skiing* (Mtapuri & Giampiccoli, 2014),
- 4L – *Landscape, Leisure, Learning, Limit* (Franch et al., 2008),
- 3E – *Education, Entertainment, Excitement* (Krippendorf, 1986),
- 3T – *Travelling, Trekking, Trucking* (Mowforth & Munt, 1998).
- Thought point: What are the distinguishing features of the new tourist?

The development of the above models confirms significant changes in the motivation for participating in tourism, which is often referred to in the literature as the appearance of a 'new tourist'. Until the mid-1980s, the field was dominated by the 3S model, which reflected mass tourism. Analysing this model, Krippendorf (1986) observed new alternative behaviour among tourists in their paying attention to the natural environment. Poon (1993) confirmed these findings and suggested that the new tourist is more focused on experience, value and independence. Pirnar et al. (2010) added: demanding and difficult to please, independent, creative, open to experiences, focused on getting to know new cultures through experiences, and more environmentally friendly. Modern tourists seek pleasure and fun, security and personalised offers responding to their preferences (Yeoman, 2008). They are interested in value for money (Dwyer et al., 2008), authentic experiences (Pine & Gilmore, 2011; Yeoman et al., 2007) and new knowledge (Buhalis & Law, 2008). Tourists are always in possession of devices allowing them to remain connected to the web at every stage of planning and undertaking a trip (Santos et al., 2016).

- Thought point: Have you used SE platforms as part of your travels as a tourist? Which tourist needs did you satisfy through the use of such platforms? How do SE offers differ from traditional offers?

The Sharing Economy in Tourism

The concept of SE is defined using terminology from Information Technology (digital economy), sociology (collaborative consumption) and economics (SE) (Dolnicar, 2018; Hamari et al., 2015; Lessig, 2008). A brief review of the literature shows that SE is a varied and dynamic phenomenon. One of the first definitions of SE (Lessig, 2008) clearly emphasises the fact that its large-scale growth is related to the spread and development of the Internet. Schor et al. (2015) found that the SE is able to function due to the existence of digital platforms (the most commonly cited are Uber and Airbnb). The second important feature of the SE is that it is social in character and has a dimension that is not necessarily financial (Belk, 2014). The SE is an alternative form of access to goods (without the need to own them) and services, conducted outside the traditionally understood market, e.g. the hotel or transport industry. Later definitions emphasised the need to belong to social groups and social media networks whose members adopt the roles of consumer-providers and consumer-users in the sharing process (Jaremen et al., 2019). In the second decade of the 21st century, attention was drawn to the change in motivation for participating in the SE towards economic motives.

- Thought point: How can the category of tourist experience be interpreted from the perspective of the experience economy? What experiences does a tourist making use of SE platforms expect (e.g. Airbnb, Uber)?

Tourist Experiences in the Sharing Economy

Tourist Experience

Many studies have addressed the problem of the 'tourist experience' ever since Cohen's founding research (Filep & Pearce, 2013; Middleton, 1988; Prebensen et al., 2014; Sharpley & Stone, 2012). It can be said that in tourism, the experience was always treated as a product component and that the tourist industry was focused on experience (Eide et al., 2017).

According to the concept of Pine and Gilmore (1999), experience acquired as the result of an encounter with material goods or a service is a *factor* of production. In tourism, it is underlined that it can be in itself an *aim* (the tourist's goal is to acquire experiences). Analysis of the four pillars of the experience economy (4E) shows that experience is created through education, entertainment, aesthetics and escapism. Education of the SE tourist-user means that they possess the skills to use new ICT and an interest in acquiring new skills (e.g. languages). Entertainment covers the positive emotions related to a visit to an attraction recommended by a resident of the place visited. Esthetics becomes apparent, for example, when immersing oneself in the local atmosphere of a place during walks along picturesque city alleyways. Tourists are also interested in escaping to a land of dreams through active participation, e.g. in a local cultural event, which takes tourists to an exciting parallel reality.

Application of the SE perspective allows the optics to be widened in research into tourist motives, and to enrich it with the concept of the 'new tourist'. Earlier, experiences had been treated merely as an addition to a product, and not as the content of tourist travel. The tourist experience is the result of a combination of experiences related to various services, the characteristics of a tourist destination and individual attitudes and perceptions, consumers' senses and feelings. A specific component of experience is authenticity, which is also included in the principles of the SE (Yeoman & McMahon-Beattie, 2019). Cohen (1988) emphasises that authenticity is a relative creation, constructed socially as the result of comparisons between tourists' expectations and perceptions. MacCannell (2002) talks about the authenticity of experiences and places. The creation of experiences requires the emotional involvement of the consumer, based on meetings (Snel, 2013), specific interactions and relations between tourists and service providers, as well as the natural environment and residents of the places visited.

Adopting the SE perspective in tourism requires consideration of changes in the direction of the greater need for experiences and is connected to the general growth in economic value (cf. Boswijk et al., 2007; Sundbo & Sørensen, 2013). The value of a purchased tourist service is measured by the category of experiences. Tourist consumption is based on non-material values that are empirical and symbolic in character: the place's atmosphere, the way in which a service is provided, communicating with the client, value for money etc.

- Thought point: What are the approaches for understanding the concept of 'experience' in tourism?

In research into tourist experiences, two approaches dominate, the first presenting experience as a process of the tourist learning and creating knowledge (Brougère, 2015), and the second approaches the tourist experience as a momentary pleasure-oriented event (Boutaud & Veron, 2008).

Learning from Tourist Experiences and Experiences from Learning

The entirety of a tourist's experiences as a user of SE platforms lasts from the moment they search for information on the Internet to the moment they return home, or even longer (the perpetuation of a tourist's memories, for example on social media). The formation of a tourist-user of SE and his system of values is connected to a large degree to the phenomenon of creating and not solely copying reality. This is because the tourist is involved emotionally and intellectually in new ideas, spaces and actions. An important role is played in this process by the Internet, mobile applications and smartphones which accompany the tourist at every stage of tourist consumption. Thanks to the skills they have acquired, the tourist is able, for example, to independently book a taxi or knows how to get to a specific place without the help of professional guides. He can then share their experience with other less advanced tourists. In the SE, we are dealing with 'empirical intelligence – experience intelligence', which results in the tourist co-designing and co-creating a service. The tourist's cognitive experience can be used by Uber to prepare suitable offers.

Tourist Experience as a Momentary Pleasure-Oriented Event

Experiences are constructed by the tourist based on relaxation on the beach by a warm sea, visiting well-known tourist attractions or riding an old train through a historical city centre. From this viewpoint, the tourist has poor connections with the surroundings they are visiting, maintains a distance from the local population, often as the result of poor knowledge of the place visited, and has limited involvement in new ideas or activities. It can be observed that tourists are concerned mainly with 'ticking off' a given place and traditional tourist attractions and are interested in 'well worn' tourist trails. The tourist experience is carefully prepared, choreographed and safe attractions that provide standardised experiences. In this case, ICT plays a varied or secondary role in tourist travel, with the Internet often a tool used to search for tourist offers before departure.

- Thought point: Think about what the differences are between the two approaches to understanding the concept of experience.

Table 4.1 presents the assumptions of the two approaches discussed and their basic features.

The experiences identified in the research presented above are not in practice separable and may even overlap. The perspective for looking at experience is determined individually every time depending on the type of tourism, the tourist

Table 4.1 Characteristics of approaches to interpreting the concept of experience – synthesis

Criterium	*Tourist experience as a momentary pleasure-oriented event (TEMPOE)*	*Tourist experience as a process of learning and creating knowledge (TELCK)*
Character of experiences	Momentary, standardised experiences.	Long-term knowledge and memory. Not normalised experiences.
Tourist behaviour	Distance and passivity, focused on the number of excursions and ticking off well-known attractions, optics on 'receiving' stimuli.	Involvement and activity, focused on excitement, adventure, surprise and creativity.
Experiences in the creation of the offer	Experience as the context of the offer.	Experience as the building block of the offer.
Value of the offer	Utilitarian and functional.	Empirical and symbolic.
Main components of economic value	Low price, quality appropriate to needs, the comfort of purchase.	Atmosphere and mood of a place, value for money.
The role of ICT in building experiences	Varied, sometimes secondary.	In the foreground at every stage of consumption.
Approach to tourist travel	Everything planned in advance following 'well-worn' tourist trails, organised programmes, attractions and shopping.	Individual and spontaneous programme decisions, search for adventure, interest in local character and authenticity.

Source: Authors' own work.

segment, the character of the tourist travel (individual/group) and the type of tourist service (transport, hotel, museum).

The next sub-chapter will use the research results to present experiences from the perspective of Polish tourists using Uber.

Experience as a Motive for Participation in the SE

Case Study of Polish Uber User

The Uber application was officially launched in 2010 in San Francisco, and three years later in Poland (first in Warsaw), then in Krakow, Gdańsk-Sopot-Gdynia, Poznań, Wrocław, Łódź, Katowice, Szczecin. Around half of the Polish market for rides is ordered via the Uber application (*Uber wykroił połowę…*, 2022).

In the process of identifying experiences as a motive for the choice of Uber services, research was conducted on a representative sample of 1003 Poles aged between 18 and 64 who participate in tourist travel. The representativeness of the sample was verified with regard to the respondents' gender, age, education and size of place of residence. The research was conducted in the last quarter of 2020. The data was collected using the CAWI technique. The selection of the sample and collection of the data were carried out by the IMAS international research agency. The research results indicated that 216 of the respondents used Uber services. Among them were 105 women and 111 men. Overall, 50.9% of the people were up to 35 years old, while 16.2% were over 55 years of age. Over half of the people (51.7%) travel for tourist purposes three or more times a year. The majority (3/4) of the respondents travel for relaxation, 49.8% travel to discover new places and 42.6% visit family and friends. The motives for using Uber services were selected and a scale was developed to measure their importance based on scales used by other researchers (Alemi et al., 2018, 2019; Lee & Wong, 2021). Forty-one items were formulated describing the factors that induce the use of Uber services. The research measured the significance of individual factors using a five-point Likert scale. Considering that experience is a unique, personal, unforgettable feeling requiring the involvement of the client on a physical, emotional and even spiritual level, it can be assumed that the motives listed in Table 4.2 are related to the acquiring of a specific type of experience.

- Thought point: Think about what influenced you in ordering Uber services. What was the hierarchy of importance of the factors for choosing Uber?

A ranking was developed for the motives for using Uber services. They were also additionally assigned to the approaches to interpreting the essence of experience described earlier: TEMPOE and TELCK (Table 4.2).

The research results indicate that the tourists studied were motivated mainly by experiences from the TEMPOE perspective. In the ranking presented above (Table 4.2), of the top ten motives, seven were characterised as this type of approach (Table 4.1). This is due to the fact that respondents were mainly induced to make use of Uber's services by the economic factor, related to saving money, time and effort. The first position on the list, however, is occupied by a factor that characterises the understanding of experience as being from the TELCK perspective. The Uber user was most often motivated by the desire to follow trends. Through their behaviour, they wished to follow a lifestyle considered modern, which they demonstrated through their skills in using new, innovative means of transport (positions 7 and 9 in Table 4.2). Subsequent motives on the ranking related to the approach that interpreted the tourist experience as a process of learning and creating knowledge. The tourist-users of Uber escape from the routine, leave well-worn tourist trails and seek less well-known attractions and authentic experiences through contact with local residents and exciting adventures. They are sensitive to the needs of the environment and are intent on enriching their knowledge (about tourist destinations), as well as acquiring new skills (positions 12–28 in Table 4.2).

Discussion of the Case Study and Its Results

The research results show that consumer choices are determined by a whole range of motives (as earlier confirmed by Fodness [1994]), with a defined hierarchical structure (according to the remarks of Pearce [1988]). The motivations are

Table 4.2 Ranking of motives for using Uber services

No.	*Item*	*Significance on a scale of 1–5 (average)*	*Approach*
1.	Using Uber is currently trendy/fashionable	4.293	TELCK
2.	Uber replaces unavailable taxis	4.249	TEMPOE
3.	Uber allows to save money	4.240	TEMPOE
4.	Uber is cheaper than a taxi	4.239	TEMPOE
5.	Uber avoids the problems and costs of parking	4.221	TEMPOE
6.	A journey with Uber lasts a shorter time than on public transport	4.204	TEMPOE
7.	I know how to use the Uber application	4.141	TELCK
8.	Uber provides a wide choice of services	4.124	TEMPOE
9.	Using Uber shows a modern lifestyle	4.119	TELCK
10.	Uber shortens the time needed to get to accommodation	4.110	TEMPOE
11.	Uber reacts faster than taxis	4.082	TEMPOE
12.	Contact with Uber drivers allows to access places only known to residents	4.079	TELCK
13.	Uber is a good value for money	4.053	TELCK
14.	Uber allows to have contact with the everyday lives and authenticity of destination	4.049	TELCK
15.	Uber is ethical and environmentally friendly	4.039	TELCK
16.	Uber provides benefits for the residents of destination	4.084	TELCK
17.	Uber makes contact with local residents easier	4.019	TELCK
18.	Uber gives the opportunity to experience adventures	4.019	TELCK
19.	Uber drivers provide more information about destination	4.010	TELCK
20.	Contact with Uber drivers enables the acquiring of new skills	3.985	TELCK
21.	I like Uber's philosophy	3.981	TELCK
22.	Uber allows to escape from places overcrowded with tourists	3.971	TELCK
23.	Uber provides more experiences through contact with people compared to traditional services	3.951	TELCK
24.	Uber is an alternative to a consumer/lavish lifestyle	3.942	TELCK
25.	Uber drivers make holiday programme more attractive	3.938	TELCK
26.	Using Uber expresses belonging to a community of people who share my lifestyle and way of travelling	3.937	TELCK
27.	I prefer authentic experiences with Uber than standard transport services	3.931	TELCK
28.	Uber gives the freedom of choice	3.919	TELCK
29.	Uber is better suited to my expectations than traditional transport	3.917	TEMPOE
30.	I have an influence on the Uber platform content	3.907	TELCK
31.	Uber provides exceptional experiences	3.905	TELCK
32.	The Uber platform allows to ask questions	3.895	TELCK
33.	I enjoy using the Uber platform	3.889	TELCK
34.	Uber is safe	3.848	TEMPOE
35.	Contact with Uber drivers makes it easier to participate in local entertainment, customs and traditions	3.845	TELCK
36.	The journey time with Uber is shorter than by private car	3.792	TEMPOE
37.	Contact with Uber drivers allows to influence their offer	3.763	TEMPOE
38.	Uber provides privacy	3.731	TEMPOE
39.	I know about Uber's services	3.684	TELCK
40.	I use the Uber platform to share my travel experiences	3.651	TELCK
41.	Uber services improve my social status	3.520	TELCK

Source: Authors' own work.

dominated by the inclination to save (as earlier noted by, e.g., Alemi et al., 2019; Vaclavik et al., 2020), as well as by the desire to have novel experiences, be trendy, discover 'the unknown' and develop knowledge and skills. The significance of novelty and culture was noted earlier by Pearce and Lee (2005), and the development of knowledge and skills by Lee and Wong (2021). In this study, the motive of experiencing close contact with authentic culture was also found to be important (this motive was also emphasised in research by Snel, 2013). The choice of Uber was considered by respondents to be ethical and environmentally friendly, which corresponds with the findings of Krippendorf (1986) and Franch et al. (2008), which pointed to the growing sense of responsibility in modern tourists. Tourists paying for services via SE platforms (here Uber) display the features of the new tourist, who often seeks active holidays in order to undergo and collect experiences. Their travel is motivated by the wish to demonstrate their lifestyle and personality, explore interesting places, 'experiencing localness', and manifest their skills in using new technology ('experiencing modernness').

Exploring motivation provides the answer to the important question: What do clients expect? It also allows offers to be shaped according to the wishes and demands of consumers, which in turn favours them to be satisfied and make repeat purchases of satisfying services. The results presented here on the motivation of Uber users, with particular emphasis on the experiences they expect, carry a crucial message both for intermediary platforms and for drivers directly providing transport services. Undeniably, experience is a criterium of consumer choice. The Uber platform should therefore adopt a marketing concept which assumes as the highest priority the deliberate creation of experiences. The usage of various aspects of the experience economy allows to provide clients services they view as valuable. The fact of being oriented towards providing experiences should be emphasised in marketing messages and the content of promotional posts. An example can be given the Airbnb platform which operates as an intermediary in the reservation of accommodation services, which, instead of beds, rooms or apartments, offers 'nights and experiences'.

When using transport services, the modern tourist is not only interested in getting from point A to point B, which can be achieved in a multitude of ways. So why do clients choose the Uber platform and not another means of transport? Research has confirmed that Uber services bring users comprehensive experiences in a variety of fields: economic, social and psychological. A key role is played in the building of these experiences by the driver. It is the driver who ultimately decides what experiences the consumer will have. In the perception of clients, an Uber driver is not only a person who knows how to drive a car and ensures a safe journey but also has a significant influence on the client's perception of the service. As a result, the driver must know what the client expects. This knowledge is provided by the results of research. Here, it is also worth mentioning the crucial role of the platform. Providing experiences based on drivers themselves presents new challenges for the platform in terms of the recruitment of drivers and the development of their competencies towards consciously shaping the experiences of users.

Conclusions

This chapter is an attempt to examine the reasons tourists have for using car-sharing from the perspective of the experience economy. The chapter integrates several research contexts, including tourist motivations, the profile of the new tourist, the experience economy and the SE. Taking into account the specifics of these approaches, the authors conceptualise the experience of the SE tourist-user, which they verify empirically using the example of the Uber platform. The scientific contribution of the chapter is therefore to shed light on the category of 'tourist experience' in the context of the features of the new tourist and the principles of the experience economy.

Like every study, the one presented in this chapter also has its limitations. At the same time, the limitations direct the researcher's thoughts towards further research. Firstly, the geographical reach of the research only included Polish citizens, which makes it impossible to use the research results to make wider generalisations. Nevertheless, it encourages further research to be conducted in different cultural settings. Secondly, the research covered only shared mobility and Uber services. It is worth therefore investigating the experiences related to various SE offers (i.e. accommodation, tourist guiding, recreation). How these experiences contribute to building the entirety of new tourists' experiences as well as which of these experiences are crucial for tourists?

Further Questions

- In the face of the further development of ICT, how will the profile of the modern tourist change, and what will they be motivated by in the future?
- What will the characteristics and structure of SE tourist experiences be like in the future, and what role will such experiences play?

Further Readings

Alemi, F., Circella, G., Handy, S., & Mokhtarian, P. (2018). What influences travellers to use Uber? *Travel Behaviour and Society*, *13*(October), 88–104. https://doi.org/10.1016/j.tbs.2018.06.002

Prebensen, N. K., Chen, J. S., & Uysal, M. (2014). *Creating experience value in tourism*. CABI Publishing.

Sharpley, R. & Stone, Ph.R. (Eds.) (2012). *Contemporary tourist experience: Concepts and consequence*. Oxon: Routledge.

References

Alemi, F., Circella, G., Handy, S., & Mokhtarian, P. (2018). What influences travellers to use Uber? *Travel Behaviour and Society*, *13*(October), 88–104. https://doi.org/10.1016/j.tbs.2018.06.002

Alemi, F., Circella, G., Mokhtarian, P., & Handy, S. (2019). What drives the use of ride-hailing in California? Ordered probit models of the usage frequency of Uber and Lyft.

Transportation Research Part C: Emerging Technologies, 102, 233–248. https://doi.org/10.1016/j.trc.2018.12.016

Belk, R. (2014). You are what you can access: Sharing and collaborative consumption online. *Journal of Business Research, 67*(8), 1595–1600. https://doi.org/10.1016/j.jbusres.2013.10.001

Boswijk, A., Thijssen, T., & Peelen, E. (2007). *The experience economy: A new perspective*. Pearson Education.

Botsman, R., & Rogers, R. (2010). Beyond zipcar: Collaborative consumption. *Harvard Business Review, 88*(10), 30–39.

Boutaud, J. J., & Veron, E. (2008). *Sémiotique ouverte*. Lavoisier.

Brougère, G. (2015). Le corps, vecteur de l'apprentissage touristique. In J. M. Decroly (Ed.), *Le Tourisme comme expérience. Regards interdisciplinaires sur le vécu touristique* (pp. 175–186). Presses Universitaires du Québec.

Buhalis, D., & Law, R. (2008). Progress in tourism management: Twenty years on and 10 years after the internet: The state of tourism research. *Tourism Management, 24*(9), 609–623. https://doi.org/10.1016/j.tourman.2008.01.005

Cohen, E. (1988). Authenticity and commodification in tourism. *Annals of Tourism Research, 5*, 371–386.

Crompton, J. L. (1979). Motivations for pleasure vacation. *Annuals of Tourism Research, 6*(4), 408–424.

Dann, G. (1977). Anomie, ego-enhancement and tourism. *Annals of Tourism Research, 4*(4), 184–194.

Dolnicar, S. (2018). *Peer-to-peer accommodation networks: Pushing the boundaries*. Goodfellow Publishers.

Dwyer, L., Edwards, D., Mistilis, N., Roman, C., Scott, N., & Cooper, C. (2008). *Megatrends underpinning tourism to 2020: Analysis of key drivers for change*. CRC for Sustainable Tourism Pty Ltd. https://opus.lib.uts.edu.au/bitstream/10453/17701/1/2010002807OK.pdf

Eide, D., Fuglsang, L., & Sundbo, J. (2017). Management challenges with the maintenance of tourism experience concept innovations: Toward a new research agenda. *Tourism Management, 63*, 452–463. https://doi.org/10.1016/j.tourman.2017.06.029

Filep, S., & Pearce, Ph. (eds.) (2013). *Tourist experience and fulfilment: Insights from positive psychology*. Routledge.

Fodness, D. (1994). Measuring tourist motivation. *Annals of Tourism Research, 21*(3), 535–581. https://doi.org/10.1177/004728759403300294

Franch, M., Martini, U., Buffa, F., & Parisi, G. (2008). 4L tourism (landscape, leisure, learning and limit): Responding to new motivations and expectations of tourists to improve the competitiveness of Alpine destinations in a sustainable way. *Tourism Review, 63*(1), 4–14. https://doi.org/10.1108/16605370810861008

Giddens, A. (1991). *Modernity and self-identity*. Polity.

Hamari, J., Sjöklint, M., & Ukkonen, A. (2015). The sharing economy: Why people participate in collaborative consumption. *Journal of the Association for Information Science and Technology*. https://doi.org/10.1002/asi

Iso-Ahola, S. E. (1982). Towards a social psychological theory of tourism motivation: A rejoinder. *Annals of Tourism Research, 9*(2), 256–262. https://doi.org/10.1016/0160-7383(82)90049-4

Jaremen, D. E., Nawrocka, E., & Żemła, M. (2019). Sharing the economy in tourism and sustainable city development in the light of agenda 2030. *Economies, 7*(4), 109. https://doi.org/10.3390/economies7040109

Knowles, T., & Curtis, S. (1999). The market viability of European mass tourist destinations. A post-stagnation life-cycle analysis. *International Journal of Tourism Research, 1*, 87–96. https://doi.org/10.1002/(SICI)1522-1970

Krippendorf, J. (1986). The new tourist – Turning point for leisure and travel. *Tourism Management*, *7*(2), 131–135. https://doi.org/10.1016/0261-5177(86)90025-7

Lee, C. K. H., & Wong, A. O. M. (2021). Antecedents of consumer loyalty in ride-hailing. *Transportation Research Part F: Traffic Psychology Behaviour*, *80*, 14–33. https://doi.org/10.1016/j.trf.2021.08.012

Lessig, L. (2008). *Remix: Making art and commerce thrive in the hybrid economy*. The Penguin Press HC.

MacCannell, D. (1976). *The tourist. A new theory of the leisure class*. Schocken Books.

Middleton, V. T. C. (1988). *Marketing in travel and tourism*. Butterworth-Heinemann.

Mowforth, M., & Munt, I. (1998). *Tourism and sustainability: New tourism in the third world*. Routledge.

Mtapuri, O., & Giampiccoli, A. (2014). A reformulation of the 3Ss model for community-based tourism: Towards an alternative model. *Man in India*, *94*(1/2), 327–336.

Pearce, P. L. (1988). *The Ulysses factor: Evaluating visitors in tourist settings*. Springer Verlag.

Pearce, P. L., & Lee, U. (2005). Developing the travel career approach to tourist motivation. *Journal of Travel Research*, *43*(3), 226–237. https://doi.org/10.1177/0047287504272020

Pine, B. J., & Gilmore, J. H. (2011). *The experience economy*. Harvard Business Press.

Pine, B. J., & Gilmore, J. H. (1999). *The experience economy: Work is theatre & every business a stage*. Harvard Business School Press.

Pirnar, I., Icoz, O., & Icoz, O. (2010, October 25-28). *The new tourist: Impacts on the hospitality marketing strategies*. EuroCHRIE Amsterdam 2010: Passion for Hospitality Excellence, Amsterdam, The Netherlands. http://eurochrie2010.nl/publications/77.pdf

Plog, S. C. (1974). Why destination areas rise and fall in popularity. *Cornell Hotel and Restaurant Quarterly*, *14*(4), 55–58. https://doi.org/10.1177/001088047401400409

Poon, A. (1993). *Tourism, technology and competitive strategies*. Commonwealth Agricultural Bureau International.

Prebensen, N. K., Chen, J. S., & Uysal, M. (2014). *Creating experience value in tourism*. CABI Publishing.

Santos, M. C., Veiga, C., & Águas, P. (2016). Tourism services: Facing the challenge of new tourist profiles. *Worldwide Hospitality and Tourism Themes*, *8*(6), 654–669. https://doi.org/10.1108/WHATT-09-2016-0048

Schor, J. B., Walker, E. T., Lee, C. W., Parigi, P., & Cook, K. (2015). On the sharing economy. *Contexts*, *14*(1), 12–19. https://doi.org/10.1177/1536504214567860

Sharpley, R. & Stone, Ph.R. (Eds.) (2012). *Contemporary tourist experience: Concepts and consequence*. Routledge.

Sigala, M. (2017). Collaborative commerce in tourism: Implications for research and industry. *Current Issues in Tourism*, *20*(4), 346–355. https://doi.org/10.1080/13683500.2014.982522

Snel, A. (2013). Experience as the DNA of a changed relationship between firms and institutions and individuals. In J. Sundbo, & F. Sørensen (Eds.), *Handbook on the experience economy* (pp. 122–145). Elgar Publishing.

Sundbo, J., & Sørensen, F. (2013). Introduction to the experience economy. In J. Sundbo, & F. Sørensen (Eds.), *Handbook on the experience economy* (pp. 1–17). Elgar Publishing.

Uber wykroił połowę rynku przejazdów zamawianych przez aplikację [Uber cut out half of the app-ordered rides market]. https://businessinsider.com.pl/firmy/sprzedaz/udzial-ubera-w-rynku-przejazdow-w-polsce/eyd8chm (accessed on 19.07.2022).

Vaclavik, M. C., Macke, J., & Faturi e Silva, D. (2020). Do not talk to strangers: A study on trust in Brazilian ridesharing apps. *Technology in Society*, *63*, 101379. https://doi.org/10.1016/j.techsoc.2020.101379

Yeoman, I. S. (2008). *Tomorrow's tourist, scenarios & trends*. Elsevier.

Yeoman, I. S., Brass, D., & McMahon-Beattie, U. (2007). Current issue in tourism: The authentic tourist. *Tourism Management*, *28*(4), 1128–1138. https://doi.org/10.1016/j.tourman.2006.09.012

Yeoman, I. S., & McMahon-Beattie, U. (2019). The experience economy: Micro trends. *Journal of Tourism Futures*, *5*(2), 114–119. https://doi.org/10.1108/JTF-05-2019-0042

5 Self-Service Technologies (SSTs) and Their Implications on Tourist Experiences

Åse Storhaug Hole, Xiang Ying Mei, Bjørnar Engh, and Thor Håkon Engen

Introduction

The development of technology and digitalisation has led to many changes in service encounters. The raise and surface of self-service technologies (SSTs) as alternatives or replacements for traditional services (Oh et al., 2013; Rust & Espinoza, 2006) have changed the behaviour among tourists due to their important involvement in service delivery. This has then changed the experiences with the service providers such as airlines, restaurants, hotels, and retail shops. The usage of SSTs can consist of two scenarios. Forced scenarios are where customers are required to use SSTs with no other options. Voluntary usage scenarios on the other hand are when customers have the option of using SSTs as an addition or alternative and can directly interact with a service representative such as frontline staff at a hotel establishment should they want to do so. Evidently, depending on the scenarios, motivations as well as the overall tourism experience may be vastly different. Moreover, there is a concern about whether such solutions impact the customer's experiences and reflections on co-production and co-creation in a positive manner (Lang et al., 2020; Lawlor, 2010). SSTs may not be positive for all types of customers as they may cause anxiety and doubts, particularly among those individuals who are less prone to technologies (Mason et al., 2023).

With this in consideration, this chapter aims to investigate SST in the tourism context and the notion of co-production of experiences. It also seeks to discuss tourists' motivation in participating in such a service production. Using the example of Coop Obs, one of the largest supermarket chains in Norway, the experiences of using SSTs such as self-checkout kiosks are explored. While supermarkets not only serve tourists, they are also key operators in the domestic tourism industry in Norway due to the important second-home market in mountain regions. Moreover, self-checkout kiosks in supermarkets are available both in Norwegian and English and are thus technically well facilitated for international tourists visiting Norway.

Self-Service Technologies (SSTs) in Tourism

A general definition of SSTs is 'technological interfaces that enable customers to produce a service independent of direct service employee involvement' (Meuter

DOI: 10.4324/9781003335924-7

et al., 2000, p. 50). SSTs thus require a potential user or customer to use technology to perform work that is part of a service, for the service to be available to the customer. This means that the customer is not in contact with employees but uses technology to get service performed. SSTs have increased substantially in the hospitality and tourism industry in recent years (Oh et al., 2013). The tourism industry, which falls under the umbrella of the service sector, has eagerly embraced such technologies and acknowledged the active role that customers play in the provision of the primary service (Rosenbaum & Wong, 2015). In the modern marketplace, SSTs are becoming the standard (Collier et al., 2015). For business operators such as hotels, restaurants, retail shops, and airlines, SSTs can free up time so that they can manage with fewer employees and thus save resources. Tourists or users can also save time, which they can use on other activities and tasks instead. SSTs in the tourism industry include the more well-known and classic offerings such as Internet travel booking and more recent platforms like mobile airline check-in facilities. This has now also further expanded to hotel self-check-in, self-ordering of food, and self-checkout when purchasing items and goods at various retail shops in tourism-related businesses (Kelly et al., 2017; Oh et al., 2013).

A sound understanding of customer meanings and perceptions is crucial since it affects how value is created in tourism consumption experiences (Helkkula et al., 2012; Kelly et al., 2017). Airlines, for instance, have made a substantial investment not only in the technology itself, including airline kiosks for self-check-in but also evaluated whether travellers consider SSTs as beneficial amenities or as barriers to receiving the services and experiences that they need (Lee et al., 2012). It is also important to note that tourism is a vast industry with many types of businesses and tourists. Naturally, SSTs cannot be adopted by all types of tourism and tourism-related businesses. For instance, it was discovered that SSTs such as self-check-in kiosks are not ideal to introduce in luxury establishments compared with their budget counterparts as luxury hotel customers want to talk to employees directly rather than using machines (Rosenbaum & Wong, 2015). Hence, although the technology and possibility exist, it may not be ideal for all service settings. Other negative aspects include the fact that many of the services in the tourism industry still require customisation (Lu et al., 2022) and some level of human interaction as tourism is fundamentally a people industry. On the other hand, technology has opened many opportunities due to the pandemic, which has had a devastating impact on the tourism industry.

SSTs and Covid-19

Covid-19 has certainly led many companies in the service sector to rethink and even fast-pace the introduction of such technology in their customer-employee encounters. Tourism can be considered a 'high-touch' industry, meaning that it depends on close human-to-human interactions and mobility (Liu & Yang, 2021, p. 2908). However, due to social distancing and lockdown, and to prevent the spreading of the virus, human contact had to be limited and even avoided causing a shift in business operations. For those establishments that were allowed to still open between lockdowns, they had to think about alternative solutions using technologies. For instance, restaurants have introduced touchless and contactless payment options and menus by either offering food ordering kiosks or even QR-codes where all ordering and payment are done with smartphones. The food can even be delivered by robots offering a 100% touchless experience, to provide a safe environment for both customers and employees. Similar solutions are also applied to the hotel industry as well as retail sectors such as supermarkets when customers are more prone to use self-checkout kiosks to limit face-to-face interactions and thereby reduce the risk of getting infected by the virus.

- Thought point: With Covid-19 under control and the world has slowly returned to a pre-covid state, will some of the SSTs continue to be used or will most tourism services resume back to personal face-to-face interactions?

Co-Production of Experiences

A key topic discussed in relation to SSTs is the co-production of experiences. As discussed in much existing research, the tourism industry as an experience-based industry has realised that providing tourists with unique and memorable experiences is key to competitiveness and long-term survival (Mei et al., 2020). To achieve this, there is the need to meet the ever-evolving tourist expectations and needs for a shopping trip, dinner at a restaurant, hotel stay, and any other activities that tourists partake in at a destination (Chathoth et al., 2013). It has been argued that one way to ensure such is to co-produce or co-create experiences with tourists. When tourists themselves take an active role in this process, then experiences become unique and tailored to each tourist rather than providing standardised services and experiences to everyone. Co-production of services is when the customer takes an active part in the production of service, and this has become an important topic in recent years. Etgar (2008, p. 97) discusses the descriptive model of the consumer co-production process, while others use the term prosumer (Kotler, 2010; Lang et al., 2020; Ritzer & Jurgenson, 2010) when highlighting the customer's role in this process. Etgar's model further describes five basic levels that should exist for co-production to occur. These levels are as follows:

1 Development of antecedent conditions such as economic, cultural, and technological conditions having to be at a certain level for consumers to engage in co-production.
2 Development of motivating factors that make consumers engage in co-production. This is key in relation to facilitating good experiences for customers when they use SSTs.
3 Visibility of costs and benefits of co-production of service. This highlights the costs and benefits of co-production and whether any benefits outweigh the costs that customers perceive.
4 Activation is when the consumer is involved in the actual execution of the co-production. This concerns activation after co-production and is about when the customer takes the product into use.

5 Generate data to evaluate the results of the process to determine whether co-production is an activity that is worth engaging in. This level concerns generating data to form a basis for evaluating the difference between the cost/benefit of co-production and alternative strategies without customer involvement (Etgar, 2008, pp. 99–103).

Another relevant term as mentioned is co-creation. The terms co-production and co-creation are closely related but not synonymous. Chathoth et al. (2013) explain that companies create innovation through co-production and co-producing with the customers. On the other hand, co-creation is when consumers and other involved stakeholders can exert more power over the product, and they are allowed to 'play' with it or modify and experiment with it in ways that the company did not expect or think about initially. A further understanding of the difference between co-production and co-creation is through an interaction between the customer and a machine. In this stance, co-production is between the customer and a machine such as a self-checkout kiosk. This takes place within the production process itself before the product or service is used, whereas 'co-creation of value' occurs when the customer uses the product or service (Vargo & Lusch, 2006). A pair of skis has little value for the customer until he or she actively uses the skis and goes on a ski trip. The ski trip gives the ski product added value through nature experiences, fresh air, and better health. The customer is then in a co-creation process with the store that sells skis, but the main product is experience. The shop offers a service, where customers can buy goods in a physical store. The customer then takes such goods and uses them outside the store. In this example, the co-production takes place inside the store when the customer participates in the process, whereas the co-creation of value occurs when the customer uses the new pair of skis on a holiday experience. While this example applies to physical goods, a similar process is also applied to full services. Another example is in the context of booking holidays with travel agents. Tourists are involved in co-production which involves the planning, production, offering, and assessment process (Arıca & Kozak, 2019). Through information sharing, information seeking, responsible behaviour, and personal interactions, tourists can customise the package of tourism products that are tailored to their needs and wants (Yi & Gong, 2013). Value in the form of hedonic and unique experiences is then co-created during their holiday at a given destination. The above discussion indicates that co-creation comes after co-production has taken place as a further step beyond co-production. Moreover, in the context of SSTs and the usage of such technologies, the notion of co-production is more relevant, as the experiences lie in the actual co-production process between customers and the machines used in SSTs.

Digitalisation and Co-Production

Technological development and digitalisation have certainly facilitated and opened numerous possibilities for co-production to occur. In its infancy, digitisation was used to improve already existing processes in the private and public sectors. In the private sector, it was about creating digital solutions, so that the customer could search and find information online, and shop online. In the public sector, digitisation was about putting information online, so that the user can search and find information on their own (Di Giulio & Vecchi, 2021). The key commonalities were to maximise efficiency while reducing costs. As technological development moves forward, the focus shifts further, from reducing costs to business operations, and in that connection how to prepare for future competition with the help of digitisation (Kræmmergaard, 2019). One definition of digitisation is using digital technologies to change the business model and to find new ways to create value and obtain income, by moving to a digital business (Heggerners, 2020; Rachinger et al., 2019). This stresses that when adapting digital technologies to find new ways to make money, the business model also needs to be changed. The concept of the business model includes how to create value for a customer, what resources are used to create this value, and how to get paid by the customer (Heggerners, 2020). Evidently, co-production does not always occur by involving technology. However, technology has certainly created the need for more opportunities for co-production to take place.

- Thought point: To which degree can co-production be integrated into facilitating tourism experiences?

Tourist's Motivation in Using SSTs

For the co-production of experience to occur, tourists must be willing to participate in such a process. Since customers are in this sense important contributors to a firm's productivity, there is a need to define which roles customers should play in this process (Meuter et al., 2005). Meuter et al. (2005) argue that some of the barriers that prevent customers to participate in this process by using SSTs such as airline self-check-in kiosks are that they are not aware of the potential benefits, including time-saving, or they are unsure of the system and the usage. Etgar (2008) adds to the discussion by dividing motivation and drivers into three categories consisting of economic, psychological, and social drivers. Economic drivers are defined as economic gain (Lusch et al., 1992). This can be either a price reduction of an item or goods that lead to financial gain for the customer. Moreover, it can also save time by using self-service checkouts as raised by Meuter et al. (2005). Psychological drivers that motivate the customers may include the fact that by participating in the co-production of a service, they can experience mastery (of using the digital tool) if they succeed in performing it. This can provide positive experiences that make the customer choose a self-service checkout in the future (Etgar, 2008, p. 101). And lastly, social drivers can also be a motivating factor for the customer to get involved in the co-production of a service. The digitisation of many societies in developed economies is happening at a fast-pace and being a 'digital native', which includes both Generations Z and Y, is associated with both status and social acceptance. People who consider themselves to be part of this group will naturally choose to use SSTs and other similar digital tools (Etgar, 2008).

Furthermore, Oh et al. (2013) investigated intrinsic motivations indicating that some customers are unwilling to use these systems as they desire human interactions and related constructs. It all depends on the travellers' intrinsic motivation. For instance, if the motivation is to save time, then customers will be more than willing to use SSTs. Some may also find it fun and exciting to use new technology, and then *fun* and *excitement* can also serve as intrinsic motivations. On the other hand, should the intrinsic motivation be to seek personal human interactions with the hotel staff, this will then counteract the adoption of SSTs as a method of service transactions (Oh et al., 2013).

Another question that arises is that not everyone is comfortable with digitalisation and the usage of SSTs for various reasons. This includes people who are unsure of the system and the usage as discussed and those who are outside of what is considered 'digital natives', or their desire for human interactions surpass all the other perceived benefits. The elderly part of the population often fits into such groups. While many elderly people are comfortable with technology, many are still turning to cash and traditional solutions. Some do not even own smartphones and are non-digital by not being on the Internet at all (Buggeland et al., 2023). This means that they are excluded from many services, and this undoubtedly impacts their service encounters and overall travel experiences negatively if the technology is not adapted to their needs and concerns. The discussion thus indicates that demographics, personal traits, and characteristics as well as attitudes are key elements that impact people's willingness in adopting new technology such as SSTs (Lee et al., 2010; Lee et al., 2012). Moreover, motivation to use SSTs may also depend on the situation even though they have previously used the technology (Kelly et al., 2017; Simon & Usunier, 2007). For instance, when customers are in a hurry, they tend to turn to SSTs (Demoulin & Djelassi, 2016). In a different situation as when tourists travel to a foreign country, they may refrain from using the SSTs at airports, train stations, and self-check-in/out kiosks as there may either be language barriers or they are just not familiar with the system, making it riskier should mistakes be made.

- Thought point: Discuss the extent to which co-production (and co-creation) is something that all tourists want to participate in.

Case Study Example – Coop Obs

As discussed, SSTs are now largely integrated into all types of services in the tourism industry as well as other secondary industries, including retail shops and supermarket outlets. Hence, SSTs are not only found when checking into airlines and hotels, but they are also found in major supermarkets and restaurants as discussed. These establishments are servicing not only international tourists but also locals and domestic tourists, who have found new appreciation and love for travelling domestically during the pandemic. For instance, in Norway, supermarkets are key operators in the domestic tourism industry due to the important second-home market in mountain regions. Additionally, since all self-checkout kiosks in supermarkets in

Norway are available both in Norwegian and English, they are also technically well facilitated for international tourists visiting Norway as their holiday destination.

This study has focused on self-checkout kiosks in one of the largest retail and supermarket chains in Norway, Coop Obs. Coop is Norway's second-largest grocery operator and currently operates approx. 1,150 grocery stores within six chain concepts, including Coop Obs which is classified as a hypermarket (Coop, 2023). Different from a supermarket, Coop Obs also sells household items, clothing, and various leisure and sport-related equipment such as ski and alpine gear, fishing gear, rollerblades and skateboards, ice skating equipment and sleight, bicycles, and scooters. Coop has chosen to implement self-service checkouts to make the checkout process easier and faster for customers. For the company to succeed in this, it is a prerequisite that Coop knows its customers and what their needs and expectations are. Before Coop started implementing these solutions, they mapped the customers' journey, to see where the new technology provides increased value for them. They finally saw the phase that it was possible to make it easier by introducing self-service checkouts so that customers would not have to stand in queues and could easily pay and finish their shopping trip. It was nevertheless challenging to use these solutions for large-scale operations. The introduction of such technology solved this challenge by having the customers scan the goods themselves as they pick and put the goods straight into a bag in the shopping cart. This solution saves customers a lot of time (Coop, 2019).

Methodology and Data Collection

Data was collected at Coop Obs Elverum, located in Inland County in Norway. This location was selected because this store is way ahead when it comes to offering SSTs. There are different solutions for customers who choose self-service checkouts, which include the ordinary self-checkout solution where goods are scanned at the kiosk when the customers are done with the shopping and ready to pay. The other solution is called Shopexpress where customers use a handheld scanner that can be picked up at the entrance to the store. The customer scans their goods and puts them straight into a shopping bag/net. The customer then goes to the exit and plugs the hand scanner into the cash register so that information from this is loaded into the cash register system and the customer then pays by card. The third method is where customers can use the system called Coopay. This is a mobile-based system where the customer downloads an app, which connects the customer's bank card to a payment solution. Customers can use their mobile phones and scan items in the store, go to the self-service checkout and scan their phone, and thus pay without a card. In addition to these three methods, customers can still use the ordinary cash register solution.

The main data collection method was observations, which was conducted on two separate days, one during lunchtime and another one in the afternoon. Before commencing the first observation, researchers tested the self-service checkouts themselves to understand the system better by scanning the products directly in the self-checkout kiosk. A few different products were bought, such as loose-weight nuts, bananas, beer, two loaves of bread, and a packet of biscuits. The packet of biscuits was just to be scanned straight in, presumably the beer too, but then the system locked up and someone from the staff came to make sure that the researchers were allowed to buy alcohol (due to the age limit). Furthermore, the nuts and bananas were weighed, and it was a bit complicated to find the right product on the screen. It was the same for finding the right baked goods, but this is a matter of habit and will get easier each time the system is used. Then a receipt was printed, and this needed to be scanned at the exit to leave the store.

The next time, the Shopekspress option was used. The products were scanned as they were picked up. The same products were bought as last time, to get to know the different solutions using the same products. Products were scanned and 'removed' several times, just to test this properly. When the researchers got to the self-checkout kiosk, the Coop membership card was scanned, the hand scanner was put in place, and all the products were loaded into the machine automatically. However, these only applied to the items that had a barcode, the other items that were typical bulk items had to be entered manually as last time. Due to the previous testing experience, it went faster this time around. This solution is probably not suitable for international tourists, domestic tourists, or even locals who do not have a Coop membership.

Furthermore, based on these two experiences, the researchers became familiar with the solutions. For large purchases, it is possible to scan the goods and put them straight into a bag in the trolley, and when it is done, just pay. Nevertheless, when purchasing a few products, it is easier to just scan the products directly in the self-checkout kiosk. Based on this test, an observation form was created where it was possible to easily record the customers' choice of checkout solutions, approximate age range, gender, number of items, and need for help and control. In addition to the observations, the researchers also carried out a quantitative study by collecting data from a sample of 526 respondents to further verify the findings gained from the observations.

Findings and Implications

In the two separate observations, 175 people used self-checkout kiosks, while 166 people used manual ones. The customers were therefore evenly distributed between the manual and the self-checkouts. For customers choosing to take part in co-production, the service must be experienced as user-friendly, and customers must be motivated to use the services. As discussed, co-production is about the customer taking an active part in the production of a service. The development of motivating factors in relation to co-production is fundamentally related to facilitating customers to have a good experience when they use self-service checkouts (Etgar, 2008). The observation shows that half choose manual checkouts and thus chose to not participate in a co-production of the service. This may indicate that many of the customers are not sufficiently motivated to adopt this technology. According to Dabholkar (1996), self-checkout kiosks need to be easy to use with a user interface that is simple and logically structured, which gives customers a positive experience. The customer's own choices indicate that some find self-checkouts to be user-friendly, and the other half do not. Nevertheless, since customers' behaviour was merely observed and direct contact was not made with them, it is difficult to determine whether this is the case or whether there were other motivations or reasons. For example, it may be because these customers have yet to discover such a checkout option, or they have not received sufficient information on how to use them (Meuter et al., 2005). The customers' experience of using self-service checkouts as part of co-production is arguably governed by their need for user-friendly services. In addition, this could also be influenced by the level of technological anxiety and the need for personal contact with frontline employees (Oh et al., 2013). When users are familiar with the SSTs, the systems, and the environment, they are presumable more willing to use the technology. Tourists who travel domestically might be more willing to use self-checkout solutions as there are fewer barriers and opportunities to fail. Thus, their co-production experiences will also likely be positive due to a sense of mastery and accomplishment. Interestingly while the co-production process occurs fundamentally between customers and the machines used in SSTs, should human assistance be required in the process, and they are available at customers' disposal, this also contributes to positive experiences.

Another key finding from the study is that over twice as many elderly people prefer the traditional manual checkouts where they must interact with the frontline staff. The findings from the quantitative study also verify that there is a clear difference between young customers and elderly customers when investigating the dimensions of (1) the ease of use, (2) technological anxiety, and (3) face-to-face contact with employees and their impact on customer's experience with using self-service checkouts. These results thus support the findings from the observations that elderly customers are more concerned about the ease of use (Dabholkar, 1996), they are more anxious about the technology and express more need for contact with service personnel (Dabholkar et al., 2003; Meuter et al., 2005). The findings are however not surprising as elderly people are more averse to the use of SSTs as they often learn to use the technology as adults (Simon & Usunier, 2007). This applies in several service settings and not just in tourism and is again connected to the level of technological anxiety.

The elderly group of the population in developed economies often has sufficient disposable income and greater commitment to travel as they have more time (Isa et al., 2020). Since elderly tourists love and appreciate travelling (Boonpat et al., 2022), they are a crucial market for many destinations and tourism activities due to their strong buying power. In the digital era, it is thus important to understand the needs, wants, and motivations of such a group. Such knowledge is key to being able to create a co-production environment in which they are willing to participate and can gain confidence and control. This will lead to positive tourism experiences on their side.

Conclusion

Continuous development of the experience economy indicates that SSTs are here to stay regardless of the pandemic as the technology will continue to develop and peoples' overall dependency on digital solutions will only be more amplified regardless. Tourism and tourism-related businesses must be not only preoccupied with the benefits of such technology on their side but also understand possible negative customer experiences as a result. Negative tourist experiences can eventually lead to the store or even the destination as a whole gaining a bad reputation, which in turn can lead to a decrease in turnover and even negative word-of-mouth.

This chapter has used Norway as a case study example and discovered that although Norway has come a long way in digitalisation, many customers still refrain from using SSTs such as self-checkout kiosks. This indicates that motivation is a strong influencer, and many are unwilling to participate in the co-production of such experiences. It could also just be that many are not familiar with the existence of the system and are therefore uncertain of their role in the co-production process. Therefore, tourism and tourism-related that plan to introduce SSTs also make sure that the self-checkout solutions are designed based on customers' premises. In addition, it is necessary to plan for good routines when it comes to training and educating the customers by ensuring that face-to-face assistance from the staff is possible should that be necessary. This is particularly relevant when comes to the elderly group of the population and those that experience technology anxiety. Implications of this study indicate that there is a need to pay more attention to an important and large group of tourists, the elderly people, and emphasise assistance, care, and personal contact with them. After all, freedom of choice, training, and support from the frontline personnel are the key elements in this context. After all, no one likes to be pushed into a situation they cannot control and manage. Additionally, SSTs may not be relevant and ideal in all types of services and service settings. Thus, it would be quite risky to consider SSTs as replacements for all service encounters and deliveries as such technology should rather be considered alternatives and additions instead. Future studies may also seek to investigate various tourism service settings in different cultures as customer attitude, personal characteristics, and demographics impact motivation to participate in the experience co-production process.

Further Questions

- With the increasing dependency on technological solutions for both the tourists and tourism and tourism-related businesses, what are the concerns that should be raised and further discussed, which will impact the tourism experience consumption?
- How can co-production and co-creation be discussed to include vastly different types of tourists such as elderly people over 60 years old as well as travellers from parts of the world where technological solutions are yet to be fully adopted?

- Considering that the elder group of the population in many parts of the world have sufficient disposable income, and time, and display a love for travel, how can the tourism industry balance technology processes while meeting the needs of such a market?

Further Readings

Lau, A. (2020). New technologies used in COVID-19 for business survival: Insights from the hotel sector in China. *Information Technology and Tourism*, *22*(4), 497–504.

Roberts, D., Hughes, M., & Kertbo, K. (2013). Exploring consumer's motivations to engage in innovation through co-creation activities. *European Journal of Marketing*, *48*(1/2), 147–169. https://doi.org/10.1108/EJM-12-2010-0637

Shin, H. & Perdue, R.R. (2019). Self-service technology research: A bibliometric co-citation visualization analysis. *International Journal of Hospitality Management*, *80*, 101–112. https://doi.org/10.1016/j.ijhm.2019.01.012

Wang, Y., So, K. K. F., & Sparks, B. A. (2017). Technology readiness and customer satisfaction with travel technologies: A cross-country investigation. *Journal of Travel Research*, *56*(5), 563–577. https://doi.org/10.1177/0047287516657891

References

Arıca, R., & Kozak, R. (2019). Co-production behaviors of travel agencies customers: A research on local cultural tourists visiting Istanbul. *Journal of Tourism and Hospitality Management*, *7*(1), 84–98.

Boonpat, O., Yolthasart, S., & Utchaya, N. (2022). Wellness tourism activity model development to promote tourism market for Thai elderly tourists in Chiang Rai province [article]. *Journal of Management Information & Decision Sciences*, *25*(2), 1–12. https://login.ezproxy.inn.no/login?url=https://search.ebscohost.com/login.aspx?direct=true&db=bsu&AN=156926161&site=ehost-live&scope=site.

Buggeland, S. A., Solheim, E. K., & Solstad, F. (2023). *Svea (82) nekter å bruke kontaktløst: – Prinsipielt helskrullete! [Svea (82) refuses to use contactless: - In principle, completely stupid!]*. VG. https://www.vg.no/nyheter/i/zE8B6w/svea-82-nekter-aa-bruke-kontaktloest-prinsipielt-helskrullete

Chathoth, P., Altinay, L., Harrington, R. J., Okumus, F., & Chan, E. S. W. (2013). Co-production versus co-creation: A process based continuum in the hotel service context. *International Journal of Hospitality Management*, *32*, 11–20. https://doi.org/10.1016/j.ijhm.2012.03.009

Collier, J. E., Moore, R. S., Horky, A., & Moore, M. L. (2015). Why the little things matter: Exploring situational influences on customers' self-service technology decisions. *Journal of Business Research*, *68*(3), 703–710. https://doi.org/10.1016/j.jbusres.2014.08.001

Coop. (2019). *Ta i bruk Coop shopexpress [Use Coop shopexpress]*. https://www.obs.no/om-oss/ta-i-bruk-coop-shopexpress

Coop. (2023). *Om Coop [About Coop]*. https://coop.no/om-coop/

Dabholkar, P. A. (1996). Consumer evaluations of new technology-based self-service options: An investigation of alternative models of service quality. *International Journal of Research in Marketing*, *13*(1), 29–51. https://doi.org/10.1016/0167-8116(95)00027-5

Dabholkar, P. A., Michelle Bobbitt, L., & Lee, E. J. (2003). Understanding consumer motivation and behavior related to self-scanning in retailing. *International Journal of Service Industry Management, 14*(1), 59–95. https://doi.org/10.1108/09564230310465994

Demoulin, N., & Djelassi, T. M. (2016). An integrated model of self-service technology (SST) usage in a retail context. *International Journal of Retail & Distribution Management, 44*(5), 540–559. https://doi.org/10.1108/IJRDM-08-2015-0122

Di Giulio, M., & Vecchi, G. (2021). Implementing digitalization in the public sector. Technologies, agency, and governance. *Public Policy and Administration, 0*(0). https://doi.org/10.1177/09520767211023283

Etgar, M. (2008). A descriptive model of the consumer co-production process. *Journal of the Academy of Marketing Science, 36*(1), 97–108. https://doi.org/10.1007/s11747-007-0061-1

Heggerners, T. A. (2020). *Digital Forretningsforståelse - fra Store Data til Små Biter [Digital business understanding - from big data to small bits* (3rd ed.). Fagbokforlaget.

Helkkula, A., Kelleher, C., & Pihlström, M. (2012). Characterizing value as an experience: Implications for service researchers and managers. *Journal of Service Research, 15*(1), 59–75. https://doi.org/10.1177/1094670511426897

Isa, S. M., Ismail, H. N., & Fuza, Z. I. M. (2020). Elderly and heritage tourism: A review. *IOP Conference Series: Earth and Environmental Science, 447*(1), 012038. https://doi.org/10.1088/1755-1315/447/1/012038

Kelly, P., Lawlor, J., & Mulvey, M. (2017). Customer roles in self-service technology encounters in a tourism context. *Journal of Travel & Tourism Marketing, 34*(2), 222–238. https://doi.org/10.1080/10548408.2016.1156612

Kotler, P. (2010). The prosumer movement. In B. Blättel-Mink & K.-U. Hellmann (Eds.), *Prosumer Revisited: Zur Aktualität einer Debatte* (pp. 51–60). VS Verlag für Sozialwissenschaften. https://doi.org/10.1007/978-3-531-91998-0_2

Kræmmergaard, P. (2019). *Digital transformation: 10 Evner din Organisation skal mestre- og 3 som du har brug for [Digital transformation: 10 skills your organisation must master - and three you that you need]* (2nd ed.). Djøf Forlag.

Lang, B., Botha, E., Robertson, J., Kemper, J. A., Dolan, R., & Kietzmann, J. (2020). How to grow the sharing economy? Create prosumers! *Australasian Marketing Journal (AMJ), 28*(3), 58–66. https://doi.org/10.1016/j.ausmj.2020.06.012.

Lawlor, J. (2010). The role of the customer as a quasi-employee in service organisations: Research agenda. In G. Gorham & Z. Mottiar (Eds.), *Contemporary issues in Irish and global tourism and hospitality* (pp. 179–239). Dublin Institute of Technology.

Lee, W., Castellanos, C., & Chris Choi, H. S. (2012). The effect of technology readiness on Customers' attitudes toward self-service technology and its adoption; the empirical study of U.S. Airline self-service check-in kiosks. *Journal of Travel & Tourism Marketing, 29*(8), 731–743. https://doi.org/10.1080/10548408.2012.730934.

Lee, H. J., Jeong Cho, H., Xu, W., & Fairhurst, A. (2010). The influence of consumer traits and demographics on intention to use retail self-service checkouts. *Marketing Intelligence & Planning, 28*(1), 46–58. https://doi.org/10.1108/02634501011014606.

Liu, C., & Yang, J. (2021). How hotels adjust technology-based strategy to respond to COVID-19 and gain competitive productivity (CP): Strategic management process and dynamic capabilities. *International Journal of Contemporary Hospitality Management, 33*(9), 2907–2931. https://doi.org/10.1108/IJCHM-10-2020-1143.

Lu, S., Kwon, J., & Ahn, J. (2022). Self-service technology in the hospitality and tourism settings: A critical review of the literature. *Journal of Hospitality & Tourism Research, 46*(6), 1220–1236. https://doi.org/10.1177/1096348020987633.

Lusch, R. F., Brown, S. W., & Brunswick, G. J. (1992). A general framework for explaining internal vs. external exchange. *Journal of the Academy of Marketing Science, 20*(2), 119–134. https://doi.org/10.1007/BF02723452.

Mason, M. C., Zamparo, G., & Pauluzzo, R. (2023). Amidst technology, environment and human touch. Understanding elderly customers in the bank retail sector. *International Journal of Bank Marketing, Ahead-of-Print*(Ahead-of-Print). https://doi.org/10.1108/IJBM-06-2022-0256.

Mei, X. Y., Hågensen, A.-M. S., & Kristiansen, H. S. (2020). Storytelling through experiencescape: Creating unique stories and extraordinary experiences in farm tourism. *Tourism and Hospitality Research, 20*(1), 93–104. https://doi.org/10.1177/1467358418813410.

Meuter, M. L., Bitner, M. J., Ostrom, A. L., & Brown, S. W. (2005). Choosing among alternative service delivery modes: An investigation of customer trial of self-service technologies. *Journal of Marketing, 69*(2), 61–83. https://doi.org/10.1509/jmkg.69.2.61.60759.

Meuter, M. L., Ostrom, A. L., Roundtree, R. I., & Bitner, M. J. (2000). Self-service technologies: Understanding customer satisfaction with technology-based service encounters. *Journal of Marketing, 64*(3), 50–64. https://doi.org/10.1509/jmkg.64.3.50.18024.

Oh, H., Jeong, M., & Baloglu, S. (2013). Tourists' adoption of self-service technologies at resort hotels. *Journal of Business Research, 66*(6), 692–699. https://doi.org/10.1016/j.jbusres.2011.09.005.

Rachinger, M., Rauter, R., Müller, C., Vorraber, W., & Schirgi, E. (2019). Digitalization and its influence on business model innovation. *Journal of Manufacturing Technology Management, 30*(8), 1143–1160. https://doi.org/10.1108/JMTM-01-2018-0020.

Ritzer, G., & Jurgenson, N. (2010). Production, consumption, prosumption: The nature of capitalism in the age of the digital 'prosumer'. *Journal of Consumer Culture, 10*(1), 13–36. https://doi.org/10.1177/1469540509354673.

Rosenbaum, M. S., & Wong, I. A. (2015). If you install it, will they use it? Understanding why hospitality customers take "technological pauses" from self-service technology. *Journal of Business Research, 68*(9), 1862–1868. https://doi.org/10.1016/j.jbusres.2015.01.014.

Rust, R. T., & Espinoza, F. (2006). How technology advances influence business research and marketing strategy. *Journal of Business Research, 59*(10), 1072–1078. https://doi.org/10.1016/j.jbusres.2006.08.002

Simon, F., & Usunier, J.-C. (2007). Cognitive, demographic, and situational determinants of service customer preference for personnel-in-contact over self-service technology. *International Journal of Research in Marketing, 24*(2), 163–173. https://doi.org/10.1016/j.ijresmar.2006.11.004.

Vargo, S. L., & Lusch, R. F. (2006). Service-dominant logic: What it is, what it is not, what it might be. In R. F. Lusch & S. L. Vargo (Eds.), *The service-dominant logic of marketing: Dialog, debate, and direction* (pp. 43–56). ME Sharp.

Yi, Y., & Gong, T. (2013). Customer value co-creation behavior: Scale development and validation. *Journal of Business Research, 66*(9), 1279–1284. https://doi.org/10.1016/j.jbusres.2012.02.026.

Part II

Marketing Experiences in the Contemporary Experience Economy

6 Value Co-Creation through Technology-Mediated Experiences

A Research Agenda

Shasha Liu, Pierre Beckendorff, and Judith Mair

Introduction

Understanding experiences is significant for scholars and practitioners because competitive advantages can be obtained by enhancing tourist experiences (Giuseppe et al., 2022; Quinlan Cutler & Carmichael, 2010). Most tourists consider themselves 'non-typical' (Prebensen et al., 2003) and seek personal and meaningful experiences (Galani-Moutafi, 2000). Accordingly, Prahalad and Ramaswamy (2004) introduced the concept of experience co-creation. They defined this concept as the 'joint creation of value by the company and the customer' (p. 8), thus emphasising the role of 'value' in the tourism experience. Accordingly, the concept of value co-creation is frequently used in discussions on tourist experiences (Campos et al., 2018). However, critical questions have been raised about the usefulness and validity of value co-creation because emerging tourist practices and experiences are not fully captured by traditional notions of co-creation (Neuhofer, 2016; Rihova et al., 2015).

Advances in technology have made information and communication ubiquitous (Weiser, 1993), challenging traditional concepts of co-creating value through tourist experiences. Specifically, advances in smartphones put 'social relations into travel ... with complex patterns of social experience conducted through communications at-a-distance' (Sheller & Urry, 2006, p. 210). Subsequently, social lives are 'full of multiple and extended connections often across long distances' (Sheller & Urry, 2006, p. 213). These observations highlight that value co-creation through technology-mediated tourist experiences occurs not only within the locus of physical interactions between tourists and service providers, but also through interactions across time and space with other actors who are not physically present (Fan et al., 2020).

The prevailing discourse in the value co-creation literature tends to emphasise the dominant role of providers and their interactions with customers within a service ecosystem. The tourist is often regarded as a passive target of marketing offerings rather than an independent co-creator of value. This perspective focuses on interactions between tourists and providers, and as such, the concept of value is rather abstract (García-Rosell et al., 2019). However, this approach neglects the role of 'hybrid' interactions with other actors in the 'customer ecosystem', which has been defined as 'a system of actors and spheres that customers are involved

DOI: 110.4324/9781003335924-9

with'(Heinonen et al., 2013, p. 107). Similarly, in a tourism context, it is proposed that the 'tourist ecosystem' can be defined as a system of interacting actors and spheres that are relevant to a touristic experience. Therefore, this chapter aims to clarify the process of value co-creation in technology-mediated tourist experiences by identifying the actors and mechanisms of co-creation and co-destruction, and the various dimensions of value.

- Thought point: Can you think of a time when you become a co-creator of tourism experiences? What did it feel like? What type of experience context was it?

Methodology

A conceptual framework analysis is employed to understand the concept of value co-creation of tourist experiences mediated by technology. Conceptual framework analysis generates a network of linked concepts by making new connections between disparate bodies of literature (Jabareen, 2009). First, the related data sources were mapped, and data collection was conducted. A keyword inventory was constructed by screening titles, abstracts, and keywords from the value co-creation literature. Second, after reviewing the selected articles, duplicate and non-relevant publications were removed from the sample by screening the selected publications. Additional refereed articles were added by inspecting the reference lists of preliminary publications to identify any studies that might have been overlooked. Third, open coding was used to analyse the contents of the database to seek similarities and differences between and across the studies included.

Findings

Technology has empowered tourists to interact with others in hybrid physical and virtual spaces. This leads to additional social interactions which can significantly influence evaluations of value. The study integrates the main approaches to value creation and shows that there are three major themes to value co-creation in technology-mediated tourist experiences. Table 6.1 provides the major themes that were synthesised from the analysis of the articles in this review, including the dimensions of value, actors, and mechanisms. Using these three themes as a conceptual framework, this chapter integrates the resources integrated, dimensional value and value co-creation and co-destruction of tourist experiences. Given the lack of research on these aspects, this study will propose a research agenda to inform further empirical research. Each of the themes identified is detailed in the following section.

Value Creation

In the consumer and marketing literature, value has been explored from three main perspectives: goods-dominant (G-D) logic, service-dominant (S-D) logic, and customer-dominant (C-D) logic. These various theoretical approaches to value co-creation are not contradictory (Saarijärvi et al., 2013). Vargo et al. (2020) argued

Table 6.1 Value in tourist experiences emerges through the co-creation process

Elements	*Description*
Actors	Tourists, providers (including government, service providers, and local businesses), social networks, other tourists, and hosts
Resources	Tourists' accumulated reality and ecosystem, including various operand resources and operant resources
Dimensions of value	Individual value Social value Lived value Imaginary value

Source: Authors' own work.

that S-D logic is the most expansive and holistic approach to value creation. The initial concept of S-D logic highlighted interactions between multiple actors from a provider's perspective, but more recent revisions have emphasised an actor-to-actor (A2A) orientation. This orientation considers all actors and emphasises that the beneficiary is always an active participant who integrates operand and operant resources for their value. Overall, value creation is an all-encompassing process which emphasises the dynamic interactions and the nature of the context (Akaka et al., 2015). These approaches can be explored further, and extended, by considering means, nature, and locus (see Table 6.2).

Some of the discussion of value has focused on the various ways that value can be understood in many different contexts, and the remainder of this chapter will concentrate on value co-creation in tourist experiences mediated by technology. Figure 6.1 extends the work of Grönroos and Voima (2013) by proposing that value in tourist experiences is co-created through a hybrid of virtual, physical, and social interactions. This happens across five actor spheres in a tourist's social life. Importantly, these interactions often take place in the tourist ecosystem without the presence or involvement of service providers (Grönroos & Voima, 2013). A tourist can be involved in interactions among multiple parties (e.g., service providers, the host, fellow travellers, companions, and their social networks) in multiple contexts (Neuhofer et al., 2013) within a tourist ecosystem at all stages of the experiences.

Consistent with previous studies on social value from interactions with multiple actors, Figure 6.1 highlights dimensional value from interactions in hybrid spaces. Compared with previousstudies, this figure highlights blended experiences through dynamic and multiple interactions between multiple actors in hybrid spaces. Accordingly, from the micro level, value co-creation and value co-destruction consist of interactions between some or all of the following in tourists' ecosystems:

1 a provider sphere
2 a tourist sphere
3 a host community sphere
4 a travel companion and other tourists' sphere
5 a social network sphere

Table 6.2 Theoretical approaches to value creation

Approach		*Value in exchange*	*Value in use*	*Value in context*	*Value in experience*
Paradigm		*G-D logic*	*S-D logic (original)*	*S-D logic (revised)*	*C-D logic*
Means	*Value*	Created by the provider	Co-created in the use of goods or services (Vargo et al., 2008)	Co-created by integrating resources in the service ecosystem (Akaka et al., 2015)	Value is formed (Heinonen et al., 2013)
	Value creation	trade-offs	A structured evaluation	A holistic and dynamic evaluation	Sense making
Nature	*Value*	Increasing wealth for the service provider (Vargo et al., 2008)	Consumer satisfaction	Increasing adaptability, survivability, and system well-being through service (Vargo et al., 2008)	Enhancing consumers' well-being
	Value creation	A structured process where service providers and consumers have distinct roles	A structured process where service providers and consumers are considered co-creators	Uniquely and phenomenologically determined by the beneficiary	An ongoing, iterative circular process where the consumer is considered an independent creator
Locus	*Value*	Embedded in products/ services	Co-created in the interaction at the consumers' end	Co-created through interaction at the beneficiary end	Emerges in the social life
	Value creation	Occurs in the control zone of the provider	Occurs in the control zone of the provider	Occurs in person at one certain point in time and space	Occurs through multiple visible and invisible experiential spaces in a consumer's social life (e.g., biological, physical, mental, social, geographical, and virtual)
Scope	*Value*	Created in production	Co-created through the use of products or services	Co-created through the use of products or services	Accumulated experience (past, current, and future experience)
	Value creation	Takes places before exchange	Created when the service provider is active	Created when the beneficiary is active	Temporal and not necessarily and directly related to the service provider's activities

Sources: Adapted from *Grönroos and Voima* (2013), Heinonen et al. (2013) and Vargo et al. (2020)

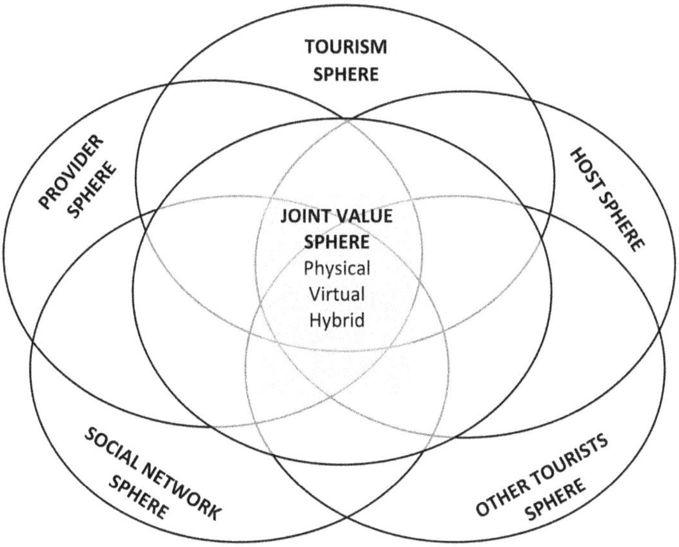

Figure 6.1 Interactions and relationships between various actors

Sources: Adapted from Edvardsson et al. (2011) and Grönroos and Voima (2013)

Although the framework is used here to explain how tourists use technology to co-create value, it is important to acknowledge that value can also be co-destroyed by the same interactions between the actors involved in tourist experiences.

Resource Integration in Value Co-Creation

Resource-advantage theory defines resources as 'tangible and intangible entities available to the firm that enable it to produce efficiently and/or effectively a market offering that has value for some market segment(s)' (Hunt, 2000, p. 138; Madhavaram & Hunt, 2008). Operand resources are static and finite, while operant resources are dynamic and infinite. Operant resources are fundamental to the creation of competitive advantage and performance for providers (Vargo & Lusch, 2004, 2008). This is because 'knowledge and skills operate on resources to solve problems, fulfil needs, and produce a favourable customer experience' (Edvardsson et al., 2011, p. 329). Further, Edvardsson et al. (2011) and Edvardsson et al. (2012) argued that resources are embedded in a social context influenced by social factors, such as culture, norms, interpretations, rules, and languages.

Value co-creation through technology-mediated tourist experiences is an ongoing, iterative circular process. Value is directly or indirectly created by integrating resources through physical or virtual interactions between multiple actors in the tourist ecosystem. In other words, a tourist can integrate both their resources and other actors' resources to co-create value through technology-mediated tourist experiences. Thus, it is necessary to understand how a tourist integrates different types of resources (including resources from other actors) to co-create value within a tourist ecosystem. A few studies have made some insightful contributions in this direction (see, for example, Campos et al., 2016; Prebensen et al., 2013). For example, Xie et al. (2021) revealed social capital as a key element that influences tourists' co-creation experiences in the virtual tourist community. However, a more systematic approach is needed to move the field forward.

Value in Tourist Experiences Mediated by Technology

Existing studies mainly consider value as a linear process within a service ecosystem (Helkkula et al., 2012) and neglect dynamic value within dynamic networks and social contexts (Blocker & Barrios, 2015). According to Helkkula et al. (2012), value in tourist experiences can be dynamically understood from four dimensions: individual and social value, imaginary and lived value, value in context, and accumulative value. Attention now turns to how value is co-created and co-destroyed at all stages of the experience through interactions with multiple actors by using these four dimensions as a framework for further discussion.

Individual Value in Tourist Experiences

Individual value is defined as 'individual service customers' sense making of value in the experience, which takes place as inner thoughts and which may or may not be externalised in the form of words or gestures' (Helkkula et al., 2012, p. 65). Such individual value can be determined by an individual's preferences, habits, needs, and values (Edvardsson et al., 2011). Individual value can be co-created through interactions between tourists and providers via two processes – the production process and the consumption process (Grönroos & Voima, 2013). The production process refers to customer engagement in a service provider's activities. The consumption process refers to a service provider's engagement with tourists' consumption of experience. Additionally, individual value can be co-created (Buhalis & Sinarta, 2019) through interactions with third-party actors. Actors from an individual's social networks can participate in the lived experiences of the tourist by providing suggestions and recommendations throughout a trip (Xiang & Gretzel, 2010). Tourists can attend to emotional and psychological needs by sharing travel experiences with their social networks (Fan et al., 2020).

Although the co-creation of value may be the aim, individual value can also be co-destroyed through interactions with providers and other actors. First, when providers and tourists fail to appropriately interpret each other's actions (Echeverri & Skålén, 2011), the individual value will be diminished. There is often a discrepancy between the market offerings and a tourist's evaluation of these offerings (O'Cass & Sok, 2015). Furthermore, as Plé and Chumpitaz Cáceres (2010) note, inappropriate or unexpected use of available resources can result in value co-destruction for at least one of the parties. Second, in some cases, personalisation can also result in value co-destruction. Privacy concerns are a challenge for personalisation

(Wozniak et al., 2016). Consumers face a dilemma known as the personalisation-privacy paradox (Awad & Krishnan, 2006). This implies that consumers are concerned about the risks to their privacy through personal information disclosure, yet they desire personalisation benefits (Lee & Cranage, 2011).

Social Value in Tourist Experiences

The creators of value are not restricted to an individual or related group but can expand to different configurations of actors in social reality (Helkkula et al., 2012). The consumption of tourist experiences does not derive solely from individuals, but rather from interactions with others (Neuhofer et al., 2012). Tourists often share or compare their experiences with others (friends, relatives, or even unknown others) in their social networks even if they travel alone. This leads to what is known as social value, defined as the social benefits from interaction with others through consumption (Sweeney & Soutar, 2001).

Generally, tourists can construct a socially dense experience, thus contributing to value co-creation in two ways – sharing tourist experiences with social networks and co-experiencing travel with social networks. First, recalling and expressing past experiences can have a significant influence on an individual's emotional and behavioural responses (Gross & John, 2003). The act of sharing or comparing experiences, emotions, and expectations with others can generate new experiences (Chen et al., 2012). Further, tourists may change their evaluation of past experiences when they share their travel experiences with others (Kim & Fesenmaier, 2017). Second, a tourist can co-experience travel activities with those in their social network in both physical and virtual spaces. Interactions with other travellers create a sense of togetherness or 'temporary communitas' (Getz, 2008). The ubiquity of technology also allows tourists to share and co-create travel experiences by interacting with others in virtual social spaces as a means to strengthen personal bonds or obtain social support (Neuhofer et al., 2014). Research shows that interaction with other tourists in online/offline communities enables tourists to feel a sense of social and cultural connection and belongingness through knowledge sharing (Paris, 2012). Thus, tourists can share something that they find interesting with a like-minded group to seek mutual understanding.

As with other types of value, however, social value can be diminished by interactions with other actors. First, tourists may feel social pressure to share an experience with social media networks. But, this may be time-consuming and forced (Neuhofer, 2016) and result in individuals neglecting the opportunity to communicate in person with travel companions or fellow tourists (Paris et al., 2015). Second, social interactions may lead to negative consequences for interpersonal authenticity. Tribe and Mkono (2017) demonstrated that some tourists suffered from self-esteem issues and self-surveillance when they paid too much attention to online impression management. Third, tourists may suffer from social surveillance. An example would be when tourists find that their social media posts are criticised by others because of social norms (e.g., lifestyle).

Lived Value in Tourist Experiences

Lived value can be defined as the perceived benefits from direct travel experiences or the use of a service. Individuals can have a 'direct experience of a particular service when they are participating in the service encounter' (Helkkula et al., 2012, p. 61). This mainly highlights that value directly emerges from physical activities. Lived value can be created through technology-mediated experiences offered by service providers. Following Pine and Gilmore (1998), technology can be used to co-create lived value by providing entertainment, education, aesthetics, and escapism.

Lived value can also be co-created by satisfying the real-time demands of travellers. Technology, connectivity, and synchronous communication facilitate real-time onsite decision-making (Buhalis & Sinarta, 2019). This allows the lived experience to be more flexible, instantaneous, and responsive to specific situations (Lamsfus et al., 2015). Furthermore, Paris and Rubin (2013) highlighted the importance of social connectedness in the context of a crisis in the destination. However, lived value can also be co-destroyed through technology-mediated interactions with others through three different pathways. First, in a technology-mediated context, the behaviour of other tourists capturing and sharing content, and interacting with online social networks can detract from the lived experiences of a tourist. Tourists are empowered to keep in touch with their everyday lives while undertaking tourism experiences (White & White, 2007). This kind of co-presence can nevertheless diminish the sense of escapism some may be seeking and may inhibit the enjoyment of the lived experience at the destination (Neuhofer, 2016). Second, lived value can be diminished if tourists are too preoccupied with creating and sharing their experiences rather than enjoying the experience itself (Tribe & Mkono, 2017). Third, lived experiences can be unintentionally diminished by using technology such as augmented and virtual reality. In some tourist settings, these technologies create a barrier between a tourist and their physical environment. For example, they can weaken the depth of connection between individuals and products and lead to a loss of situational awareness and cognitive overload (Han et al., 2019).

Imaginary Value in Tourist Experiences

Value derives from not only the visible interactions between the customer and provider in physical spaces, but also from the imagination (e.g., mental and virtual spaces) (Grönroos & Voima, 2013; Heinonen et al., 2013). Imaginary value emerges at all stages of the travel experience (i.e., before, during, and after the trip). Imagination can be stimulated by signs, pictures, and written and spoken words (Lengkeek, 2000). Therefore, tourists can conjure up images and be mentally transported to the destination by gaining insight from shared experiences on social media or advertisements (Tussyadiah & Fesenmaier, 2009).

Imagination can also be sparked at the destination. Providers can stimulate tourist emotions, cultural experiences, knowledge, and skills, by constructing a narrative (Mathisen et al., 2014), or by using technology. For example, tourists can be transported to ancient Greek life by using interactive technology in a museum. On the other hand, potential tourists can also derive imaginary value from the lived travel experiences of others. Tourists who create digital content often tailor their experiences with a particular social media audience in mind (Marwick, 2012, p. 390). Finally, imaginary value can be co-created after the trip when a tourist recalls their memories or reminisces about their travel by sharing their travel experiences online. When a tourist shares their travel experiences (e.g., photos, blogs, videos, and souvenirs) with others, they may fantasise about past experiences (Pera, 2017). However, technology-mediated tourist experiences can also lead to the co-destruction of imaginary value. On one hand, imagination may be suppressed by social interactions. Tribe and Mkono (2017) used the term 'mindlessness' to describe the negative impacts of social interactions on tourists' experiences. Pre-packaged vacations and curated digital content that emphasise the most symbolic or 'must-see' sites can also suppress the imagination both before a trip and when travellers are at the destination. This destroys the element of surprise and reduces creativity, causing tourists to follow a scripted routine rather than mindfully engaging with their travel experiences (Tribe & Mkono, 2017). However, studies to date are abstract in nature, rather than revealing how different contents of imagination are stimulated.

Technology has empowered tourists to have more opportunities to interact with others in hybrid physical and virtual spaces. This therefore leads to more social interactions which can significantly influence evaluations of value. Table 6.3 provides a summary of the actors and mechanisms, which interact to facilitate value co-creation in technology-mediated tourism experiences.

- Thought point: Take a look at Table 6.3 summarising the dimensions of value, actors, and mechanisms. What kinds of interaction would add value to experiences? What kinds of interactions would diminish experience value?

Cast Study Examples – Using Technology to Co-Create Experiences

Technology (e.g., the Internet, social media, and the Metaverse) has allowed tourists to co-create value with their social networks, with other social media users, and with tourism providers to source travel information for their travel decisions or co-create travel experiences. For example, it is expected that Metaverse will change the travel industry. Metaverse refers to the immersive virtual spaces where people can communicate with others via digital avatars (Gursoy et al., 2022). It can be considered a supplementary way to generate demand for tourism and may inspire virtual tourism purchases, which provide a new way to book tourism experiences and lead to an increase in the volume of physical travellers. In terms of co-creation, airlines could co-create individual value with tourists during check-in through Metaverse. For instance, Qatar Airways offers opportunities for tourists to check in (e.g., seat selection) and virtually experience travel by launching Qverse (www.qatarairways.com/QVerse) where travellers can interact with the Metahuman cabin crew named Sama before they even leave home. Similarly, Celebrity Cruises 'Wonderverse', which is considered to be the first virtual cruise ship, makes it possible to connect with tourists globally through the Metaverse before booking a trip. Tourists are able to move around on the virtual cruise ship as avatars. They can interact with

Table 6.3 Value co-creation and co-destruction in tourist experiences with multiple actors

Value	*Actors*	*Mechanisms*	
		Co-creation	*Co-destruction*
Individual value	Providers	• Providers' engagement, such as personalisation • Tourist engagement, such as identifying their needs by using online filters	• A discrepancy between the market offerings and tourists' evaluation of these offerings • Inappropriate or unexpected use of the available resources • Negative consequences from personalisation or recommendations: uninvited recommendations, economic discrimination, privacy concerns
	The third-party actors	• Learning from others or asking suggestions from others • Mingling with the host: sharing economy	• Seeking inauthenticity: preventing tourists from experiencing destinations serendipitously and creatively
Social value	Providers The third-party actors	• Sharing of tourist experiences • Co-experience travel activities • Attending 'temporary communitas'	• Social pressure to share an experience • Suffering from online impression management
Lived value	Providers	• Tourist engagement with four tourist realms: entertainment, education, aesthetics, and escapism • Satisfying their real-time demands	• Obstacles between tourists and products or services in the use of technology (e.g., AR OR VR): preventing a deeper connection between tourists and products, loss of situational awareness, overloaded cognition and some program errors
	The third-party actors	Satisfying their real-time demands	• Co-presence with others distracts tourists from the lived experiences • Competing with other tourists for resources
Imaginary value	Providers	• Spontaneous memory by advertisement from social media • Controlled memories from onsite stimulus (e.g., VR, AR, and interactive technology)	The unambiguous context could suppress tourists to imagine.
	The third-party actors	• Spontaneous memory by shared travel experience from social media • Sharing their travel experiences	

Source: Authors' own work.

other tourists/Metahuman staff (e.g., ship designers and leaders) and immersively explore virtual destinations (e.g., the Endicott Arm and Dawes Glacier in Alaska). In these cases, the Metaverse can serve as a marketing tool for potential tourists by co-creating individual value, social value, and imaginary value with the service providers and other tourists.

Social media (e.g., platforms such as Instagram, YouTube, Facebook, and Twitter) has helped tourists to co-create social value by sharing their travel experiences with their social networks and other social media users. This allows tourists to share their travel experiences with broader social networks in different formats (e.g., texts, photos, videos, or live streaming). Tourists can enhance their social image, boost social bonding, and get social support by getting likes and comments from their social networks. Meanwhile, tourism providers have benefited from tourists' word-of-mouth on these social media platforms because potential tourists are inspired to travel by these posts or are influenced towards selecting particular destinations during their decision-making process. In order to enhance their competitiveness, tourism providers often actively encourage tourists to share their travel experiences on social media, such as offering incentives and creating unique or interesting spaces for photographs. For example, to encourage the sharing of experiences on social media, many hotels create 'Selfie Stations' for photographs, which have their branding and imagery included. Some tourism destinations have also launched social media campaigns to encourage tourists to share posts on social media. For example, Tourism Australia launched a campaign called 'There's nothing like Australia' which encourages tourists to share their travel videos by telling stories about why they love Australia.

Social media also serves as a crucial platform for advertising. Tourism providers offer personalised travel experiences to potential tourists on social media. Tourism providers can predict travel preferences by collecting and analysing the personal information of potential tourists on social media and then using these data insights to push recommend travel-related advertisements. For example, video platforms (e.g., TikTok) can access their audiences' interests and browsing history to push personalised advertisements recommending travel products, services, and experiences.

- Thought point: Can travel experience value be diminished by interactions with others through the use of technology?

Conclusion

This chapter has elaborated on the process of value co-creation and co-destruction in technology-mediated tourist experiences by identifying the actors, and mechanisms from a multi-dimensional value perspective. While many of these ideas exist in the literature on value co-creation, the concept is fragmented. Therefore, the key contribution of this chapter lies in integrating the different strands of literature. It provides a framework for the research that follows and proposes a research agenda to take this new knowledge forward.

The insights presented in this chapter raise several significant research opportunities that can inform future studies on value co-creation in technology-mediated

Table 6.4 Research agenda

Value co-creation aspect	*Research topics*
Resources	Identification and categorisation of value co-creation resources
	Resource management
	Application of technology
Dimensions of value	Personalisation
	Decision-making
	Self-development
	Lived and imaginary value
Value co-destruction	Value co-destruction (antecedents and consequences)
	Recovering value

tourist experiences in a hybrid of physical, social, and virtual spaces (see Table 6.4). The first issue is that the resources integrated to co-create tourist experiences should be explored and identified in future research. Second, research opportunities are apparent when considering the dimensions of value (e.g., individual, social, lived, and imaginary values). Third, while most research focuses on harmonious interactions, the negative consequences of these interactions should not be overlooked (Kirova, 2021). In the tourism context, although there are some insightful studies, the focus has been on explaining what value co-destruction is, rather than systematically and empirically discussing the actors, resources, and mechanisms involved.

Practically, this chapter demonstrates that travel providers and destinations need to consider value within a wider tourist ecosystem to better understand how smartphones can facilitate value co-creation and reduce the prospect of value co-destruction. Understanding how tourists use technology to co-create experiences is a starting point for creating better experiences. First, in terms of individual value, tourism providers should work to provide personalised products and services. Technology has empowered a tourist to directly interact with service (tourism) providers to personalise their travel experiences. Thus, tourism providers should take advantage of technology to explore how best to co-create personalised experiences, whilst remaining cognizant of the negative consequences of social interactions such as privacy concerns, economic discriminations, and ethnic discriminations. Second, when it comes to social value, tourism providers should design interactive or fun activities which can trigger tourists to share with their social networks on social media or through smartphones. Third, immersive technologies (e.g., 360-degree video, AR/VR) (X. Fan et al., 2022) would be useful for lived value by boosting flow experience and affective engagement. Fourth, technologies such as virtual and augmented reality can also be used to provide tourists with sensory and cultural elements in physical and virtual spaces to facilitate the imaginary experience. Thus, tourism providers need to take advantage of these technologies for imaginary experiences when designing experiences and marketing strategies.

- Thought point: Think of a trip you experienced last time. Can you think of a way that you could co-create more value with others through information technology?

Further Questions

- How do tourists use smartphones to manage operant resources and operand resources to co-create value in tourist experiences with multiple actors within a tourist ecosystem?
- How is value co-created in hybrid physical, social, and virtual spaces?
- How can value be recovered, and by whom, when value co-destruction takes place?

Further Readings

Fan, X., Jiang, X., & Deng, N. (2022). Immersive technology: A meta-analysis of augmented/virtual reality applications and their impact on tourism experience. *Tourism Management, 91*, 104534. https://doi.org/10.1016/j.tourman.2022.104534

Payne, A. F., Storbacka, K., & Frow, P. (2008). Managing the co-creation of value. *Journal of the Academy of Marketing Science, 36*(1), 83–96. https://doi.org/10.1007/s11747-007-0070-0

Ranjan, K. R., & Read, S. (2016). Value co-creation: Concept and measurement. *Journal of the Academy of Marketing Science, 44*(3), 290–315. https://doi.org/10.1007/s11747-014-0397-2

References

Akaka, M. A., Vargo, S. L., & Schau, H. J. (2015). The context of experience. *Journal of Service Management, 26*(2), 206–223. https://doi.org/10.1108/JOSM-10-2014-0270

Awad, N. F., & Krishnan, M. S. (2006). The personalization privacy paradox: An empirical evaluation of information transparency and the willingness to be profiled online for personalization. *MIS Quarterly, 30*(1), 13–28. https://doi.org/10.2307/25148715

Blocker, C. P., & Barrios, A. (2015). The transformative value of a service experience. *Journal of Service Research, 18*(3), 265–283. https://doi.org/10.1177/1094670515583064

Buhalis, D., & Sinarta, Y. (2019). Real-time co-creation and nowness service: Lessons from tourism and hospitality. *Journal of Travel & Tourism Marketing, 36*(5), 563–582. https://doi.org/10.1080/10548408.2019.1592059

Campos, A. C., Mendes, J., do Valle, P. O., & Scott, N. (2016). Co-creation experiences: Attention and memorability. *Journal of Travel & Tourism Marketing, 33*(9), 1309–1336. https://doi.org/10.1080/10548408.2015.1118424

Campos, A. C., Mendes, J., Valle, P. O., & Scott, N. (2018). Co-creation of tourist experiences: A literature review. *Current Issues in Tourism, 21*(4), 369–400. https://doi.org/10.1080/13683500.2015.1081158

Chen, T., Drennan, J., & Andrews, L. (2012). Experience sharing. *Journal of Marketing Management, 28*(13–14), 1535–1552. https://doi.org/10.1080/0267257X.2012.736876

Echeverri, P., & Skålén, P. (2011). Co-creation and co-destruction: A practice-theory based study of interactive value formation. *Marketing Theory, 11*(3), 351–373. https://doi.org/10.1177/1470593111408181

Edvardsson, B., Skålén, P., & Tronvoll, B. (2012). Service systems as a foundation for resource integration and value co-creation. *Review of Marketing Research, 9*, 79–126. https://doi.org/10.1108/S1548-6435(2012)0000009008

Edvardsson, B., Tronvoll, B., & Gruber, T. (2011). Expanding understanding of service exchange and value co-creation: A social construction approach. *Journal of the Academy of Marketing Science, 39*(2), 327–339. https://doi.org/10.1007/s11747-010-0200-y

Fan, D. X. F., Hsu, C. H. C., & Lin, B. (2020). Tourists' experiential value co-creation through online social contacts: Customer-dominant logic perspective. *Journal of Business Research, 108*, 163–173. https://doi.org/10.1016/j.jbusres.2019.11.00

Fan, X., Jiang, X., & Deng, N. (2022). Immersive technology: A meta-analysis of augmented/virtual reality applications and their impact on tourism experience. *Tourism Management, 91*, 104534. https://doi.org/10.1016/j.tourman.2022.104534

Galani-Moutafi, V. (2000). The self and the other: Traveler, ethnographer, tourist. *Annals of Tourism Research, 27*(1), 203–224. https://doi.org/10.1016/S0160-7383(99)00066-3

García-Rosell, J.-C., Haanpää, M., & Janhunen, J. (2019). 'Dig where you stand': Values-based co-creation through improvisation. *Tourism Recreation Research, 44*(3), 348–358. https://doi.org/10.1080/02508281.2019.1591780

Getz, D. (2008). Event tourism: Definition, evolution, and research. *Tourism Management, 29*(3), 403–428. https://doi.org/10.1016/j.tourman.2007.07.017

Giuseppe, M., Scott, M., Marcello, A., & Giacomo, D. C. (2022). Collaboration and learning processes in value co-creation: A destination perspective. *Journal of Travel Research, 62*(3). https://doi.org/10.1177/00472875211070349

Grönroos, C., & Voima, P. (2013). Critical service logic: Making sense of value creation and co-creation. *Journal of the Academy of Marketing Science, 41*(2), 133–150. https://doi.org/10.1007/s11747-012-0308-3

Gross, J. J., & John, O. P. (2003). Individual differences in two emotion regulation processes: Implications for affect, relationships, and well-being. *Journal of Personality and Social Psychology, 85*, 348–362. https://doi.org/10.1037/0022-3514.85.2.348

Gursoy, D., Malodia, S., & Dhir, A. (2022). The metaverse in the hospitality and tourism industry: An overview of current trends and future research directions. *Journal of Hospitality Marketing & Management, 31*(5), 527–534. https://doi.org/10.1080/19368623.2022.2072504

Han, D.-I. D., Weber, J., Bastiaansen, M., Mitas, O., & Lub, X. (2019). Virtual and augmented reality technologies to enhance the visitor experience in cultural tourism. In *Augmented reality and virtual reality* (pp. 113–128): Springer.

Heinonen, K., Strandvik, T., & Voima, P. (2013). Customer dominant value formation in service. *European Business Review, 25*(2), 104–123. https://doi.org/10.1108/09555341311302639

Helkkula, A., Kelleher, C., & Pihlström, M. (2012). Characterizing value as an experience: Implications for service researchers and managers. *Journal of Service Research, 15*(1), 59–75. https://doi.org/10.1177/1094670511426897

Hunt, S. D. (2000). *A general theory of competition: Resources, competences, productivity, economic growth.* https://doi.org/10.4135/9781452220321

Jabareen, Y. (2009). Building a conceptual framework: Philosophy, definitions, and procedure. *International Journal of Qualitative Methods, 8*(4), 49–62. https://doi.org/10.1177/160940690900800406

Kim, J., & Fesenmaier, D. R. (2017). Sharing tourism experiences: The posttrip experience. *Journal of Travel Research, 56*(1), 28–40.

Kirova, V. (2021). Value co-creation and value co-destruction through interactive technology in tourism: The case of 'La Cité du Vin' wine museum, Bordeaux, France. *Current Issues in Tourism, 24*(5), 637–650. https://doi.org/10.1080/13683500.2020.1732883

Lamsfus, C., Wang, D., Alzua-Sorzabal, A., & Xiang, Z. (2015). Going mobile: Defining context for on-the-go travelers. *Journal of Travel Research, 54*(6), 691–701. https://doi.org/10.1177/0047287514538839

Lee, C. H., & Cranage, D. A. (2011). Personalisation–privacy paradox: The effects of personalisation and privacy assurance on customer responses to travel web sites. *Tourism Management*, *32*(5), 987–994. https://doi.org/10.1016/j.tourman.2010.08.011

Lengkeek, J. (2000). Imagination and differences in tourist experience. *World Leisure Journal*, *42*(3), 11–17. https://doi.org/10.1080/04419057.2000.9674191

Madhavaram, S., & Hunt, S. D. (2008). The service-dominant logic and a hierarchy of operant resources: Developing masterful operant resources and implications for marketing strategy. *Journal of the Academy of Marketing Science*, *36*(1), 67–82. https://doi.org/10.1007/s11747-007-0063-z

Marwick, A. (2012). The public domain: Surveillance in everyday life. *Surveillance & Society*, *9*(4), 378–393. https://doi.org/10.24908/ss.v9i4.4342

Mathisen, L., Prebensen, N. K., Chen, J. S., & Uysal, M. (2014). *Storytelling in a co-creation perspective*.

Neuhofer, B. (2016). *Value co-creation and co-destruction in connected tourist experiences*. Paper presented at the Information and Communication Technologies in Tourism 2016, Cham.

Neuhofer, B., Buhalis, D., & Ladkin, A. (2012). Conceptualising technology enhanced destination experiences. *Journal of Destination Marketing & Management*, *1*(1), 36–46. https://doi.org/10.1016/j.jdmm.2012.08.001

Neuhofer, B., Buhalis, D., & Ladkin, A. (2013). *Co-creation through technology: Dimensions of social connectedness*. Paper presented at the Information and Communication Technologies in Tourism 2014, Cham.

Neuhofer, B., Buhalis, D., & Ladkin, A. (2014). Co-creation through technology: Dimensions of social connectedness. In *Information and communication technologies in tourism 2014* (pp. 339–352). Springer.

O'Cass, A., & Sok, P. (2015). An exploratory study into managing value creation in tourism service firms: Understanding value creation phases at the intersection of the tourism service firm and their customers. *Tourism Management*, *51*, 186–200. https://doi.org/10.1016/j.tourman.2015.05.024

Paris, C. M. (2012). *Flashpacking: A discussion of independent travel in a digital world*. Paper presented at the Information and Communication Technologies in Tourism 2012: Proceedings of the International Conference in Helsingborg, Sweden, January 24–27, 2012.

Paris, C. M., Berger, E. A., Rubin, S., & Casson, M. (2015). *Disconnected and unplugged: Experiences of technology induced anxieties and tensions while traveling*, Cham.

Paris, C. M., & Rubin, S. (2013). *Backpacking, social media, and crises: A discussion of online social convergence*, Berlin, Heidelberg.

Pera, R. (2017). Empowering the new traveller: Storytelling as a co-creative behaviour in tourism. *Current Issues in Tourism*, *20*(4), 331–338. https://doi.org/10.1080/13683500.2014.982520

Pine, B. J., & Gilmore, J. H. (1998). *Welcome to the experience economy* (Vol. 76, No. 4, pp. 97–105). Harvard Business Review Press.

Plé, L., & Chumpitaz Cáceres, R. (2010). Not always co-creation: Introducing interactional co-destruction of value in service-dominant logic. *Journal of Services Marketing*, *24*(6), 430–437. https://doi.org/10.1108/08876041011072546

Prahalad, C. K., & Ramaswamy, V. (2004). Co-creation experiences: The next practice in value creation. *Journal of Interactive Marketing*, *18*(3), 5–14. https://doi.org/10.1002/dir.20015

Prebensen, N. K., Larsen, S., & Abelsen, B. (2003). I'm not a typical tourist: German tourists' self-perception, activities, and motivations. *Journal of Travel Research*, *41*(4), 416–420. https://doi.org/10.1177/0047287503041004011

Prebensen, N. K., Vittersø, J., & Dahl, T. I. (2013). Value co-creation significance of tourist resources. *Annals of Tourism Research*, *42*, 240–261. https://doi.org/10.1016/j.annals.2013.01.012

Quinlan Cutler, S., & Carmichael, B. (2010). The dimensions of the tourist experience. In P. L. M. Morgan & B. Ritchie (Eds.), *The experience of tourism and leisure: Consumer and managerial perspectives* (pp. 3–26). Channel View Publications.

Rihova, I., Buhalis, D., Moital, M., & Gouthro, M.-B. (2015). Conceptualising customer-to-customer value co-creation in tourism. *International Journal of Tourism Research*, *17*(4), 356–363. https://doi.org/10.1002/jtr.1993

Saarijärvi, H., Kannan, P. K., & Kuusela, H. (2013). Value co-creation: Theoretical approaches and practical implications. *European Business Review*, *25*(1), 6–19. https://doi.org/10.1108/09555341311287718

Sheller, M., & Urry, J. (2006). The new mobilities paradigm. *Environment and Planning A: Economy and Space*, *38*(2), 207–226. https://doi.org/10.1068/a37268

Sweeney, J. C., & Soutar, G. N. (2001). Consumer perceived value: The development of a multiple item scale. *Journal of Retailing*, *77*(2), 203–220. https://doi.org/10.1016/S0022-4359(01)00041-0

Tribe, J., & Mkono, M. (2017). Not such smart tourism? The concept of e-lienation. *Annals of Tourism Research*, *66*, 105–115. https://doi.org/10.1016/j.annals.2017.07.001

Tussyadiah, I. P., & Fesenmaier, D. R. (2009). Mediating tourist experiences: Access to places via shared videos. *Annals of Tourism Research*, *36*(1), 24–40. https://doi.org/10.1016/j.annals.2008.10.001

Vargo, S. L., Koskela-Huotari, K., & Vink, J. (2020). Service-dominant logic: Foundations and applications. In *The Routledge handbook of service research insights and* ideas (pp. 3–23), Routledge.

Vargo, S., & Lusch, R. (2004). Evolving to a new dominant logic. *Journal of Marketing*, *68*, 1–17. https://doi.org/10.1509/jmkg.68.1.1.24036

Vargo, S. L., & Lusch, R. F. (2008). Service-dominant logic: Continuing the evolution. *Journal of the Academy of Marketing Science*, *36*(1), 1–10. https://doi.org/10.1007/s11747-007-0069-6

Vargo, S. L., Maglio, P. P., & Akaka, M. A. (2008). On value and value co-creation: A service systems and service logic perspective. *European Management Journal*, *26*(3), 145–152.

Weiser, M. (1993). Hot topics-ubiquitous computing. *Computer*, *26*(10), 71–72.

White, N. R., & White, P. B. (2007). Home and away: Tourists in a connected world. *Annals of Tourism Research*, *34*(1), 88–104. https://doi.org/10.1016/j.annals.2006.07.001

Wozniak, T., Liebrich, A., Senn, Y., & Zemp, M. (2016). Alpine tourists' willingness to engage in virtual co-creation of experiences. In *Information and communication technologies in tourism 2016* (pp. 281–294): Springer.

Xiang, Z., & Gretzel, U. (2010). Role of social media in online travel information search. *Tourism Management*, *31*(2), 179–188. https://doi.org/10.1016/j.tourman.2009.02.016

Xie, L., Guan, X., Liu, B., & Huan, T.-C. T. C. (2021). The antecedents and consequences of the co-creation experience in virtual tourist communities: From the perspective of social capital in virtual space. *Journal of Hospitality and Tourism Management*, *48*, 492–499. https://doi.org/10.1016/j.jhtm.2021.08.006

7 Exploration of Transmedia Storytelling as a Marketing Strategy in the Tourism Industry

A Case Study of the Love Ladder in Chongqing

Han Li, Kai Xin Tay, and Zi Bai Luo

Introduction

In recent years, tourists have not only been drawn to unique tourism resources because of the risks that come with travelling but also both the physical and mental aspects of a cultural experience within a destination (Carr, 2006; Richards, 2002). As a result, the majority of people get their information on the Internet, such as on social media (Yuliarti et al., 2021). Therefore, telling stories is shown as a potentially powerful way to raise awareness about an attraction. Another critical factor to emphasise in E-tourism storytelling marketing is the homogenisation of tourism products (Hartman et al., 2019; Ryu et al., 2019; Yuliarti et al., 2021). Storytelling about a destination is known as a tool to build up its reputation and image, especially when it comes to vying for tourism and economic growth during the digital age (Bassano et al., 2019).

Folk stories attempt to awaken the affection of tourists, to evoke a sense of empathy for the characters as well as the plot in the stories. In such instances, an attitudinal change is a way to achieve marketing goals with potential customers (Laing & Frost, 2019; Pan & Chen, 2019). For this matter, Pan and Chen (2019) explained that the content of the story has to be easy to memorise and consonant. The authors also place emphasis on how a well-planned storytelling marketing tactic can enable businesses to build infinite value in their brand image. Thanks to transmedia platforms, stories can be widely distributed and readily accessible by people when compared to conventional marketing strategies (i.e., printed media like brochures and flyers). Adding a mythical touch to a story about an attraction can also significantly boost brand awareness and competitiveness in the tourism industry, as well as visit intention (Bassano et al., 2019; ben Youssef et al., 2018; Chautard & Collin-Lachaud, 2019; Pan & Chen, 2019).

A story is more meaningful than beauty statements or empty slogans, as it can trigger emotional responses from people (Dimache et al., 2017; Frude & Killick, 2011; Woodside et al., 2008). Once people get emotional about something, it is easier for them to carry out irrational recognitions and develop an unconscious preference for the elements delivered in the story. As an example, family-related tales can build a strong bond among family members (Frude & Killick, 2011). Swiss psychologist Carl Jung's 'archetypes' theory mentioned that every story,

DOI: 10.4324/9781003335924-10

whether real or fictional, often reflects a value orientation of consumers, as well as the embodiment of the meaning as expected by consumers (Jung, 2011). Such a thing is termed the prototype' of the story in people's minds. A story should burrow deep in the hearts of consumers; there must be a 'prototype' to awaken their deep desire, to meet their core needs (Pan & Chen, 2019). Storytelling has been successfully deployed to promote tangible products, but little to none had used this tactic in E-tourism. Hence, this chapter is to study the effects of transmedia storytelling marketing on visit intention, using content analysis in the context of a Chinese destination called the Love Ladder in Chongqing, Jiangjin.

Theoretical Background

Storytelling for Tourist Destination

Storytelling marketing is known as a process for visitors to accept the local culture and taboos of a location. Cultural products are known to be the creation of great novelty, which can bring enormous economic benefits to tourist businesses (Cooke & Lazzeretti, 2008). If culture is the soul of tourism, tourism is the vector of it. Tourism without a cultural blessing lacks depth and connotation, while a culture without tourism eventually loses its motivation to valorise itself (Friedrichs, 2016). Tourism and culture are, therefore, tightly intertwined (Datzira-Masip, 2006; Zakaria et al., 2014). Before writing up a story, the first question one has to think about is: 'What kind of stories might make people feel that our products are meaningful and linked to the personal experience of consumers?' (Loebbert, 2003).

The theme in a story is one of the key characteristics of a brand. The theme forms the induction and generalisation of events, which is the basic, yet highly important concept affecting the development of any story (Yang, 2006). A theme affects the main concept of a story's development, while it is the essence of different story forms (Miller, 2014). It is generally used to guide the narration of the story, provide emotional communication, and convey deeper connotations (Joubert et al., 2019; Su et al., 2020). The theme of the story is notably an embodiment of the company's core worth (Aimé, 2021; Smith & Wintrob, 2013). The same applies to the promotion of the destination's brand for e-tourism marketing, where the planned narration is made necessary to create an image for the destination. The creation of the brand's core value should be the core content of the story's choice.

In the content design of the story, McKee divides the constituent elements in a story into different types, namely early story design, structure, characters and plots, time, and place of the story (McKee & Fryer, 2006). Fog et al. (2005) also summed up the constituent of a brand's story in content by using the actual cases of story marketing, from the information, characters, plot, and conflict in each of them. Escalas (2004) conveyed the constituent of the contents of a story into four points: Story implication, process conflict, task role, and plot design. It is then stated that the more complete these elements are, the more effective it is to establish memory and resonance from the audience. The story describes events through the plot. As an integral part of the story, the plot must be logical and reasonable. One of the functions of the plot is to help the audience understand the events that make up the story (Polkinghorne, 1991).

The more vivid the plot is, the more it can help the audience imagine the scenes in the story. This would then foster the desire to relate the story to their own experiences, triggering reflection on the story (McKee, 2011). Simmons (2002) believed that conflict should be included in the storyline since stories without conflict are both boring and unattractive. However, Fog et al. (2005) added that the conflict within the setting must also be reasonable. How to introduce the conflict? What are the key points of the story that cannot be reversed? What is the climax of the story? How should the morals of the story be presented? There lies a barrage of problems that must be answered.

In terms of a story's characteristics, a good story should be pleasant to the ear. To put it simply, the story must gain a higher level of meaning behind its seemingly simple appearance. It should transcend from being a pile of words, projecting and reflecting people's feelings and attitudes. For this, McKee and Fryer (2006) explained that the story must fulfil four conditions: telling the real people and things, telling the truth people know, telling social norms, and making the audience believe. Ryu et al. (2019) examined the effects of story structures in multiple brands, specifically on hotel consumers' perceptions of brand image. The study found that a well-structured brand story is equipped with the capability to entice loyalty and increase hotel sales. A well-structured story includes clarification of the plot, recognisable historical references, and the usage of first-person narration (Ryu et al., 2019).

Aside from me, a fascinating story must not only have a sufficiently large amount of information but also awaken human emotions in the audience (Joubert et al., 2019; Laing & Frost, 2019; McKee, 2011; McKee & Fryer, 2006). By comparatively analysing other successful destinations through the lens of storytelling marketing in e-tourism, one would be able to determine the appropriate and appealing story theme, content, plot, and characteristics, therefore using them as a pull factor to trigger visit intention. This study provides a comprehensible conceptual system of tourism destination storytelling marketing, which are the elements required to form a good destination story.

- Though points: What does storytelling mean to you? Why are story themes and content important in the marketing field? What kind of stories might make people feel that the products are meaningful and linked to the personal experience of consumers?

Case Study – The Love Ladder

The main story starts with 20-year-old Liu Guojiang, who fell in love with a widowed mother, Xu Chaoqing. The two lovers ran off to live together in peace for over 50 years. In a twist that can rival Shakespeare's Romeo and Juliet, friends, and relatives around the two criticised the relationship due to their age difference, as well as the fact that Xu already had children. Desperate to escape the gossipy and scornful nature of their communities, the pair eventually eloped to live in a cave in Jiangjin county, which locates in the Chongqing municipality. In the second year of their shared life in the mountain, Liu began to meticulously hand-carve a long flight of stairs for his wife to travel down the mountain easily. His efforts lasted for more than 50 years.

Half a century later, in 2001, a group of adventurers who were exploring the forests came across the elderly couple and their 6,000 hand-carved steps. The coupled had lived in peace for over 50 years until Liu, aged 72 years old, returned from his daily farm work one day and collapsed. Xu sat with her husband in his final moments, murmuring prayers as he took his last breath in her arms. Even upon his death, no one was able to unclasp the grip Liu had on Xu's hand. This story was then told throughout the nation, to the point that the tale was awarded to be China's greatest love story of the year in 2006. Because of the tale of the Love Ladder, the mountain came to be known by tourists as a renowned and unique location. Figure 7.1 shows the popularity of online searches of the term 'Love Ladder' from 2011 to 2020. This topic of discussion only got increasingly popular on social media when Xu passed away in 2012, the same year that the government began to promote the location with storytelling marketing.

After hearing the story, many travelled to the mountain from all over the world out of their emotional reactions to the tale. With more people visiting the destination, the local government has decided to boost the economy by establishing Love Ladder as a tourist attraction. Their work included building better roads to the mountain and renovating the couple's old home. In the process of their marketing efforts, TV dramas and songs based on the Love Ladder were created. The local government has established the 'Jiangjin love Tourism Culture Research Association', holding the 'Chinese Tanabata Oriental love festival' for 12 consecutive times. In recent years, the local government has commissioned several poets to compose poems for the Love Ladder, while introducing a variety of popular shows

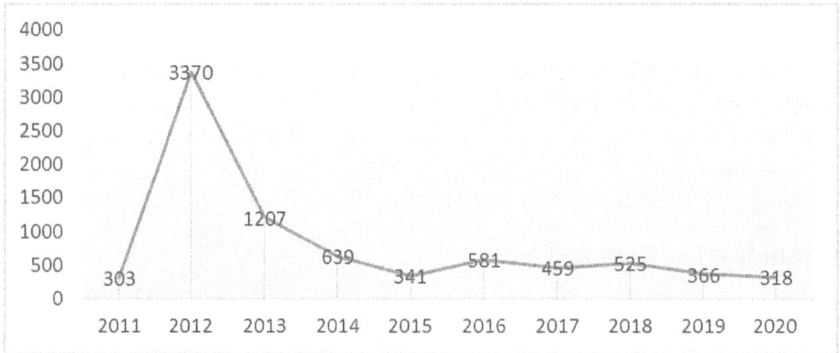

Figure 7.1 The trending topic 'Love Ladder' on social media

Source: Authors' own work

such as 'Township Treaty' and 'Chinese New Song Sound'. There was even a love-themed marathon held locally to market the location.

- Though points: How do you feel about the Love Ladder story? Does the story of the Love Ladder entice you to visit the destination?

Methodology

A text analysis software, ROST CM6 was brought into use to provide interpretive data for this study. After extracting comments from online platforms about the Love Ladder, the texts were then carefully analysed and dissected, to initiate the transformation of the uncertain text into quantitative data. The purpose of this is to identify the visitor's recognition, emotional experience, and visit intention concerning the location, as influenced by the story. Purposive sampling was also applied to the study, particularly through online searches that include the Chinese keyword 'Love Ladder' on Baidu. As a result, as many as 832 comments about the story of Love Ladder were obtained from netizens' reviews on travel websites, e.g., Ctrip and Antcom, as well as other social media platforms, e.g., Sina Weibo, Baidu Tieba, Tianya Community, and Douban Community. These comments displayed both positive and negative expressions towards the story. Since the nature of the study lay in exploring people's recognition, emotional experience, and visit intention from the masses, the negative comments were omitted in the screening step. To further avoid any arising biases and prejudice from the researchers on the comments, each author was tasked with screening and removing the texts separately. Consequently, a total of 620 online reviews and 18 travel notes (amounting to 50,718 words) were analysed by using the ROST CM6 Software. The frequencies of certain words in the comments were obtained and thematised into four different categories: story structures (e.g., story theme, characters, plot, and historical connection), media, emotional experience (e.g., sentiment), and visit intention.

Findings

The findings include examples of original quotes from the netizens' comments, which are classified using the thematization method (as shown in Table 7.1). The frequency of words is also summarised, as processed by ROST CM6 (as shown in Table 7.2).

The theme of the Love Ladder story can be captured from words with higher frequencies, including *love* and *love story,* which have appeared as many as 611 times out of 620 comments. This indicates that the netizens understand the story theme well (that it is a love story). The main characters in the story *Liu Guojiang* and *Xu Chaoqing*, as well as a handful of other side characters (Elderly, Youth etc.), were mentioned 383 times from the 620 comments. This suggests that the characters are at the focal point in the story since they initiate a connection between themselves and the prototypical personas stored in visitors' memories. The plot of Love Ladder can be captured from words, including *Over 6000 Steps, Over 50 years* and

Table 7.1 Text coding table

Categories	*List of comments*
Story theme	349. The story is so touching. Love is always beautiful and worth looking forward to. We should all try our best to love the people we love.
Story character	56. In my lifetime, I must go to the place where Liu Guojiang and Xu Chaoqing resided in. I want to see the place of such a beautiful love story for myself and hike up their Love Ladder.
Story plot	66. This "young man" spent 56 years digging and casting more than 6000 steps for this "older woman". Such courage and perseverance are truly a showcase of the power of love! There is no need for a vow. Love ladder – 56 years of love, spanning more than 6000 steps. This is the most romantic gift in the world.
Historical connection	67. In the past, when I heard of the story about the Love Ladder, I thought that this sort of love was too sacred and distant. However, when I experienced walking on such a long dirt path and climbed the 6000-step stone ladder myself, I realised that this kind of love can be so real that it can be felt from a touch.
Story Media	193. I liked the song "Ladder of Heaven" and the story behind it, so I went and walked on this "Love Ladder" on November 12, 2018, to feel the sincerity and persistent love story. I hope that everyone here, including me, can experience this wonderful kind of love for us.
Sentiment	98. I just heard about this earthmoving story today, it is so touching that I can't sleep. If I don't witness it, I'm afraid I will regret it for the rest of my life.
Visit intention	72. I always felt that it is a sacred place, and I always had a yearning for it. So, on the 10th, I set foot on that land with my friends to feel the power of that lifelong love. The Love Ladder is a pilgrimage to pure love, and I am a mere devout believer.

Source: Authors' own work

Table 7.2 Summary of words frequency table

Categories	*Word frequency*
Story theme	Love (512 time), love story (99 times)
Story character	Elderly (114 times), Liu Guojiang (67 times), Xu Chaoqing (59 times), youth (49 times), protagonist (29 times), maidservant (26 times), man (21 times)
Story plot	Over 6,000 steps (79 times), over 50 years (16 times), believe (56 times)
Historical connection	Real (70 times), real person and true thing (13 times)
Story Media	Movie (63 times), song (20 times), TV drama (12 times)
Sentiment	Burst into tears (24 times), tears (15 times), moved (155 times), touching (68 times), feeling (34 times), deeply (20 times), shocked (16 times), envy (15 times), regret (15 times), yearn for (13 times)
Visit intention	Want to go (13 times), going (19 times), yearn for (13 times), have been there (12 times)

Source: Author' own work

Believe, which appeared 151 times out of 620 comments. Through these words alone, a completed story can be pieced together. According to the frequency of words mentioned in the Love Ladder story, authenticity has been mentioned many times. Specific words, such as *real, real person, and true thing*, were found 83 times in the 620 comments, which indicates that a sense of truthfulness to the tale is more likely to win the trust and emotional resonance of visitors.

As for the form of storytelling, *Movies, Songs,* and *TV Dramas* are selected as the three forms of mediums worth keeping an eye on. These key terms have been mentioned 95 times out of the 620 comments, which indicates that several forms of the story are well known to visitors and that different forms of mediums affect different visitors. When it comes to the reactions from visitors after listening to the story, words with similar meanings such as *moved* and *tears* were mentioned 336 times. Storytelling marketing here was shown to be stimulating the visitor's *emotions* and *feelings*, obtaining emotional power for the visitors' subsequent behaviours. The story of Love Ladder has attracted a large number of potential visitors, drawing them to the scenic area. This is evident in how many online users have been spotted talking about their willingness to visit. Words expressing their wishes of *going* to the location as well as *having been* to the Love Ladder were also displayed in the word frequency statistics. It fully shows that the story possesses a positive impact on the visitor's *willingness to travel* and *practical action.*

- Though points: Would you write reviews after reading a destination story? Do you read the reviews when selecting a place to visit? What story structure will trigger your intent to visit a destination? What story media should the destination marketer use to promote the place?

Discussion of the Case

In the construction of the story, the theme of the story should be very clear with a positive impact intended for the audience. The confirmation of the theme can be said to be the primary task of the story in the marketing of the scenic area. As mentioned by Loebbert (2003), storytellers should place their focus on telling a story that can bring rich meaning to consumers. For example, the themes that human beings yearn for in a story, such as love, are easier to awaken emotional pursuit in tourists. Character development is also extremely important to the composition of a story, as it is often the embodiment of the meaning expected by visitors. Peng (2012) mentioned 12 kinds of characters that can provoke a sense of psychological motivation from consumers. Some of them include creators, heroes, and rulers. In this study, it was found that ordinary people as characters can also meet the psychological needs of consumers, as stories of ordinary people tend to be relatable and therefore able to easily resonate with visitors.

The plot of the story was also found in the comments, the story must follow the development logic of the plot. The story structure should focus on the emergence, process, and solution of the problems or difficulties (Simmons, 2002; McKee, 2011; Fog et al., 2005). This is further elaborated in the form of the words '*more than 6000 levels*' and '*more than 50 years*' from the comments. They display the capability of the audience to piece together the complete story, showing that they can perceive it from their impression of the story. From the aspect of historical connections that the story makes, the authenticity of the story is highlighted, making it more acceptable to visitors, as well as arousing an emotional resonance from them. For this matter, Presas et al. (2014) argued that potential visitors want to experience something authentic and real and that creating a fake story would only generate negative responses.

It is also worth noting that the effects are much different if the same story is distributed on different channels. Any narrative form can become the carrier of the story's message and narration can be found in novels, films, music, paintings, etc. (Yu, 2010). The aesthetic needs vary in different groups of tourists. If the story is to influence the emotional experience of tourists, the form of expression should achieve the aesthetic expectations and informational desires of relevant groups, which requires the communication medium of the story to adapt. Through the analysis of online reviews about the stories of Love Ladder, the results show that the story marketing mechanism in tourism destinations can be separated into two dimensions: tourists' perception of stories and tourists' emotional experience of said stories. These dimensions conform to the effect hierarchy model that was constructed by Lavidge and Steiner (1961). In the mechanism of tourism destination story marketing, the first level of stimulation (awareness of the destination), the second level of stimulation (emotional development), and the travel decision from the effect hierarchy model are involved.

Regardless of its effectiveness as mentioned above, the story marketing process should still be strictly evaluated. For example, due to the special circumstances of the case or the biases that might arise from the method, comments from online sources are not sufficient to reflect a story's full effect, and the structure of story marketing may vary from region to region. Therefore, it is necessary to further verify feedback from other sources by comparing multiple scenic areas as the follow-up procedure. In addition, to further deepen the understanding of the study, it is necessary to study specific behaviours that tourists commonly produce, which would involve the actual evaluation of the story's impact. This study provides the basis for qualitative research. In the following research into this topic, it is necessary to connect the impact of storytelling marketing with specific variables that can be measured for verification.

Deficiencies of Story Marketing in the Scenic Area of Love Ladder

The story does not have much depth to it. The story is very attractive to visitors, but to generate greater marketing power, there is a need to deeply interpret the background of the story (Fog et al., 2005; Ryu et al., 2019; Wu & Chen, 2020). This is even supported by the comments, some of which have repeatedly mentioned that '*we can't satisfy many curiosities in our hearts just from these fragments. I hope to know more*'. Therefore, it can be said that the structure of the story lacks depth in terms of local and social background. The connotations made in the story are still too obscured to its audience. Many scenic areas work with the theme of love. If Love Ladder wants to rise in the ranks among these scenic spots and possess a strong market appeal, it is obvious that it can't achieve this only by appealing to a single emotion. The beauty of the story about the Love Ladder lies not only in the love shared by the two main characters but also in its progressive breakthroughs from conventional concepts. With the times changing, the lack of relevance and discontinuous marketing efforts became the causes of the attraction's failure to face different groups of target audiences. At the same time, the decrease in popularity and attention also weakened the marketing effects of Love Ladder.

Further Development

'*The truth of the love ladder story*', '*specific regions and environments*', and '*manually digging the ladder to maintain its original appearance*' were some of the phrases repeated in the tourists' comments. '*I hope the government will not allow the scenic area to be commercialised*', and '*I hope the love ladder can maintain its original appearance*' ... some people had also written down their wishes within the comment sections, which were then echoed by others who share the sentiment. In other words, maintaining the original appearance is the unanimous desire of tourists. Thus, when shaping the scenic area, the destination manager must make efforts to maintain the original ecology of the scenic area to preserve the story's authenticity. Furthermore, the activities there should be designed in a way that is not detrimental to the original appearance of the scenic area, while more focus should be placed on refining meaningful moments of the story. As the social environment transforms, the aesthetics and the formats of the story will also need to be changed accordingly. To strengthen the psychological impact on tourists through stories, the mediums and methods of narration must meet the aesthetic expectations of tourists. This indicates that the original form of the story, as a block of text, is no longer suitable for current trends in the story market. Therefore, it is necessary to consider the conventional demands and create short videos which will boost the influence of the story. Introducing newer media forms to this topic will also allow story marketing to meet the general population's aesthetic preferences, to increase its popularity.

Conclusion

Culture is the foundation of tourism, and the symbolism of culture is an important part of the tourism experience. Through the presented case of the Love Ladder, it is found that many tourists hold reverence for the unique regional background described in the Love Ladder's tale and are eager to experience the local culture. Through interpretations of local cultures, such as folk marriages, the original contents of the story are enriched and transformed, thus refining the story in a way that tourists can truly experience Love Ladder's cultural charm for themselves.

Under the unfavourable circumstances that the search volume and attention of the Love Ladder are gradually declining, the department in charge should pay close attention to the market's demands. For instance, the change in tourists' position in tourism marketing has gradually blurred the boundary between the publisher and the receiver of the marketing plans. Tourists no longer only act as information receivers, but they now also play the role of promoters to a certain extent. Therefore, it is necessary to pay close attention to the market's demand, reshape the story, and adjust the marketing strategy accordingly. This is so that it can better meet the demands of the masses and achieve better marketing results.

In the future, the research should be conducted and demonstrated by using different methods and theories. At the same time, regarding research directions, the impact of the story's influencing factors on tourists' perception and behavioural willingness should be analysed, respectively. This is stated as this process can accurately determine the core elements of the story in marketing, which can then be used to make the marketing method more concise. As for research methods, a variety of tactics should be adopted to carry out a comparative analysis, such as in-depth interviews with tourists or questionnaires to further combine qualitative and quantitative analysis in one study. Meanwhile, comparative research on scenic areas aside from the Love Ladder should also be carried out, to provide comprehensive and scientific theoretical support for the development of story marketing in the field of tourism.

Further Questions

- What are the impacts of the story's influencing factors on tourists' perception and behavioural willingness towards visit intention?
- What are the core elements of the story in marketing that can be used to make the marketing method more concise?
- How can storytelling function as a marketing strategy to promote the destination in the technology era of the experience economy?
- Think of a famous destination story you are familiar with. How did they promote the place using storytelling?

Further Readings

Dimache, A., Wondirad, A., & Agyeiwaah, E. (2017). One museum, two stories: Place identity at the Hong Kong Museum of History. *Tourism Management*, *63*, 287–301. https://doi.org/10.1016/j.tourman.2017.06.020

Hartman, S., Parra, C., & de Roo, G. (2019). Framing strategic storytelling in the context of transition management to stimulate tourism destination development. *Tourism Management*, *75*, 90–98. https://doi.org/10.1016/j.tourman.2019.04.014

Ryu, K., Lehto, X. Y., Gordon, S. E., & Fu, X. (2019). Effect of a brand story structure on narrative transportation and perceived brand image of luxury hotels. *Tourism Management*, *71*, 348–363. https://doi.org/10.1016/j.tourman.2018.10.021

Su, L., Cheng, J., & Swanson, S. R. (2020). The impact of tourism activity type on emotion and storytelling: The moderating roles of travel companion presence and relative ability. *Tourism Management*, *81*. https://doi.org/10.1016/j.tourman.2020.104138

Woodside, A. G., Sood, S., & Miller, K. E. (2008). When consumers and brands talk: Storytelling theory and research in psychology and marketing. *Psychology & Marketing*, *25*(2), 97–145. https://doi.org/10.1002/MAR.20203

References

Aimé, I. (2021). The dynamic construction of brand storytelling. https://doi.org/10.1080/0965254X.2021.1908404

Bassano, C., Barile, S., Piciocchi, P., Spohrer, J. C., Iandolo, F., & Fisk, R. (2019). Storytelling about places: Tourism marketing in the digital age. *Cities*, *87*, 10–20. https://doi.org/10.1016/J.CITIES.2018.12.025

ben Youssef, K., Leicht, T., & Marongiu, L. (2018). Storytelling in the context of destination marketing: An analysis of conceptualisations and impact measurement, *Journal of Strategic Marketing*, *27*(8), 696–713. https://doi.org/10.1080/0965254X.2018.1464498

Carr, A. (2006). Cultural tourism: The partnership between tourism and cultural heritage management. *Tourism Analysis*, *11*(2), 165–167. https://doi.org/10.3727/108354206778001530.

Chautard, T., & Collin-Lachaud, I. (2019). Introducing the storytelling analysis methodology in marketing: Principles, contributions and implementation. *Recherche et Applications en Marketing (English Edition)*, *34*(3), 27–46. https://doi.org/10.1177/2051570719841225

Cooke, P. N., & Lazzeretti, L. (2008). *Creative cities, cultural clusters and local economic development*. Edward Elgar Publishing Limited. https://books.google.com.my/books?hl=en&lr=&id=iGHykkVY49MC&oi=fnd&pg=PA155&dq=cultural+product+is+high+end+goods&ots=g9kd3YArRg&sig=feR-IuqGoUFlNn5sVCp3EM7e1sE#v=onepage&q=high%20novelty&f=false

Datzira-Masip, J. (2006). Cultural heritage tourism — Opportunities for product development: The Barcelona case. *Tourism Review*, *61*(1), 13–20. https://doi.org/10.1108/EB058466/FULL/XML

Dimache, A., Wondirad, A., & Agyeiwaah, E. (2017). One museum, two stories: Place identity at the Hong Kong Museum of History. *Tourism Management*, *63*, 287–301. https://doi.org/10.1016/j.tourman.2017.06.020

Escalas, J. E. (2004). Narrative processing: Building consumer connections to brands. *Journal of Consumer Psychology*, *14*(1–2), 168–180. https://doi.org/10.1207/s15327663jcp1401&2_19

Fog, K., Budtz, C., & Yakaboylu, B. (2005). Storytelling: Branding in practice. *Storytelling: Branding in Practice*, 1–238. https://doi.org/10.1007/B138635

Friedrichs, J. (2016). An intercultural theory of international relations: how self-worth underlies politics among nations. *International Theory*, *8*(1), 63–96. https://doi.org/10.1017/S1752971915000202

Frude, N., & Killick, S. (2011). Family storytelling and the attachment relationship. *Psychodynamic Practice*, *17*(4), 441–455. https://doi.org/10.1080/14753634.2011.609025

Hartman, S., Parra, C., & de Roo, G. (2019). Framing strategic storytelling in the context of transition management to stimulate tourism destination development. *Tourism Management*, *75*, 90–98. https://doi.org/10.1016/j.tourman.2019.04.014

Joubert, M., Davis, L., & Metcalfe, J. (2019). Storytelling: The soul of science communication. *Journal of Science Communication*, *18*(5), E. https://doi.org/10.22323/2.18050501.

Jung, C. G. (2011). *Four archetypes* (Shamdasani Sonu, Ed.; Vol. 9). Princeton University Press. https://doi.org/10.1515/9781400839155

Laing, J. H., & Frost, W. (2019). Presenting narratives of empathy through dark commemorative exhibitions during the Centenary of World War One. *Tourism Management*, *74*, 190–199. https://doi.org/10.1016/j.tourman.2019.03.007

Lavidge, R. J., & Steiner, G. A. (1961). A model for predictive measurements of advertising effectiveness. *Journal of Marketing*, *25*(6), 59. https://doi.org/10.2307/1248516.

Loebbert, M. (2003). *Storymanagement : der narrative Ansatz für Management und Beratung*. 261. https://books.google.com/books/about/Storymanagement.html?id=RVHbAAAACAAJ

McKee, A. (2011). What is textual analysis? In *Textual analysis*. https://doi.org/10.4135/9780857020017.n1

McKee, R., & Fryer, B. (2006). Storytelling that moves people. *Harvard Business Review Online*. http://www.hbsp.org

Miller, C. H. (2014). *Digital storytelling: A creator's guide to interactive entertainment* (3rd ed.). Routledge. https://doi.org/10.4324/9780203425923

Pan, L.-Y., & Chen, K. (2019). A study on the effect of storytelling marketing on brand image, perceived quality, and purchase intention in ecotourism. *Ekoloji*, *107*, 705–712. http://www.ekolojidergisi.com/article/a-study-on-the-effect-of-storytelling-marketing-on-brand-image-perceived-quality-and-purchase-5686

Peng, C. (2012). *Research on brand narrative theory: The construction and dissemination of brand stories*. Doctorial Observation, Wuhan University.

Polkinghorne, D. E. (1991). Narrative and self-concept. *Journal of Narrative and Life History*, *1*(2–3), 135–153. https://doi.org/10.1075/JNLH.1.2-3.04NAR.

Presas, P., Guia, J., & Muñoz, D. (2014). Customer's perception of familiness in travel experiences. *Journal of Travel and Tourism Marketing*, *31*(2). https://doi.org/10.1080/10548408.2014.873307

Richards, G. (2002). Tourism attraction systems: Exploring cultural behavior. *Annals of Tourism Research*, *29*(4), 1048–1064. https://doi.org/10.1016/S0160-7383(02)00026-9

Ryu, K., Lehto, X. Y., Gordon, S. E., & Fu, X. (2019). Effect of a brand story structure on narrative transportation and perceived brand image of luxury hotels. *Tourism Management*, *71*, 348–363. https://doi.org/10.1016/j.tourman.2018.10.021

Smith, K., & Wintrob, M. (2013). Brand storytelling: A framework for activation. *Design Management Review*, *24*(1), 36–41. https://doi.org/10.1111/DREV.10227

Simmons, R. (2002). *Odd girl out: The hidden culture of aggression in girls*. Mariner Books. https://books.google.com.my/books?hl=en&lr=&id=tcCCFzrEdioC&oi=fnd&pg=PP2-&dq=Simmons+(2002)+&ots=CFkcp3Q78d&sig=9iFFVzv0dARGsZZbGree-WkRGCE#v=onepage&q=Simmons%20(2002)&f=false

Su, L., Cheng, J., & Swanson, S. R. (2020). The impact of tourism activity type on emotion and storytelling: The moderating roles of travel companion presence and relative ability. *Tourism Management*, *81*. https://doi.org/10.1016/j.tourman.2020.104138

Woodside, A. G., Sood, S., & Miller, K. E. (2008). When consumers and brands talk: Storytelling theory and research in psychology and marketing. *Psychology & Marketing*, *25*(2), 97–145. https://doi.org/10.1002/MAR.20203.

Wu, J., & Chen, D. T. V. (2020). A systematic review of educational digital storytelling. *Computers and Education*, *147*. https://doi.org/10.1016/j.compedu.2019.103786

Yang, N. (2006). *Chinese and western comparative poetics: Contrast and integration*. Culture and Arts Publishing.

Yu, L. (2010). "Narrative" becomes the beauty of "brand" *("叙事"成"品牌"之美)*. https://wap.cnki.net/touch/web/Journal/Article/QGSQ201012016.html

Yuliarti, M. S., Rahmanto, A. N., Priliantini, A., Naini, A. M. I., Anshori, M., & Hendriyani, C. T. (2021). Storytelling of Indonesia tourism marketing in social media: Study of Borobudur and Danau Toba Instagram account. *Jurnal Komunikasi*, *13*(1), 107. https://doi.org/10.24912/jk.v13i1.9209

Zakaria, A. Z., Salleh, I. H., & Rashid, M. S. A. (2014). Identity of malay garden design to be promoted as the cultural tourism product in Malaysia. *Procedia - Social and Behavioral Sciences*, *153*, 298–307. https://doi.org/10.1016/J.SBSPRO.2014.10.063

8 Travellers' Creation and Dissemination of User-Generated Content

A Review and Theoretical Implications

Deepti Jog

Introduction

In pursuit of better travel decisions, potential tourists get exposed to two sources of information, one being online destination marketing content and the second being user-generated content (UGC) based on the subjective evaluation of people's travel experiences. Social media has essentially redefined how individuals communicate and behave online, resulting in a new information consumption and information dissemination medium. It has thus evolved as a significant source for consumers to obtain first-hand information and eliminate ambiguity surrounding their purchase decisions. According to recent statistics, there were 4.24 million new social media users in January 2022, which has shown an increase of over 10% in the last year (Hootsuite, 2020). The users rely on social media platforms for multidimensional interaction and information exchange, for communication, reviewing, spreading invitations, and sharing pictures, photos, and videos. In the tourism sector, UGC shared on social media has become an essential and popular innovative tourism tool.

The exponential growth in UGC and its well-established link to tourism explains how persuasive information will help others make their travel decision. It is observed that travellers differentiate and assess UGC based on trustworthiness, proficiency, perceived usefulness, and perceived ease of use. Such content generated through social media by users has revolutionised tourism communications. It is seen as a rich source of information for travel decision-making. Subsequently, this has made past visitors more influential in the minds of prospective travellers, and the significant impact created by tourism-related firms has contracted.

Contemporary travellers are carried away by realistic online expectations and believe in recreating the experiences. In this vein, travellers perceive these peer-to-peer reviews as more reliable than the marketing material on the destination marketing organisation (DMO) website or related sources. For example, websites like Tripadvisor and European Travel Commission (2009) believe that out of hundreds of millions of potential hotel visitors, 88% of visitors' choice is affected by what they see on the review sites (Raj & Kajla, 2018). This rapid growth of information generated by consumers of tourism services over the past decade calls for a detailed review of how it has progressed based on technology over time. The different forms of user-generated travel content are also largely undefined and unrehearsed within

DOI: 10.4324/9781003335924-11

the tourism industry. This chapter examines the inclusion of other forms of UGC created and disseminated by travellers and how it has transitioned over time with technological advancements.

The chapter focuses on two critical evaluations basis theoretical research. First, how UGC contributes to destination marketing in the tourism sector. Second, examine the impact of this information accessible to travellers and its impact on their decision-making. We apply for a systematic literature review. Our study extends previous work by understanding the different forms of UGC in the travel industry and its development over time with the inclusion of technology.

Social Media and Tourism

Tourism Organisations, Travellers, and Social Media

Tourism Organisations: From the marketing perspective, UGC persuades target groups like tourists. Such content creation has led tourism marketers to focus on design strategies to maximise marketing opportunities and attract tourists by involving prior visitors in marketing communication. A process commonly known as content co-creation is a value-creation effort put together by the customer and company that contributes to the sustainable growth of tourism organisations (Tuan et al., 2019). For instance, sentiment analysis of the Tweets about Bali-Indonesia performed by Raj and Kajla (2018) provided a positive image of the destination.

Traveller: For travellers, social media has made creating and sharing travel experiences with friends, family, and the larger anonymous group ubiquitous. Along with sharing their travel experiences, travellers thus have access to much more travel-related information and travel companies through social media platforms. Information shared by potential, actual, or former customers about a destination over the internet substantially shapes tourists' awareness, expectations, and behaviours. Due to this, DMOs have started to understand that the destinations now have to abandon the traditional top-down approach and favour the bottom-up approach by including co-created branding strategies. For this, destinations have started engaging with empowered travellers in value co-creation. Prahalad and Ramaswamy (2004) provided the first reference of the value co-creation concept, and after that, value co-creation in tourism is investigated from multiple facets, including strategy, marketing, and management. In the tourism and hospitality domain, while understanding the critical role of service experiences in creating value, value co-creation has gained further momentum. Such travel-generated content makes a unique form of intercommunication and builds the online reputation for destination brands. In an organisational context, 'reputation has been defined as the perceptual representation of a company's past actions and prospects that describe the firm's overall appeal to all its key constituents compared to other leading rivals' (Fombrun, 1996, p. 72). The traveller-generated content is expected to enhance the reputation and eventually generate value if applied cohesively to the destination's branding efforts or tourism organisations (Oliveira & Panyik, 2015). Tourism organisations are particularly interested in the mosaic of people sharing their travel experiences in addition to allocating ratings and scores to specific services in the form of rankings and strive to provide such opportunities to travellers.

In the same study by Raj and Kajla (2018) mentioned above, sentiment analysis of Bali-Thailand revealed prominent negative tweets. These unpleasant incidents, mentioned on Twitter, including rabies, draughts, and drug use, were indeed reported in local news. Such examples indicate the prominent role played by UGC in providing realistic destination information to prospective travellers.

Digitisation of Travellers – Word-of-Mouth

Electronic Word-of-Mouth (e-WoM) in Travel Planning and Decisions

At an individual level, UGC helps travellers express their opinions and permits interaction with others to gather or disseminate information. The proliferation of UGC in marketing communications challenges the equilibrium of tourism marketing communication prompting extensive change and organisational restructuring. 'Word of mouth involves the exchange of ephemeral oral or spoken messages between a contiguous source and a recipient who communicates directly in real life' (Stern, 1994, p. 7). Word-of-mouth (WoM) occurs spontaneously. e-WoM (electronic WoM), on the other hand, becomes a permanent record rather than a brief comment and thus gets repeated constantly and continues to exist (Craig et al., 2015). The transition from WoM to e-WoM in the tourism scenario has strengthened the need for DMOs to systematically understand and exploit customers' opinions.

The producers of shared content are called prosumers as (s)he creates content. By generating, updating, sharing, and discussing online material on various platforms, including content-sharing websites, blogs, wikis, and social networks, prosumers give life to the idea of e-WoM. e-WoM tremendously impacts a company's reputation, sales, and, eventually, survival (Kietzmann et al., 2011). Due to this, DMOs and tourism organisations engage with the guests to co-create UGC.

An interesting example of content co-creation is travellers sharing their opinions on tripadvisor.com. Tripadvisor.com uses these consumer opinions as marketing the largest site for unbiased travel reviews (which) gives you the real story about hotels, attractions, and restaurants worldwide. It hosts more than 1,926,031 unbiased reviews and is updated to every minute and every day by real travellers; it contains 'been there, done that' inside information; and 'the best deals for your travel dates' (tripadvisor.com, 2011).

Contribution of UGC to Destination Marketing

The Evolution of Destination Marketing through UGC

UGC in the tourism marketing strategy stems from information and communication technologies (ICTs). ICTs provide a more accessible means of communication with consumers and businesses, which is sophisticated and dynamic (Buhalis & Deimezi, 2004). AI-based chatbots are used by companies such as MakeMyTrip, Kayak, Skyscanner, and Cheapflights for customer service, including travel planning, booking, providing suggestions and recommendations, and other support activities (Pillai & Sivathanu, 2020). The assessment of this data is done using data analytics tools. The use and application of big data in tourism studies have been observed to reveal some unique and interesting facts in recent years. This data is generated by travellers inadvertently. However, ICTs aid tourists in forming memories by creating and storing their travel experiences in different forms, including textual, imagery, or audio-visual recordings (Lu et al., 2018). For travel aspirants, such content helps to plan their holidays. Several studies have focused on factors that impact the acceptance of UGC for travel decision-making.

Machine learning techniques in marketing are helping marketers to overcome the difficulties in tracking consumers' digital footprint. Such technologies on mobile devices bring the potential for creating context-related information (Buhalis & Foerste, 2015). Similarly, tourism data is assessed using advanced techniques and algorithms to gain more significant insights into the destination perception by travellers. With this advent, the tourism destination is no longer moulded by marketing content such as brochures, printed documents, or other advertisements, and UGC shapes the perception of tourists towards the destination (Leung et al., 2013). Facebook, YouTube, and other visual sites such as Instagram are popular UGC platforms (Nusair et al., 2017).

Travellers' acceptance of UGC for planning their travel has contributed to knowledge and experience. Although, one school of thought on UGC talks about such content being shared on platforms that adopt mainstream, non-elixated values, which stimulates questions regarding the authentication of the content shared. The second school of thought highlights that travellers are embracing the information supplied by other people through UGC and social networking sites on the internet and using it for travel-related decisions. Such information received by prospective travellers (those who have never been to a destination before) helps them abolish the intangible nature of the hospitality and travel aspects. Several cross-sectional studies have assessed UGC and information science in the tourism domain to compare the differential views surrounding the acceptance of such content. In order to better understand how DMOs can incorporate the use of social media platforms through the system of value co-creation, a honeycomb of social media functionality can be applied. The seven functional blocks include identity, conversations, sharing, presence, relationships, reputation, and groups (see Figure 8.1). These seven blocks help examine value-creation aspects from the traveller (social media user) perspective and organisation. Popular forms of UGC in tourism include photographs, tweets and reviews, and blog posts.

UGC, in the form of images or photographs, influences prospective travellers by conveying tourism experiences and creating memories, outlining the cognitive and affective destination image, and thus inspiring travellers (Paül i Agustí, 2018). Content in the form of photographs can indicate how tourists associate and interpret the destination (Zhao et al., 2018) and convey a unique view of the destination (Hunter, 2015). Studies have assessed the cognitive and affective elements of the images to understand and reflect tourists' received destination image (He et al., 2022). On a broader scale, such photos are classified into primary and secondary

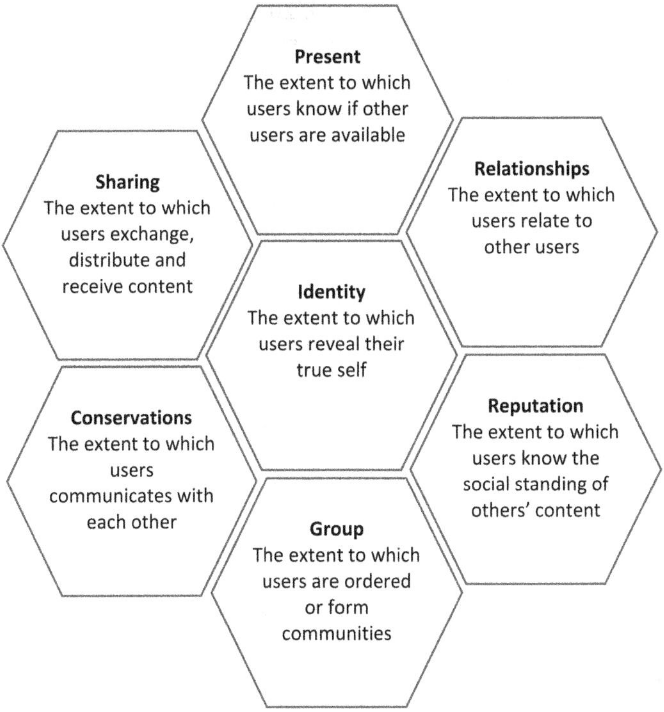

Figure 8.1 A honeycomb of social media functionality
Source: Adapted from Kietzmann et al. (2011, p. 243)

ones (Hunter, 2015). Primary images are formed by the visitors' and residents' experiences (Hunter, 2015). The travel agents create and project the secondary images wherein agents project travellers' experiences (MacKay & Fesenmaier, 1997). Some different techniques used to evaluate pictures include semiotic analysis (Hunter, 2015), visual analytics systems to perform sentiment analysis (Cao et al., 2020), and semantic network analysis (He et al., 2022).

In the case of social media content such as Twitter, everyone is free to express themselves in the form of their personal opinions and views, thus creating an immense set of data. Such data can bring smartness to managerial decisions in many sectors, including tourism, by identifying management issues. With such data, tourism businesses can monitor their market standing basis information concerning their strength (number of times the destination or particular tourism business is mentioned), the types of comments about the destination or the tourism business under scrutiny (positive, negative, or neutral tone of the tweets), popularity (comparative understanding of the destination or a tourism business as compared with the competitors), reach (number of visitors at the destination or the number of tourists who opted for the service offering of the specific tourism brand) (Revilla Hernández et al., 2016). Thus, Twitter plays a significant part in online reviews in the tourism industry (Sotiriadis & Van Zyl, 2013). Tweets are studied using multiple techniques, including sentiment analysis (Raj & Kajla, 2018), geo-located twitter opinion polarity analysis (Mostafa, 2019), network mapping analysis (Park et al., 2016), context-aware recommendation systems (Meehan et al., 2012), destination image analysis using big data tools (Marine-Roig & Clavé, 2015). Tourism literature has highlighted the importance of reviews posted by travellers in planning travel for tourists. Travel aspirants study the reviews and comment other travellers post on travel forums, blogs, and other social media platforms (Zhang et al., 2018).

A blog is 'a small website, usually maintained by one person, that is updated regularly and has a high concentration of repeat visitors' Barrett (2002, p. 106). Such peer-to-peer content (user-generated) is more reliable than the marketing material on the DMO's website or other sources (Gal-Tzur et al., 2020). Advancements in communication technology have led to the popularity of blogs, enabling people to engage more easily in social commentaries (McCabe & Foster, 2006). Travel blogs have become a powerful vehicle that drives people to tell their stories and helps build better relationships with potential visitors. Blogs are a set of combined text, videos, images, and audio that portray virtual stories full of experiences; as a result of which, they offer the opportunity to reveal tourists' interpretations of tourism products and experiences and to express tourists' impressions, perceptions, thoughts, and feelings. This information may include all that may otherwise not be revealed in a more constrained research environment, such as personal interviews (Banyai & Glover, 2012).

- Thought Point: Take a look at Figure 8.1, showing the seven functional blocks include identity, conversations, sharing, presence, relationships, reputation, and groups. Which functional blocks would you say connect to each social media platform mentioned above? Which platforms would be more critical from the perspective of the content creator (traveller) and the tourism organisation?

Travel Decision-Making Using the User-Generated Information

UGC Evolved as Relevant Information Source for Travellers

This section focuses on technology acceptance in the tourism sector, particularly regarding travellers' intention to use UGC for travel planning. Traditionally, travellers relied on uni-directional messages coming from the marketers, which rendered them powerless, as they received information deemed necessary by marketers (Bacile et al., 2014). Including UGC as a credible source of information has made two-way communication possible. UGC is available through WoM communication and provides non-commercial and up-to-date information for travellers (Yoo & Gretzel, 2011). This can be attributed to the application of ICT, and Web 2.0 changed how consumers communicate (Ukpabi & Karjaluoto, 2018). Travellers benefit from such information as it gives them a better understanding of the destination and its associated products and services. Such information further helps travellers by reducing pre-purchase doubt or risk, reducing the search time for travel information, and getting ideas for trips or even evaluating alternatives (Vermeulen & Seegers, 2009).

In an exciting study by Tsao et al. (2015), it was identified that roughly 80% of travellers assert they refer to reviews while planning their trip, and 53% of them claim that they would avoid booking a hotel that has not been reviewed by visitors previously. Thus, for travellers, UGC is expected to be genuine and frank and convey creators' real experiences (Wang, 2012). For travellers, travel costs constitute a vital component. In this vein, UGC is considered a reliable source for travellers to evaluate the value they will pay for certain travel-related services, involuntarily acting as a risk-reduction measure (Parra-López et al., 2011).

For instance, Bernoff and Schadler (2010) discuss monitoring QuickBooks' product reviews published on Amazon.com. According to the monitoring process findings, customers resented some pushy marketing techniques implemented into the software platform. As a result, QuickBooks decided to scale back the effort it put into its software-based cross-selling strategy. QuickBooks' above example is an interesting example of brands using the product and service reviews posted by consumers to build their brand image. It was very likely that the positive reviews contributed significantly to the brand image formation. However, concerning negative reviews, businesses are subject to emotional reactions, including reprimanding or becoming defensive. A better approach could be devising a strategy to turn negative opinionising consumers into satisfied ones (Mangold & Smith, 2012).

UGC and Content Co-Creation

UGC applications in destination marketing and management have hazed the shield among customers, organisations, and suppliers (Achrol & Kotler, 2012). On this basis, value co-creation has gained much attention after the growing popularity of UGC as a credible source in travel decision-making. Due to this, brands have started to create virtual communities that can help empower users' words, elevate social interactions, and thus make such content created by users to be used by the brand in their marketing efforts (Pham et al., 2022). Positioning a traveller as a reigning king in the destination brand identity, DMOs have seen to achieve better results (increased visitor numbers, tourism revenue) by way of applying coherent strategies to partner with the travellers (actual and potential) through multiple available channels (Oliveira & Panyik, 2015). Images or pictures are marketing signs to create effective advertising messages and destination branding strategies (Zhang et al., 2019). Along the same line, destination planners and managers avail the facility to connect with travellers at multiple two-way communications and experience touchpoints through traveller satisfaction, loyalty, and WoM (Krey et al., 2021).

As an implicit indicator of quality, branding would greatly influence travellers' decision-making process and intention, especially before planning a trip. In the tourism and hospitality field, the empirical studies evaluating UGC and value co-creation, particularly experiential value co-creation, have been limited. Several platforms that pave the way to such content co-creation include articles, comments, reviews, tweeter posts, discussions in forums or chats, and uploaded images, videos, or audio files (Munar, 2012).

In areas concerning destination brand image formation, the role of content co-creation using UGC, mainly through social media platforms, has gained momentum (Skinner, 2018). It would not be incorrect to say that a modest traveller actively indulges in creating a destination brand (Oliveira & Panyik, 2015). Some other studies in the area of UGC in tourism have focused on the development of virtual tourism societies (Wang et al., 2002), travel reviews and feedback (Yoo & Gretzel, 2008), e-tourism (Buhalis & Deimezi, 2004), and other social-media platform-based strategies for destinations (Munar et al., 2013). Existing studies have further evaluated tourism content co-creation in multiple contexts, including festival tourism (Rihova et al., 2018); adventure tourism (Prebensen & Xie, 2017); and inter-industry collaboration in tourism (Mathis et al., 2016).

- Thought point: By keeping because of the destination that you have visited in the recent past, enlist some of the co-created content that guided your choice of destination. Can you think of how the DMOs can create more opportunities for value co-creation for travellers?

Value Co-Creation in Content Co-Creation

The competitive tourism markets are forcing tourism and hospitality service managers to partner with customers/travellers to create value through personalised experiences (value co-creation) (Lei et al., 2019). Content co-creation is 'the act of creating products and services through the collaboration between customers, managers, employees, and other beneficiaries of the company' (Ramaswamy & Gouillart, 2010, p. 4). Content co-creation has gained significant attention in tourism research and industry (Oliveira & Panyik, 2015).

Co-creation symbolises a new era in the experience economy in the context of travel experiences. Travel experiences in the experience economy depend on users and employees, wherein co-creation is based on employee-user interaction and co-creators of value (Antón et al., 2018). Such co-creation strategies are applicable in the tourism domain (considering tourism a service industry) and allow the collection of rich consumer data that can be explored using techniques such as sentiment analysis (Buhalis & Foerste, 2015).

Although co-creation is considered a significant contributor to tourism growth, some studies have highlighted the negative contribution of UGC in the form of value co-destruction. Kwikchex, an online reputation management company acting on behalf of 800 hotels and restaurants, plans to publish a list of 1000 of (TripAdvisor) reviewers that it suspects of fraudulent and defamatory products (Gupta & Herman, 2011). In this case, the studies assessing the travellers' UGC primarily enumerate how posting negative information on social media can lead to value co-destruction for a brand (Dolan et al., 2019). In a deterring view, it is identified that social-media engagement of travellers and travel service providers has facilitated the travellers to complain (Champoux et al., 2012).

Case Study Examples

Penang State, Malaysia

There are multiple examples of DMOs using co-creation opportunities as a part of their digital marketing strategy. The research conducted by Oliveira and Panyik (2015) taking Penang State Tourism as an example demonstrated the active role of DMOs in using Instagram connected to Twitter to allow interaction with the traveller. The research further stated that the hashtags (#) can be effectively used to promote specific events, campaigns, or the destination brand itself (e.g., #visitmalaysia, #penang, and #heritage).

Ceutí, Spain

In another study conducted in Ceutí, co-creation efforts were directed towards building a smart city tourism image of the destination by way of structuring innovative communication channels between visitors and destination attraction through an interactive app (App called Be Memories discussed by Gomez-Oliva et al., 2019) that shares information about the intangible heritage wherein the content is co-created by residents of the destination. Another example of participative co-creation in tourism significantly focuses upon (re) defining and (re) configuring archaeological heritage sites by way of sharing stories that designate emotions and values attached to the past (Ross & Saxena, 2019).

Maldives

Another example is Maldives' unique journey to recovery. The Maldives is a tropical island in the Indian Ocean. Tourism is the most profitable economic industry, contributing 39.6% to the Maldives' total GDP. The island is a picturesque tourist destination with more than a thousand coral reefs, extensive sunshine, and beaches with white sand. Due to this, the destination hosts more tourists than the nation's total population. However, the island tourism destination is facing a significant problem as coral reefs are dying, and the question arises as to whether tourism impacts the coral reefs. Some of the primary reasons for this are listed to be, rising ocean temperatures, pollution, and changes in water salinity. However, another intriguing study related coral reefs' destruction to excessive Oxybenzone in water. Oxybenzone is a chemical sunscreen agent that functions as a photo stabiliser in sunscreen and is said to be extremely harmful to marine flora and fauna. Since more sunscreen is being dumped into water bodies yearly, the effects could be severe. Oxybenzone is hazardous, and one drop of it has the potential to harm hundreds of litres of water. However, there are no formal studies supporting the role of Oxybenzone on coral reef bleaching and destruction in the Maldives. DMOs in Maldives, on the other hand, consider that this could be a significant reason for the coral reef's destruction and want to take measures to control such destruction from happening further. However, the destination authorities cannot take any legitimate measures due to a lack of formal evidence. However, at their end, DMOs wish to sensitise their visitors using value co-creation techniques.

- Thought Point: Take a look at how destinations create opportunities for content co-creation. Further, based on your understanding of the Honeycomb of social media functionality, can you think of the right social media platforms that should be chosen by the DMOs in the Maldives to reach the right visitor categories? Additionally, suggest some measures by which DMOs can use a content co-creation approach to sensitise travellers against using Oxybenzone-containing sunscreen in the Maldives.

Conclusion

In the experience economy, the tourist experience is characterised as where tourism consumption and production coincide. The co-creation efforts provide opportunities to create value through consumer experiences. The co-creation of DMOs and travellers has shifted the market from a firm-centric to a consumer-centric viewpoint, with the purchaser at the forefront. The tourist is assumed to play an essential role in the final link of the production chain, realising an encounter between the DMO and the tourist by assembling the resources required to produce a tourism experience in a consumption set.

Tourists undoubtedly form some perceptions of a destination when they are able to obtain sufficient destination information prior to their trip. Destination managers should promote a holistic image based on the experiences elicited by a destination in congruence with the travellers. Destination managers should also put in efforts to create opportunities for travellers to participate in so-called content co-creation efforts. Further, the co-creation of brand identity by firms and customers online has become imperative in the digital era. This has led users to actively contribute to brand image creation and re-creation in consumers' minds through UGC (Borges-Tiago et al., 2019). Tourism research recognises the significance of UGC influences on tourist behaviour. Content co-creation is a relatively new process and is developing rapidly (Nyangwe & Buhalis, 2018). The study highlights several areas that are considered to be the positives in the use of UGC from the perspective of DMOs and tourism. The study contributes to the existing literature by highlighting how UGC contributes to the field of destination marketing through value co-creation efforts. Further access to such traveller-created information has led prospective travellers to make informed decisions.

Further Questions

- Think of a well-known destination you are familiar with. Can you recollect the functional blocks (Figure 8.1) that were the focus of the destinations' marketing efforts?
- How do you think the velocity of conversations and other information flows could affect the current or future position of the destination in the market?

Further Readings

Filieri, R., Alguezaui, S., & McLeay, F. (2015). Why do travellers trust TripAdvisor? Antecedents of trust towards consumer-generated media and its influence on recommendation adoption and word of mouth. *Tourism Management, 51*, 174–185. https://doi.org/10.1016/j.tourman.2015.05.007

Mulvey, M. S., Lever, M. W., & Elliot, S. (2020). A cross-national comparison of intragenerational variability in social media sharing. *Journal of Travel Research, 59*(7), 1204–1220. https://doi.org/10.1177/0047287519878511

Rathore, A. K., Joshi, U. C., & Ilavarasan, P. V. (2017). Social media usage for tourism: A case of Rajasthan tourism. *Procedia Computer Science, 122*, 751–758. https://doi.org/10.1016/j.procs.2017.11.433

References

Achrol, R. S., & Kotler, P. (2012). Frontiers of the marketing paradigm in the third millennium. *Journal of the Academy of Marketing Science, 40*(1), 35–52. https://doi.org/10.1007/s11747-011-0255-4

Antón, C., Camarero, C., & Garrido, M. J. (2018). Exploring the experience value of museum visitors as a co-creation process. *Current Issues in Tourism, 21*(12), 1406–1425. https://doi.org/10.1080/13683500.2017.1373753

Bacile, T. J., Ye, C., & Swilley, E. (2014). From firm-controlled to consumer-contributed: Consumer co-production of personal media marketing communication. *Journal of Interactive Marketing, 28*(2), 117–133. https://doi.org/10.1016/j.intmar.2013.12.001

Banyai, M., & Glover, T. D. (2012). Evaluating research methods on travel blogs. *Journal of Travel Research, 51*(3), 267–277. https://doi.org/10.1177/0047287511410323

Barrett, C. (2002). Anatomy of a weblog. In *We've got a blog: How weblogs are changing our culture* (pp. 89). Perseus Publishing.

Bernoff, J., & Schadler, T. (2010). *Empowered: unleash your employees, energize your customers, transform your business*. Harvard Business Press.

Borges-Tiago, M. T., Tiago, F., Veríssimo, J. M., & Silva, T. (2019). A brand-new world: Brand-endorsers-users fit on social media. *Academia Revista Latinoamericana de Administración, 32*(4), 472–486. https://doi.org/10.1108/ARLA-02-2019-0047

Buhalis, D., & Deimezi, O. (2004). E-tourism developments in Greece: Information communication technologies adoption for the strategic management of the Greek tourism industry. *Tourism and Hospitality Research, 5*(2), 103–130. https://doi.org/10.1057/palgrave.thr.6040011

Buhalis, D., & Foerste, M. (2015). DoCoMo marketing for travel and tourism: Empowering co-creation of value. *Journal of Destination Marketing & Management, 4*(3), 151–161. https://doi.org/10.1016/j.jdmm.2015.04.001

Cao, M. Q., Liang, J., Li, M. Z., Zhou, Z. H., & Zhu, M. (2020). TDIVis: Visual analysis of tourism destination images. *Frontiers of Information Technology & Electronic Engineering, 21*(4), 536–557. https://doi.org/10.1631/FITEE.1900631

Champoux, V., Durgee, J., & McGlynn, L. (2012). Corporate Facebook pages: When "fans" attack. *Journal of Business Strategy, 33*(2), 22–30. https://doi.org/10.1108/02756661211206717

Craig, C. S., Greene, W. H., & Versaci, A. (2015). E-word of mouth: Early predictor of audience engagement: How pre-release "e-WOM" drives box-office outcomes of movies. *Journal of Advertising Research, 55*(1), 62–72. https://doi.org/10.2501/JAR-55-1-062-072

Dolan, R., Seo, Y., & Kemper, J. (2019). Complaining practices on social media in tourism: A value co-creation and co-destruction perspective. *Tourism Management*, *73*, 35–45. https://doi.org/10.1016/j.tourman.2019.01.017

European Travel Commission. (2009). *The Russian outbound travel market with special insight into the image of Europe as a destination*. World Tourism Organization (WTO).

Fombrun, C. J. (1996). *Reputation: Realising value from the corporate image*. Harvard Business School Press. https://archive.org/details/reputationrealiz0000fomb

Gal-Tzur, A., Bar-Lev, S., & Shiftan, Y. (2020). Using question & answer forums as a platform for improving transport-related information for tourists. *Journal of Travel Research*, *59*(7), 1221–1237.

Gomez-Oliva, A., Alvarado-Uribe, J., Parra-Meroño, M. C., & Jara, A. J. (2019). Transforming communication channels to the co-creation and diffusion of intangible heritage in smart tourism destination: Creation and testing in Ceutí (Spain). *Sustainability*, *11*(14), 3848.

Gupta, S., & Herman, K. (2011). *TripAdvisor, Harvard business school marketing unit case 511–1004*. Harvard Business Publishing Education.

He, Z., Deng, N., Li, X., & Gu, H. (2022). How to "read" a destination from images? Machine learning and network methods for DMOs' image projection and photo evaluation. *Journal of Travel Research*, *61*(3), 597–619. https://doi.org/10.1177/0047287521995134

Hootsuite, W. A. S. Y. (2020). *Digital 2020. Global digital overview*. https://www.hootsuite.com/resources/digital-2020

Hunter, W. C. (2015). The visual representation of border tourism: Demilitarised zone (DMZ) and Dokdo in South Korea. *International Journal of Tourism Research*, *17*(2), 151–160. https://doi.org/10.1002/jtr.1973

Kietzmann, J. H., Hermkens, K., McCarthy, I. P., & Silvestre, B. S. (2011). Social media? Get serious! Understanding the functional building blocks of social media. *Business Horizons*, *54*(3), 241–251. https://doi.org/10.1016/j.bushor.2011.01.005

Krey, N., tom Dieck, M. C., Wu, S., & Fountoulaki, P. (2021). Exploring the influence of touch points on tourist experiences at crisis impacted destinations. *Journal of Travel Research*, *62*(1), 39–54. https://doi.org/10.1177/00472875211053657

Lei, S. I., Ye, S., Wang, D., & Law, R. (2019). Engaging customers in value co-creation through mobile instant messaging in the tourism and hospitality industry. *Journal of Hospitality & Tourism Research*, *44*(2), 1–23. https://doi.org/10.1177/1096348019893066

Leung, D., Law, R., Van Hoof, H., & Buhalis, D. (2013). Social media in tourism and hospitality: A literature review. *Journal of Travel & Tourism Marketing*, *30*(1–2), 3–22. https://doi.org/10.1080/10548408.2013.750919

Lu, Y., Chen, Z., & Law, R. (2018). Mapping the progress of social media research in hospitality and tourism management from 2004 to 2014. *Journal of Travel & Tourism Marketing*, *35*(2), 102–118. https://doi.org/10.1080/10548408.2017.1350249

MacKay, K. J., & Fesenmaier, D. R. (1997). Pictorial element of destination in image formation. *Annals of Tourism Research*, *24*(3), 537–565. https://doi.org/10.1016/S0160-7383(97)00011-X

Mangold, W. G., & Smith, K. T. (2012). Selling to Millennials with online reviews. *Business Horizons*, *55*(2), 141–153. https://doi.org/10.1016/j.bushor.2011.11.001

Marine-Roig, E., & Clavé, S. A. (2015). Tourism analytics with massive user-generated content: A case study of Barcelona. *Journal of Destination Marketing & Management*, *4*(3), 162–172. https://doi.org/10.1016/j.jdmm.2015.06.004

Mathis, E. F., Kim, H. L., Uysal, M., Sirgy, J. M., & Prebensen, N. K. (2016). The effect of co-creation experience on outcome variable. *Annals of Tourism Research, 57*, 62–75. https://doi.org/10.1016/j.annals.2015.11.023

McCabe, S., & Foster, C. (2006). The role and function of narrative in tourist interaction. *Journal of Tourism and Cultural Change, 4*(3), 194–215. https://doi.org/10.2167/jtcc071.0

Meehan, K., Lunney, T., Curran, K., & McCaughey, A. (2012). VISIT: Virtual intelligent system for informing tourists. In M. Merabti & O. Abuelma'atti (Eds.), *PGNET, Liverpool*. Liverpool John Moores University, School of Computing & Mathematical Sciences.

Mostafa, M. M. (2019). Clustering halal food consumers: A Twitter sentiment analysis. *International Journal of Market Research, 61*(3), 320–337. https://doi.org/10.1177/1470785318771451

Munar, A. M. (2012). Social media strategies and destination management. *Scandinavian Journal of Hospitality and Tourism, 12*(2), 101–120. https://doi.org/10.1080/15022250.2012.679047

Munar, A. M., Gyimóthy, S., & Cai, L. (2013). Tourism social media: A new research agenda. In *Tourism social media: Transformations in identity, community and culture* (Vol. 18, pp. 1–15). Emerald Group Publishing Limited. https://doi.org/10.1108/S1571-5043(2013)0000018003

Nusair, K., Hua, N., Ozturk, A., & Butt, I. (2017). A theoretical framework of electronic word-of-mouth against the backdrop of social networking websites. *Journal of Travel & Tourism Marketing, 34*(5), 653–665. https://doi.org/10.1080/10548408.2016.1218404

Nyangwe, S., & Buhalis, D. (2018). Branding transformation through social media and co-creation: Lessons from Marriott international. In *Information and communication technologies in tourism 2018* (pp. 257–269). Springer. https://doi.org/10.1007/978-3-319-72923-7_20

Oliveira, E., & Panyik, E. (2015). Content, context and co-creation: Digital challenges in destination branding with references to Portugal as a tourist destination. *Journal of Vacation Marketing, 21*(1), 53–74. https://doi.org/10.1177/1356766714544235

Park, S. B., Ok, C. M., & Chae, B. K. (2016). Using Twitter data for cruise tourism marketing and research. *Journal of Travel & Tourism Marketing, 33*(6), 885–898. https://doi.org/10.1080/10548408.2015.1071688

Parra-López, E., Bulchand-Gidumal, J., Gutiérrez-Taño, D., & Díaz-Armas, R. (2011). Intentions to use social media in organising and taking vacation trips. *Computers in Human Behavior, 27*(2), 640–654. https://doi.org/10.1016/j.chb.2010.05.022

Paül i Agustí, D. (2018). Characterising the location of tourist images in cities. Differences in user-generated images (Instagram), official tourist brochures and travel guides. *Annals of Tourism Research, 2018, 73*, 103–115. https://doi.org/10.1016/j.annals.2018.09.001

Pham, H. L., Pham, T., & Nguyen, T. T. (2022). Value co-creation in branding: A systematic review from a tourism perspective. *European Journal of Tourism Research, 32*, 3203–3203. https://doi.org/10.54055/ejtr.v32i.2597

Pillai, R., & Sivathanu, B. (2020). Adoption of AI-based chatbots for hospitality and tourism. *International Journal of Contemporary Hospitality Management*. https://doi.org/10.1108/IJCHM-04-2020-0259

Prahalad, C. K., & Ramaswamy, V. (2004). Co-creation experiences: The next practice in value creation. *Journal of Interactive Marketing, 18*(3), 5–14. https://doi.org/10.1002/dir.20015

Prebensen, N. K., & Xie, J. (2017). Efficacy of co-creation and mastering on perceived value and satisfaction in tourists' consumption. *Tourism Management*, *60*, 166–176. https://doi.org/10.1016/j.tourman.2016.12.001

Raj, S., & Kajla, T. (2018). Tourism analytics: Social media analytics framework for promoting Asian tourist destinations using big data approach. *Journal for Global Business Advancement*, *11*(1), 64–88. https://doi.org/10.1504/JGBA.2018.093204

Ramaswamy, V., & Gouillart, F. J. (2010). *The power of co-creation: Build it with them to boost growth, productivity, and profits*. Simon and Schuster. https://books.google.co.in/books?hl=en&lr=&id=EyXjhU_8myIC&oi=fnd&pg=PA3&dq=Ramaswamy,+V.,+%26+Gouillart

Revilla Hernández, M., Santana Talavera, A., & Parra López, E. (2016). Effects of co-creation in a tourism destination brand image through Twitter. *Journal of Tourism, Heritage & Services Marketing (JTHSM)*, *2*(1), 3–10. https://doi.org/10.5281/zenodo.376341

Rihova, I., Buhalis, D., Gouthro, M. B., & Moital, M. (2018). Customer-to-customer co-creation practices in tourism: Lessons from customer-dominant logic. *Tourism Management*, *67*, 362–375. https://doi.org/10.1016/j.tourman.2018.02.010

Ross, D., & Saxena, G. (2019). Participative co-creation of archaeological heritage: Case insights on creative tourism in Alentejo, Portugal. *Annals of Tourism Research*, *79*, 102790. https://doi.org/10.1016/j.annals.2019.102790

Skinner, H. M. (2018). Who really creates the place brand? Considering the role of user generated content in creating and communicating a place identity. *Communication and Society*, *31*(4), 9–24.

Sotiriadis, M. D., & Van Zyl, C. (2013). Electronic word-of-mouth and online reviews in tourism services: The use of Twitter by tourists. *Electronic Commerce Research*, *13*(1), 103–124. https://doi.org/10.1007/s10660-013-9108-1

Stern, B. B. (1994). A revised communication model for advertising: Multiple dimensions of the source, the message, and the recipient. *Journal of Advertising*, *23*(2), 5–15. https://doi.org/10.1080/00913367.1994.10673438

Tsao, W. C., Hsieh, M. T., Shih, L. W., & Lin, T. M. (2015). Compliance with eWOM: The influence of hotel reviews on booking intention from the perspective of consumer conformity. *International Journal of Hospitality Management*, *46*, 99–111. https://doi.org/10.1016/j.ijhm.2015.01.008

TripAdvisor. (2011). TripAdvisor [webpage]. Retrieved from https://www.tripadvisor.com/

Tuan, L. T., Rajendran, D., Rowley, C., & Khai, D. C. (2019). Customer value co-creation in the business-to-business tourism context: The roles of corporate social responsibility and customer empowering behaviours. *Journal of Hospitality and Tourism Management*, *39*, 137–149. https://doi.org/10.1016/j.jhtm.2019.04.002

Ukpabi, D. C., & Karjaluoto, H. (2018). What drives travellers' adoption of user-generated content? A literature reviews. *Tourism Management Perspectives*, *28*, 251–273. https://doi.org/10.1016/j.tmp.2018.03.006

Vermeulen, I. E., & Seegers, D. (2009). Tried and tested: The impact of online hotel reviews on consumer consideration. *Tourism Management*, *30*(1), 123–127. https://doi.org/10.1016/j.tourman.2008.04.008

Wang, H. Y. (2012). Investigating the determinants of travel blogs influencing readers' intention to travel. *The Service Industries Journal*, *32*(2), 231–255. https://doi.org/10.1080/02642069.2011.559225

Wang, Y., Yu, Q., & Fesenmaier, D. R. (2002). Defining the virtual tourist community: Implications for tourism marketing. *Tourism Management*, *23*(4), 407–417. https://doi.org/10.1016/S0261-5177(01)00093-0

Yoo, K. H., & Gretzel, U. (2008). What motivates consumers to write online travel reviews? *Information Technology & Tourism*, *10*(4), 283–295. https://doi.org/10.3727/109830508788403114

Yoo, K. H., & Gretzel, U. (2011). Influence of personality on travel-related consumer-generated media creation. *Computers in Human Behavior*, *27*(2), 609–621. https://doi.org/10.1016/j.chb.2010.05.002

Zhang, K., Chen, Y., & Li, C. (2019). Discovering the tourists' behaviors and perceptions in a tourism destination by analysing photos' visual content with a computer deep learning model: The case of Beijing. *Tourism Management*, *75*, 595–608 https://doi.org/10.1016/j.tourman.2019.07.002

Zhang, H., Gordon, S., Buhalis, D., & Ding, X. (2018). Experience value co-creation on destination online platforms. *Journal of Travel Research*, *57*(8), 1093–1107. https://doi.org/10.1177/0047287517733557

Zhao, Z., Zhu, M., & Hao, X. (2018). Share the Gaze: Representation of destination image on the Chinese social platform WeChat Moments. *Journal of Travel & Tourism Marketing*, *35*(6), 726–739. https://doi.org/10.1080/10548408.2018.1432449

9 Designing for Highly Involving Experiences

Immersion in Virtual and 'Real-World' Experiencescapes

Veronica Blumenthal and Olga Gjerald

Introduction

Organisations operating within the experience economy are continuously competing to attract customers and facilitate high-quality, memorable experiences for their patrons. In such a context, being able to design highly involving/ immersive experiences products can be a major competitive advantage, as studies have shown that experiencing immersion is connected to emotional engagement, which is central to the creation of memorable experiences (Jennett et al., 2008; Kim, 2014). Providing guests with memorable experiences can furthermore have a positive effect on profitability since the positive emotions connected with such experiences foster revisit intentions and the spread of positive word of mouth (Kim et al., 2010). But how can tourism managers and experience product designers facilitate such highly involving, immersive experiences for their guests?

This chapter presents an overview of the literature on immersion, drawing on research from both tourism and human-computer interaction (HCI) studies to explain what immersion is, how it can be understood, and different theories on the nature of the immersion process. The chapter then presents a case study on the nature of the immersion process in the context of virtual gaming experiences, before concluding with advice on how experience providers can use experience design to create highly involving, immersive experience products.

What Is Immersion?

Immersion is an experience concept that has grown out of several different research fields, including anthropology, education research, consumer behaviour psychology, and tourism although HCI research has by far been the most dominating field. In recent years, however, it has received increased attention from tourism academics and practitioners alike, as demands are changing and travellers increasingly seek high-quality, engaging experiences (Tussyadiah, 2014). As a consequence of immersion's roots in a potpourri of different research fields, there are a plethora of

DOI: 10.4324/9781003335924-12

meanings and definitions being ascribed to the term. According to Carr (2006), the different definitions of immersion can be divided into two categories:

- **Perceptual definitions of immersion**
  Immersion is understood to be a perceptual phenomenon and the term is used to describe the experience environment, certain types of technologies, or particular elements in the experience design. These types of definitions dominate the field of HCI.
- **Psychological definitions of immersion**
  Psychological definitions of immersion focus on the cognitive features of the experience and understand immersion as a psychological state experienced in the mind of the individual. These types of definitions are dominant in the field of tourism and consumer behaviour.

These differences are important to be aware of when interpreting research on immersion, as these two types of definitions of immersion refer to related, but different concepts: immersion as a feature of technology and immersion as a psychological state. This chapter focuses on the latter, applying an understanding of immersion as the deepest form of involvement (Brown & Cairns, 2004) and Mainemelis' (2001, p. 557) definition of immersion as 'the feeling of being fully absorbed, surrendered to, or consumed by an activity, to the point of forgetting one's self and one's surroundings'.

Readers familiar with experience concepts such as flow, peak, and extraordinary experiences might spot certain similarities between this description of immersion and these more well-known experience concepts, which also involve loss of self-consciousness and a distorted sense of time. Flow, a concept first introduced by Csikszentmihalyi (1990, p. 4), is 'the state in which people are so involved in an activity that nothing else matters'. A description that is similar to immersion, which has been described as the deepest form of involvement (Brown & Cairns, 2004). The difference between immersion and flow, however, lay in the eight components that flow has been described to consist of clear goals, intrinsically rewarding, a high degree of concentration, loss of self-consciousness, distorted sense of time, direct and immediate feedback, a balance between ability level and challenge, and a sense of personal control (Csikszentmihalyi, 1990). While some of these components, such as a distorted sense of time and loss of self-consciousness, are also part of the immersion, other components, such as challenge and clear goals, are not. Challenge has been considered to be particularly essential to flow, as the flow can only be experienced when there is a balance between challenge and skills and the consumer uses their skills optimally. Immersion, however, does not require optimal use of skills. Nor does it require a balance between challenge and skills, as research has shown that it is possible to become immersed when there is no challenge present, for example when enjoying the sunset from a sundeck (Hansen & Mossberg, 2013; Pine & Gilmore, 1999) or when the challenge exceeds the consumer's capabilities (Jennett et al., 2008). Flow is furthermore considered to involve a serene mindset (Csikszentmihalyi, 1990), which is not necessarily the case for immersion, where emotions and anxiety can run high (Jennett et al., 2008). In other words, although immersion and flow share some commonalities and immersion can be experienced as a part of the flow experience (Arnould & Price, 1993), immersion and flow are two separate, albeit closely related, experience constructs.

Peak experiences are described as 'Moments of great awe, intense happiness, even rapture, ecstasy, and bliss – moments of pure, positive happiness, when all doubts, all fears, all inhibitions, all weakness were left behind' (Maslow, 1964, p. 9). These experiences take the individual to unexpected emotional highs and make them feel connected to a larger phenomenon; to something external to, and larger than themselves (Schouten et al., 2007). Peak experiences also overlap with immersion to some extent, as they involve a lack of self-awareness, absence of time-consciousness, and total attention (Hansen & Mossberg, 2013). The same can be said for extraordinary experiences (Arnould & Price, 1993; Privette, 1983) which similarly to immersion is characterised by a sense of absorption, attention, and a 'spontaneous letting-be' (Arnould & Price, 1993, p. 25). As the name implies, however, extraordinary experiences are experiences that are out of the ordinary – that go beyond the realm of everyday life (Bhattacharjee & Mogilner, 2014). This is not necessarily the case for immersion, which can also be experienced in relation to more mundane daily life experiences, for example during work (Mainemelis, 2001).

Immersion is an important dimension of all these types of experiences (Arnould & Price, 1993; Lindberg & Østergaard, 2015) and has been described as one of the fundamental building blocks of these higher level experience concepts (Blumenthal & Jensen, 2019; Hansen & Mossberg, 2013). While immersion is a central dimension in these experience types, it is also a state that can be experienced independently, without being part of the state of flow or during a peak experience for example. Immersion can be experienced while visiting a museum (Lunardo & Ponsignon, 2019), playing a video game (Cairns et al., 2014), or enjoying a classical music concert (Carù & Cova, 2005), during horseback riding (Hansen & Mossberg, 2016), on a glacier hike (Løvoll, 2019), while reading a book (Douglas & Hargadon, 2001) or in any deeply engaging experience context, whether in a commercial context or not.

- Thought point: Can you think of a time when you became immersed in an experience? What did it feel like? What type of experience context was it in?

Immersion: A Relevant Concept in the Experience Economy

What makes the concept of immersion particularly relevant for academics and practitioners operating within the tourism industry is the connection between immersion and memorable experiences. Experiencing the state of immersion can in itself lead to an experience becoming memorable, as there is a strong connection between immersion and emotional engagement (Brown & Cairns, 2004; Jennett et al., 2008), which is a key to the formation of memorable experiences (Johnston & Clark, 2001; Kim, 2014; Servidio & Ruffolo, 2016). Memorable experiences, in turn, give rise to positive emotions towards the experience provider, which fosters revisit intentions and positive word of mouth (Kim et al., 2010; Slåtten et al., 2011). Understanding the process leading up to the state of immersion (the immersion process) can thus provide valuable insight into the factors and processes involved in creating engaging, highly involving experiences which can be crucial to the ability of experience providers to attract new and repeat visitors.

The Immersion Process and the Factors that Influence It

Because of the close connection between immersion and other related experience concepts, research on immersion as an independent experience context has remained scarce. Consequently, our understanding of the nature of the immersion process has remained limited and contested. The first to develop a model of the immersion process was Brown and Cairns (2004), who developed their model on the basis of immersion in computer games. Proposing a model of the immersion process as progressive and sequential, where players progress through degrees of involvement, ranging from engagement to engrossment before finally reaching a state of total immersion. During this process, the consumer – or player in this case – has to overcome a number of barriers, to be able to progress from one stage to the next, before reaching the state of immersion. This player's transition from one stage to the next is one-directional and cannot be reversed, as the player cannot return to an earlier stage of the process, given that the barriers (such as learning the controllers and understanding the game) have already been overcome and cannot be reversed. Due to its one-directional nature, this model does not address what happens after the consumer has reached the state of immersion.

A second model of the immersion process was later developed by Carù and Cova (2005). Their model was developed in the context of classical music concerts and addresses the issue of what happens after the consumer has reached the state of immersion. They propose that there are two paths leading to the state of immersion – dependent on the consumer's prior experience with the activity or activity contexts. Experienced visitors can become immersed instantly, while inexperienced visitors go through a gradual and cyclical process of familiarisation, progressing through the stages of nesting and investigating before reaching the stamping stage where they are familiar enough with the situation to become immersed. The consumer might however only experience the state of immersion momentarily before returning to the nesting stage, restarting the whole process. Contrary to Brown and Cairns' model, it is the consumer's gradual familiarisation with the experience and the experience contexts that drive the immersion process rather than increasing levels of involvement. They also propose that the process is cyclical rather than one-directional.

A third model of the immersion process was purposed by Hansen and Mossberg (2013). This model was developed based on a nature-based tourism context and suggests that the immersion process is dynamic in nature with consumers fluctuating in and out of different degrees of immersion throughout the duration of the experience.

Each of these three models (illustrated in Figure 9.1) not only represents three rather different interpretations of the immersion process but was also developed in

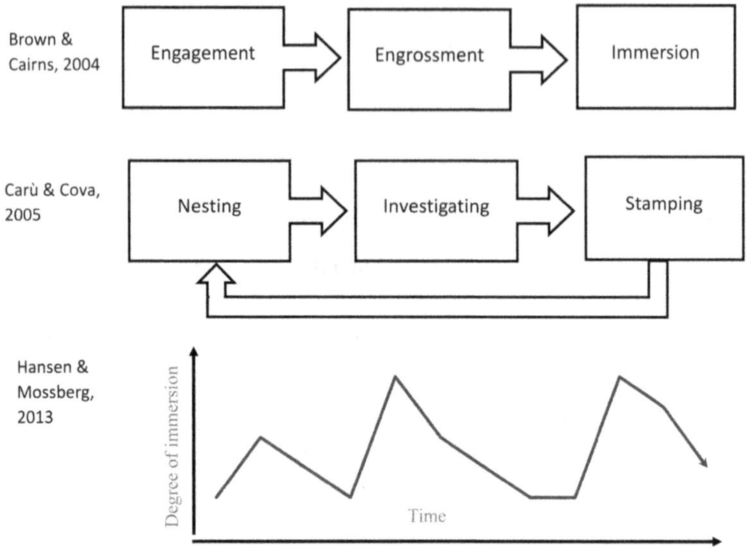

Figure 9.1 The three theories on the nature of the immersion process

Source: Adapted from Blumenthal and Jensen (2019)

three rather different experience contexts: computer games, classical music concerts, and nature-based tourism. Leading to speculations on whether the experience context might influence the progression of the immersion process and how it unfolds. Prior research has indicated that the experiencescape (Mossberg, 2007), the social and physical surroundings in which the experience takes place, and the visitors' interactions with different elements in the experiencescape play a key role in the immersion process. And as virtual experiencescapes are radically different from analogue 'real-world' experiencescapes, it is pertinent to ask whether the immersion process is significantly different in computer games compared to in a museum visit or a nature-based tourism activity.

- Thought point: Do you think there is a difference between the immersion process in virtual and 'real-world' experiences?

This is an important question as technology-enhanced and technology-dependent experience products are on the rise in tourism (Burt & Louw, 2019; Tussyadiah et al., 2018; Yung & Khoo-Lattimore, 2019) and understanding possible differences between the immersion process in analogue, technology-enhanced or technology-dependent experiences is important to our understanding of the factors that influence the immersion process. Such insights can furthermore have important practical implications for experience designers seeking to design highly engaging experience products with varying degrees of technology integration.

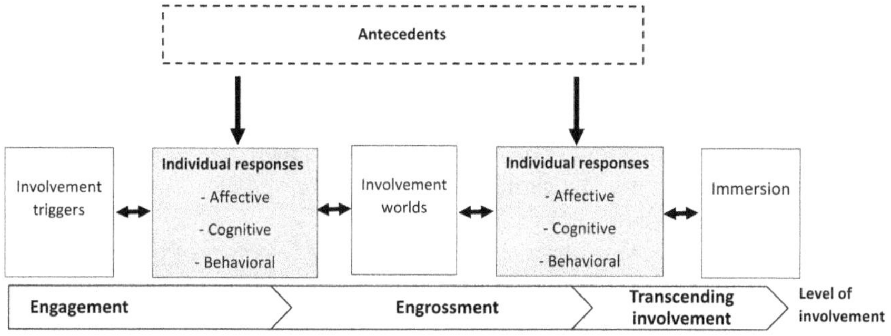

Figure 9.2 Blumenthal's generic immersion process model

Source: Adapted from Blumenthal (2021)

In an effort to explore this question, we conducted three consecutive case studies on the immersion process across three different experience contexts with varying degrees of technology integration: an analogue Viking ship sailing experience (Roskilde Viking Ship Museum), a technology-enhanced escape room experience (Escape Reality Trondheim), and virtual (technology dependent) gaming experiences offered at House of Nerds (HoN) Oslo. This resulted in the development of a new generic model of the immersion process, as well as three context-specific immersion process models from each of the three case contexts. The generic model is presented in Figure 9.2 and in the following section, we present the case study conducted at HoN and discuss similarities and differences between the immersion process identified in this context compared to the remaining immersion process models.

Case Study: Introducing House of Nerds (NoN)

Immersion in Virtual Experience Contexts vs. Immersion in Analogue Experience Contexts

HoN is a commercial gaming centre located in the Norwegian capital of Oslo. The centre offers visitors the opportunity to participate in a variety of different virtual gaming experiences on PC, consoles (GameCube, PlayStation, etc.), and retro gaming devices (Nintendo SNES) in a gaming-themed experience context. The experience products on offer here represent technology-enabled experience products that are fully dependent on technology for the experience to happen and that are dependent on the visitors' active participation in the co-creation of the experience. What makes this context particularly interesting from an immersion perspective is that it represents a duality in terms of experiencescapes. They involve visitors 'travelling' into a virtual experiencescape that to some extent is separate from the experiencescape in which the visitors are physically present. Consequently, visitors have to relate to two different experiencescapes: the 'real-world' experiencescape in which they are physically present and the virtual experiencescape to which they 'travel' through the game.

To be able to explore the immersion process in this experience context, 14 semi-structured interviews were conducted with HoN visitors who represented variations in game type (strategy, action, etc.) game settings (tournament, alone, online, with friends), play duration, and prior experience with HoN and the game they were playing during their visit. The interviews were supported by informants drawing experience line charts, indicating the development of their involvement in the experience during the course of their gaming session.

The interview data were analysed using an adapted version of the coding process characteristic of the Straussian grounded theory approach: open, axial, and selective coding (Strauss & Corbin, 1990). The first stage, the open coding stage, can however be described as semi-open, as we set out with four tentative, but pre-defined, categories: immersion, engagement, engrossment, and transcending involvement (representing the involvement levels identified in the two previous studies from the Viking Ship Museum and the Escape Room). In the second stage of the analysis, the axial coding, the codes derived from the 'semi-open' coding were grouped into categories and categorised into a hierarchy of abstraction, before the main category, and the relationship between the identified categories was established during the selective coding. To ensure proper grounding of the theory in the data and to reduce the effect of confirmation bias (Klayman, 1995), the selective coding stage of this study consisted of two consecutive phases. In the first phase, the relationships between the categories identified in the present data and the pre-defined involvement levels were identified. Before we in the second phase compared them to the categories and relationships identified as influential to the immersion process in the two previous case studies (Viking Ship Museum and Escape Room).

The Nature of the Immersion Process in a Virtual Experience Context

Findings uncover an immersion process that contains elements from both Hansen and Mossberg (2013) and Brown and Cairns' (2004) models of the immersion process and that follow the same structure as the immersion process identified in our two previous case studies (Blumenthal, 2020; Blumenthal & Jensen, 2019), although with several context-specific factors influencing the process. A context-specific model of this process is illustrated in Figure 9.3.

The process was found to consist of three levels of involvement (engagement, engrossment, and transcending involvement) and three stages that were connected to each involvement level: involvement triggers, involvement worlds, and the state of immersion. The process was held together by four mechanisms: (1) involvement as the driving force driving the immersion process forward. (2) The visitors' active participation as co-creators interacting with the different stimuli they were exposed to. (3) The influence the individual visitors' responses have on how they experience the involvement triggers, involvement worlds, and the state of immersion. (4) How antecedents (appraisals, external and personal antecedents) influence how the visitors respond to involvement triggers, involvement worlds, and the state of immersion.

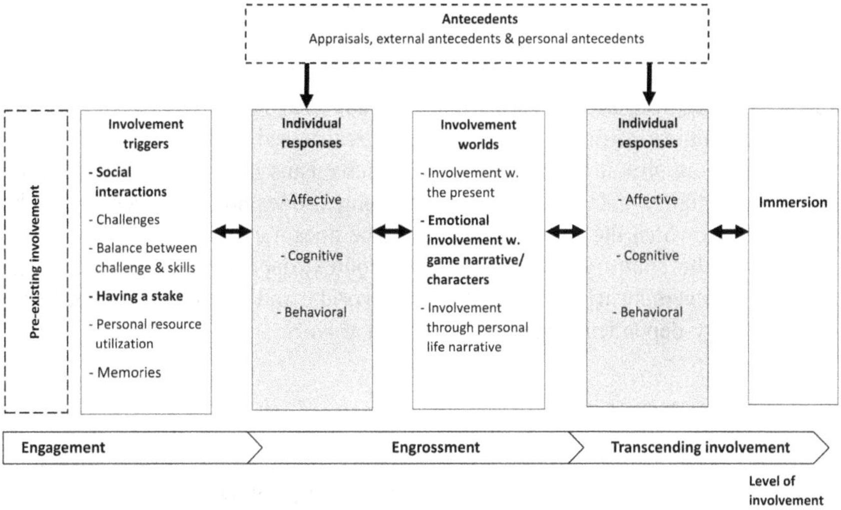

Figure 9.3 The immersion process in virtual gaming experiences – published under Creative Commons CC BY license

Source: Blumenthal and Gjerald (2022, p. 13)

The observant reader would have noticed that the three levels of involvement in Figures 9.2 and 9.3 overlap with Brown and Cairns' (2004) three degrees of involvement illustrated in Figure 9.1. However, unlike Brown and Cairns, we find that visitors fluctuate between different levels of involvement throughout the experience and that transition between the different degrees is fluent. Hence, although we identify similar involvement levels, our findings do not support the sequential one-directional progression of the immersion process as suggested by Brown and Cairns (2004). Instead, our findings align with the fluctuating model of the immersion process proposed by Hansen and Mossberg (2013). A key difference, however, is that while Hansen and Mossberg describe a process where visitors fluctuate between different degrees of immersion, we argue that visitors fluctuate between different levels of involvement, rather than immersion, as we understand immersion to be the deepest form of involvement – and humans do not have the capacity to sustain a deep level of involvement over a longer period of time. We hence see immersion as an 'either-or-state', a state you temporarily enter as you research peak level of involvement, but that cannot be sustained over a longer period of time.

The immersion process identified in the virtual gaming context examined at HoN hence shares many similarities with previously developed immersion process models from both analogue and technology-enhanced experience contexts and thus appears to be comparable across different experience contexts. This is not the first study to uncover similarities between the individual processes involved in virtual and analogue experience contexts. It has for example been found that the emotional engagement experienced when visiting a managed visitor attraction physically is comparable to the emotional engagement experienced when visiting the same attraction virtually (Wagler & Hanus, 2018). And that 'real-world' analogue experiences and virtual consumer experiences can elicit the same emotions in consumers (Chirico & Gaggioli, 2019), which indicates that virtual experiences trigger many of the same subjective processes as analogue 'real-world' experiences.

That the core structure and underlying mechanisms of the immersion process appear to be comparable across experience context does not, however, imply that the context in which the experience takes place does not influence the immersion process. On the contrary, we find multiple context-dependent differences in the concrete involvement triggers, involvement worlds, and antecedents identified in the technology-dependent experiences offered at HoN.

Context-Specific Influences on the Immersion Process

Six factors were identified as involvement triggers in the virtual experience context offered at HoN: (1) memories, (2) challenges, (3) personal resource utilisation, (4) social interactions, and (5) having a stake. Of these, 1–4 had previously been identified in some form in the previous case studies, while 'having a stake' represented a novel involvement trigger. This involvement trigger related to the feeling of having a stake in the game, for example, because the player had managed to progress to a certain level in the game or because they were playing in a tournament and wanted to win. Hence, it could be the competitive nature of these games rather than their virtual nature that led to the identification of this novel involvement trigger in this context.

As illustrated in Figure 9.3, three different involvement worlds or paths leading to the state of immersion were also identified. These involvement worlds represented a step deeper into the immersion process and were characterised by intense focus and a strong attentional direction. What separated the three involvement world categories from one another was the direction of this attentional focus. *Involvement with the present* represented an externally directed focus characterised by a strong focus on the present moment. The second involvement world, *involvement through personal life narrative*, was characterised by a more internally directed focus, where the visitors' focus was directed inwardly towards their personal life narrative rather than towards the present moment. The third and final involvement world, *emotional involvement with the game narrative/character(s)*, represented a novel involvement world as it had not been identified in the two previous case studies. What was unique about this involvement world was that it was the visitors' emotional involvement with the game narrative, or with the game's characters that were the visitors' focus of attention and that led them down the path to immersion.

Another novel finding from HoN was the identification of the category *pre-existing involvement* which seemed to function as a pre-experience *involvement booster* that could increase the visitors' level of involvement going into the experience. The category consisted of a combination of the visitors' prior knowledge, experience, and skills (both tacit and explicit) and their pre-existing relationship with the character(s) in the game. This factor seemed to boost the visitors' level of involvement going into the experience as visitors who had a pre-existing involvement with the game they were playing during their visit, generally seemed to start their gaming session at a higher level of involvement than visitors who did not have such a pre-existing involvement with the game. This harkens back to Carù and Cova's (2005) immersion process model which suggested that visitors with prior experience with the activity or experience context could become immersed instantly, while inexperienced visitors needed to go through a process of familiarisation before they were able to become immersed. Our findings moderate this, as they suggest that while pre-existing involvement with activity might speed up the visitors' progression through the immersion process, it does not fast-track them directly to a state of immersion. More systematic research is however needed to determine how the experience context, particularly the activity type, influences how pre-existing involvement influences the immersion process in different experience contexts.

In terms of the duality involved in the virtual gaming experiences where the visitors 'travel' into the virtual experiencescape from the physical experiencescape they are physically present, it was found incidents that arose in both experiencescapes could influence the visitors' level of involvement with the experiment. Identified involvement triggers such as social interactions could occur both in the virtual experiencescape and in the physical experiencescape and could trigger involvement regardless of where they took place. Similarly, factors such as game design features (virtual experiencescape) and the physical experience were both found to influence the visitors' level of involvement with the experience, through their role as antecedents influencing the visitors' responses to the different incidents that occurred during the experience.

- Thought point: Take a look at Table 9.1 summarising different involvement triggers and involvement worlds. Which involvement triggers would you say connect to involvement with the present? Involvement through personal life narrative? And emotional involvement with a narrative or story characters?

Table 9.1 Involvement triggers and involvement worlds that facilitate immersion

Involvement triggers	*Involvement worlds*
Physical challenges ('I can handle this')	Involvement with the present
Group assimilation ('I am part of a team')	Involvement through personal life narrative
Personal resource utilisation ('I can use my skills')	Emotional involvement with a narrative or story characters
Intellectual challenges ('I can solve this')	
Memories ('I remember')	
Imagination ('I can imagine myself …')	
Social interactions ('I am exchanging ideas with …')	
Having a stake ('I commit')	

Sources: Adapted from Blumenthal and Jensen (2019), Blumenthal (2020), Blumenthal and Gjerald (2022).

Conclusion

Based on the findings above, we can conclude that although there are contextual differences in terms of the specific antecedents, involvement triggers, involvement worlds, and individual responses that influence the immersion process in different contexts, the core structure of the immersion process, and the mechanism that holds it together appear to be comparable across contexts. Suggesting the immersion process in conventional 'real-world' tourism experiences could be comparable to the immersion process in virtual technology-dependent experiences and that visitors experience the same state of immersion in both experience contexts. This has important implications, as it implies that findings from HCI, where research on immersion is more developed, might be transferable to conventional tourism experience products, opening up a plethora of interesting avenues for future research.

Future research should test the proposed immersion process model in experience contexts that go beyond the context of managed visitor attractions, which were used in all three case studies described in this chapter. Furthermore, it would be interesting to see the immersion process model employed in a real-life field experiment to test its functionality as an experience design tool and the degree to which it can be used as a tool to create highly involving, immersive experience products.

The findings presented in this chapter offer important practical implications for attraction managers and experience product designers seeking to facilitate immersive experiences for their visitors. Since the results point to a close connection between the identified involvement triggers and the experience context – namely the experiencescape and the experience design. Indicating that the experience designers can facilitate immersion by manipulating the experiencescape and using experience design to incorporate several involvement triggers into their experience products. Prior research has for example shown that experience design can be used to facilitate social interactions by designing experience products that require visitors to work together to research a common goal (Arnould & Price, 1993). We recommend incorporating several involvement triggers into the experience products, both to harvest the cumulative benefits of exposing visitors to several involvement triggers during the experience and to trigger involvement among a broader range of visitors as individual visitors were found to respond differently to different involvement triggers (Blumenthal, 2020).

In addition to involvement triggers, three different involvement worlds, or paths, leading visitors to the state of immersion, were identified. Similar to the involvement triggers, our findings indicated that these paths could also be facilitated through experience/experiencescape design. 'Involvement with the present', for example, appeared to be facilitated by enclaved, themed, and safe experiencescapes offering opportunities for active participation. Whereas 'involvement through personal life narrative' was facilitated by an experiencescape designed to trigger the visitors' memories and experience designed that allowed time for reflection. Lastly, 'emotional involvement with narrative and/or characters', which was only identified in the context of virtual games, could be facilitated by incorporating an emotionally engaging narrative into the experience design.

- Thought point: Think of an experience product you are familiar with. Can you think of a way that you could include involvement triggers to make the experience more involving?

Further Questions

- Would the proposed immersion process model also apply to unfacilitated experience contexts?
- So far, 'three involvement worlds' or paths leading to the state of immersion have been identified, can you think of more?
- What about shared immersion? Can the experience of being immersed be shared? And what consequences can sharing an immersive experience have for visitors?
- Is immersion necessarily always a positive thing? Can the experience of immersion also be negative? What are the potential negative consequences of immersion?

Further Readings

Blumenthal, V., & Gjerald, O. (2022). 'You just get sucked into it': Extending the immersion process model to virtual gameplay experiences in managed visitor attractions. *Leisure Studies*, 1–20. https://doi.org/10.1080/02614367.2022.2049627

Blumenthal, V., & Jensen, Ø. (2019). Consumer immersion in the experiencescape of managed visitor attractions: The nature of the immersion process and the role of involvement. *Tourism Management Perspectives*, *30*, 159–170. https://doi.org/10.1016/j.tmp.2019.02.008.

Hansen, A. H., & Mossberg, L. (2013). Consumer immersion: A key to extraordinary experiences. In J. Sundbo & F. Sørensen (Eds.), *Handbook on the experience economy* (pp. 209–227). Edward Elgar Publishing. https://doi.org/10.4337/9781781004227.00017.

Mossberg, L. (2007). A marketing approach to the tourist experience. *Scandinavian Journal of Hospitality and Tourism*, *7*(1), 59–74. https://doi.org/10.1080/15022250701231915.

Sundbo, J., & Sørensen, F. (2013). Introduction to the experience economy. In J. Sundbo & F. Sørensen (Eds.), *Handbook on the experience economy* (pp. 1–18). Edward Elgar Publishing. https://doi.org/10.4337/9781781004227.00005.

References

Arnould, E., & Price, L. (1993). River magic: Extraordinary experience and the extended service encounter. *Journal of Consumer Research*, *20*(1), 24–45. https://doi.org/10.1086/209331.

Bhattacharjee, A., & Mogilner, C. (2014). Happiness from ordinary and extraordinary experiences. *Journal of Consumer Research*, *41*(1), 1–17. doi:10.1086/674724

Blumenthal, V. (2020). Consumer immersion in managed visitor attractions: The role of individual responses and antecedent factors. *Scandinavian Journal of Hospitality and Tourism*, *20*(1), 4–27. https://doi.org/10.1080/15022250.2020.1725624.

Blumenthal, V. (2021). *"You just get sucked into it": The immersion process in managed visitor attractions* [PhD thesis, University of Stavanger]. https://hdl.handle.net/11250/2725789

Blumenthal, V., & Gjerald, O. (2022). 'You just get sucked into it': Extending the immersion process model to virtual gameplay experiences in managed visitor attractions. *Leisure Studies*, 1–20. https://doi.org/10.1080/02614367.2022.2049627.

Blumenthal, V., & Jensen, Ø. (2019). Consumer immersion in the experiencescape of managed visitor attractions: The nature of the immersion process and the role of involvement. *Tourism Management Perspectives*, *30*, 159–170. https://doi.org/10.1016/j.tmp.2019.02.008.

Brown, E., & Cairns, P. (2004). *A grounded investigation of game immersion* [Conference paper]. CHI '04 Extended Abstracts on Human Factors in Computing Systems, Vienna, Austria. https://doi.org/10.1145/985921.986048.

Burt, M., & Louw, C. (2019). Virtual reality enhanced roller coasters and the future of entertainment – Audience expectations. *World Leisure Journal*, *61*(3), 183–199. https://doi.org/10.1080/16078055.2019.1639274.

Cairns, P., Cox, A., & Nordin, A. I. (2014). Immersion in digital games: Review of gaming experience research. In M. C. Angelides & H. Agius (Eds.), *Handbook of digital games* (pp. 337–361). John Wiley & Sons, Inc. https://doi.org/10.1002/9781118796443.ch12.

Carr, D. (2006). Play and pleasure. In D. Carr, D. Buckingham, A. Burn, & G. Schott (Eds.), *Computer games: Text, narrative and play* (pp. 45–58). Polity Press.

Carù, A., & Cova, B. (2005). The impact of service elements on the artistic experience: The case of classical music concerts. *International Journal of Arts Management*, *7*(2), 39–54.

Chirico, A., & Gaggioli, A. (2019). When virtual feels real: Comparing emotional responses and presence in virtual and natural environments. *Cyberpsychology, Behavior, and Social Networking*, *22*(3), 220–226. https://doi.org/10.1089/cyber.2018.0393.

Csikszentmihalyi, M. (1990). *Flow: The psychology of optimal experience*. New York: Harper Perennial.

Douglas, J. Y., & Hargadon, A. (2001). The pleasures of immersion and engagement: Schemas, scripts and the fifth business. *Digital Creativity*, *12*(3), 153–166. https://doi.org/10.1076/digc.12.3.153.3231.

Hansen, A. H., & Mossberg, L. (2016). Tour guides' performance and tourists' immersion: Facilitating consumer immersion by performing a guide plus role. *Scandinavian Journal of Hospitality and Tourism*, *17*(3), 1–20. https://doi.org/10.1080/15022250.2016.1162347.

Hansen, A. H., & Mossberg, L. (2013). Consumer immersion: A key to extraordinary experiences. In J. Sundbo & F. Sørensen (Eds.), *Handbook on the experience economy* (pp. 209–227). Edward Elgar Publishing. https://doi.org/10.4337/9781781004227.00017.

Jennett, C., Cox, A. L., Cairns, P., Dhoparee, S., Epps, A., Tijs, T., & Walton, A. (2008). Measuring and defining the experience of immersion in games. *International Journal of Human – Computer Studies*, *66*(9), 641–661. https://doi.org/10.1016/j.ijhcs.2008.04.004.

Johnston, R., & Clark, G. (2001). *Service operations management*. Financial Times Prentice Hall.

Kim, J.-H. (2014). The antecedents of memorable tourism experiences: The development of a scale to measure the destination attributes associated with memorable experiences. *Tourism Management*, *44*(C), 34–45. https://doi.org/10.1016/j.tourman.2014.02.007.

Kim, J.-H., Ritchie, J. R. B., & Tung, V. W. S. (2010). The effect of memorable experience on behavioral intentions in tourism: A structural equation modeling approach. *Tourism Analysis*, *15*(6), 637–648. https://doi.org/10.3727/108354210X12904412049776.

Klayman, J. (1995). Varieties of confirmation bias. *Elsevier Science & Technology 32*, 385–418. https://doi.org/10.1016/S0079-7421(08)60315-1.

Lindberg, F., & Østergaard, P. (2015). Extraordinary consumer experiences: Why immersion and transformation cause trouble. *Journal of Consumer Behaviour*, *14*(4), 248–260. https://doi.org/10.1002/cb.1516.

Løvoll, H. S. (2019). The inner feeling of glacier hiking: An exploratory study of "immersion" as it relates to flow, hedonia and eudaimonia. *Scandinavian Journal of Hospitality and Tourism*, *19*(3), 300–316. https://doi.org/10.1080/15022250.2019.1581084.

Lunardo, R., & Ponsignon, F. (2019). Achieving immersion in the tourism experience: The role of autonomy, temporal dissociation, and reactance. *Journal of Travel Research*, *59*(7), 1151–1167. https://doi.org/10.1177/0047287519878509.

Mainemelis, C. (2001). When the muse takes it all: A model for the experience of timelessness in organization. *Academy of Management Review*, *26*(4), 548–565. https://doi.org/10.2307/3560241.

Maslow, A. H. (1964). *Religions, values, and peak-experiences*. Columbus: Ohio State University Press.

Mossberg, L. (2007). A marketing approach to the tourist experience. *Scandinavian Journal of Hospitality and Tourism*, *7*(1), 59–74. https://doi.org/10.1080/15022250701231915.

Pine, B. J., & Gilmore, J. H. (1999). *The experience economy: work is theatre & every business a stage*. Boston, Mass: Harvard Business School Press.

Privette, G. (1983). Peak experience, peak performance, and flow: A comparative analysis of positive human experiences. *Journal of Personality and Social Psychology*, *45*(6), 1361–1368. https://doi.org/10.1037/0022-3514.45.6.1361

Schouten, J., McAlexander, J., & Koenig, H. (2007). Transcendent customer experience and brand community. *Journal of the Academy of Marketing Science*, *35*(3), 357–368. https://doi.org/10.1007/s11747-007-0034-4

Servidio, R., & Ruffolo, I. (2016). Exploring the relationship between emotions and memorable tourism experiences through narratives. *Tourism Management Perspectives*, *20*, 151–160. https://doi.org/10.1016/j.tmp.2016.07.010

Slåtten, T., Krogh, C., & Connolley, S. (2011). Make it memorable: Customer experiences in winter amusement parks. *International Journal of Culture, Tourism and Hospitality Research*, *5*(1), 80–91. https://doi.org/10.1108/17506181111111780.

Strauss, A., & Corbin, J. (1990). *Basics of qualitative research: Grounded theory procedures and techniques*. Thousand Oaks: Sage.

Tussyadiah, I. P. (2014). Toward a theoretical foundation for experience design in tourism. *Journal of Travel Research*, *53*(5), 543–564. https://doi.org/10.1177/0047287513513172.

Tussyadiah, I. P., Jung, T. H., & Tom Dieck, M. C. (2018). Embodiment of wearable augmented reality technology in tourism experiences. *Journal of Travel Research*, *57*(5), 597–611. https://doi.org/10.1177/0047287517709090.

Wagler, A., & Hanus, M. D. (2018). Comparing virtual reality tourism to real-life experience: Effects of presence and engagement on attitude and enjoyment. *Communication Research Reports*, *35*(5), 456–464. https://doi.org/10.1080/08824096.2018.1525350.

Yung, R., & Khoo-Lattimore, C. (2019). New realities: A systematic literature review on virtual reality and augmented reality in tourism research. *Current Issues in Tourism*, *22*(17), 2056–2081. https://doi.org/10.1080/13683500.2017.1417359.

Part III

Technological Tools and Social Media in Conceptualising Experience Economy

10 Hospitality Micro Enterprises (MEs) during COVID-19

Changing Experiences through Service Innovation and Digital Tools

Terry Lantai

Introduction

Many Micro Enterprises (MEs) in the tourism and hospitality sectors were forced to shut down or reduce their operations significantly due to various government-enforced restrictions and social distancing during the height of the pandemic. While the impact may have been devastating for all tourism and hospitality businesses, it arguably caused an even more detrimental effect on the smaller operators. MEs are often faced with limited resources compared with their larger counterparts and chain operations. For many owners of MEs, their business may be their livelihood in that they have invested significant time and effort and the business is thus more than simply a job (Mei, 2022). Hence, business survival through innovation is necessary in order to transform the business. It has been argued that the pandemic also serves as an 'opportunity' for tourism and hospitality businesses to 'grow back better', by 'preparing for tomorrow' and 'managing the crisis and mitigating the impact' (UNWTO, 2020, pp. 148–159). Thus, the crisis serves as an opportunity to build a 'new normal' (Price et al., 2022). In terms of crises, it has also been stressed that MEs and smaller businesses are more resilient and quicker to adapt to changes (Ates & Bititci, 2011; Price et al., 2022). Moreover, the significant number of such businesses in the tourism and hospitality sectors indicates that they are an important contributor to a country or region in economic development (Price et al., 2022).

This chapter aims to explore service innovation among hospitality MEs, which was expedited due to COVID-19, lockdowns, and government restrictions. The main focus is restaurant businesses in the MEs size category as they were likely to be among the most vulnerable to the effects of the pandemic (Price et al., 2022). Moreover, the chapter discusses the importance of such small establishments by differentiating Small and Medium-Sized Enterprises (SMEs) and MEs and the general innovation notion in the tourism and hospitality sectors. The case studies of the mobile payment app Vipps and other food delivery apps in Norway were used as examples.

Small Enterprises in Service Sectors

Most research on smaller enterprises has been on SMEs. It has been estimated that SMEs account for 99 per cent of all businesses and between 60 and 70 per cent of jobs in most OECD countries. In addition to the economic contribution, SMEs play

DOI: 110.4324/9781003335924-14

a particularly important role in many peripheral regions as they often contribute to local identity and social cohesion (OECD, 2021). SMEs also play a vital role in many non-OECD countries as they are the backbone of industrial development in the countries' peripheral regions (Saleh & Ndubisi, 2006). SMEs in many regions however are often challenged with innovation barriers and skills development difficulties as only less than one-half of start-ups survive for more than five years (OECD, 2021). Generally, SMEs from these regions are less competitive and innovative in comparison to companies located in more urban areas (Skuras et al., 2008). While significant studies are focusing on SMEs in general, more specific studies on SMEs in the service sectors including tourism and hospitality sectors are needed. Many business operators in the service industries are typical SMEs due to lower entry costs and resource requirements (OECD, 2021). Innovations in the SMEs in service sectors such as tourism and hospitality, which are non-technological-driven, are very different from general businesses. For instance, the use of research and development (R&D) and patents as proxies for innovative activity is incomplete, particularly when considering SMEs in the tourism and hospitality industries (Coad et al., 2019). For such industries, the innovation lies in the services and processes rather than physical products based on R&D.

MEs in the Tourism and Hospitality Sectors

MEs are a subset of SMEs and many researchers have thus investigated SMEs as one group without specifying and distinguishing MEs. In the tourism and hospitality sectors, it can be assumed that a majority of businesses are MEs, including family-owned businesses (Camilleri & Valeri, 2021). There are various definitions of MEs, some are based on the number of employees and others in combination with the annual turnover. Generally, MEs are defined as enterprises having ten employees or fewer. Whereas in countries such as Norway, it is less than five employees (Norwegian Government Security and Service Organisation, 2002). Additionally, per European Union (EU)'s definition, MEs also have an annual turnover not exceeding 2 million EU (European Commission, 2021). MEs are credited as a significant contributor to the economic growth of a community (Muske & Woods, 2004) as they represent a substantial sub-segment of all small businesses. For instance, of the 25 million SMEs in the EU, 93 per cent of these are MEs (European Commission, 2021, p. 11). In Norway, for instance, nine of ten enterprises are MEs (Statistics Norway, 2022). MEs thus play an important role in the creation of employment and generate income in most countries.

For many businesses, success arises in the total investments into the enterprise. These include tangible elements such as financial inputs as well as non-tangible elements of more social and mental nature (Baluku et al., 2018). There is much focus on the entrepreneur or the owner of the MEs as the businesses represent more than an enterprise. Self-employment is also dominating in these sectors (Camilleri & Valeri, 2021). This is in contrast to knowledge-intensive business services (KIBS) and industries such as various financial services (accounting, management consultancy), services related to information and communication technology (ICT), technical engineering, and R&D activities (Baláž, 2004). Logically, tourism and hospitality operators and especially MEs are faced with resource scarcity, even more so than the general SME category. Resource constraints are common in MEs in such sectors, not only in terms of the financial resources as the owner must take on many responsibilities and roles. These roles include being negotiator, manager, investor, and accountant to performing and delivering the service themselves to the customer. In addition to the daily operations, other tasks such as marketing, branding, and planning for strategies for long-term survival contribute to a significant workload.

Innovation in Hospitality and Tourism MEs

As discussed, innovation is often not linked with services and especially not among MEs in non-technological-driven sectors such as tourism and hospitality. However, there are many examples of innovation in these sectors in a non-traditional sense in the classic innovation literature. This includes service delivery, approach to services and the way services are facilitated to create new and unique tourism experiences. Innovation is a term that can be difficult to define and classify (Hall & Williams, 2008; Korres, 2007). In earlier innovation literature, the 'father' of innovation Schumpeter (1934) defines the notion from an economic perspective as a new activity that leads to economic growth. Later from a sociological point of view, it is understood as a means of renewal of social behaviour (LaPiere, 1965). Steele (1975, p. 19) further explains that innovation is essentially the process of creating change and the concept is simply 'the introduction of new things or methods'. Nevertheless, the challenging part is that such change is disruptive and uncertain (Mansfield, 1963; Schaper & Volery, 2007; Schön, 1982). Innovations in service sectors have been found to be more social or organisational in nature as it is essentially a people-driven industry compared with the commercial sector where technology is the focus (Gallouj & Weinstein, 1997). This is also relevant when considering innovation in tourism and hospitality MEs, which is more market-driven and people-intensive rather than research-driven (OECD, 2021). Hence, service innovations are usually driven by practical experiences (Sundbo et al., 2007). Camisón and Monfort-Mir (2012) further explain that the service sector may be less innovative when comes to R&D but not in regard to new products and processes. They are quick to respond to new opportunities and more oriented to small incremental advances (Ates & Bititci, 2011; Price et al., 2022). Subsequently, it is stressed that tourism and hospitality MEs also respond faster to crises by adapting to changes as the situation arises due to a non-hierarchical structure of the business.

- Thought point: Think about some examples of innovation in tourism and hospitality MEs. This could be innovation in processes, services, and products that are offered.

Service Innovation in Restaurants due to COVID-19

The hospitality industry along with many operators in the tourism industry took a massive hit during the height of the pandemic. While government restrictions and social distancing measures in place required some restaurants to close down completely, other restaurants managed to stay open by reducing capacity or by only offering takeout. This has resulted in a significant decrease in revenue, with many restaurants struggling to stay afloat. The shift to takeout and delivery services has been the only choice and a lifeline for some. Nevertheless, the reduced dining-in traffic and lack of in-person dining experiences had led to a changed service environment for customers and employees. The concern for personal safety is relevant not only among customers but also among employees. For restaurants that relied merely on takeout and food delivery, it was important to ensure a safe environment for both staff and customers. Thus, various contactless and touchless food ordering and delivery options were adopted and introduced by several restaurants (Kumar & Shah, 2021).

Technological developments and the wide usage of the Internet and social media have already changed the playing field by levelling the competitive condition between MEs and larger enterprises before COVID-19. For instance, due to social media platforms such as Facebook, hospitality MEs can have a business page at a fraction of the cost compared with full developed websites and traditional advertising channels. Restaurants can post their menus, update their opening hours, announce any promotions and activities, and interact with their customers in real-time at completely no cost at all. Moreover, creating additional Facebook ads is easy and cost-effective. It can be set to target certain customers in a fixed radius and does not require any special set of skills as everything is made intuitive and user-friendly (Meta, 2023). Thus, for MEs with resource scarcity and ME owners dealing with work overload or who do not possess marketing and advertising skills, this has been a game changer. The technological advancement and digitalisation in many parts of the world including Norway and Scandinavia have also led to other types of digital tools including various types of food delivery apps and mobile payment apps that gained importance in people's daily lives. While these apps and services were already established pre-COVID, their usage and dependency exploded during the lockdowns.

Food Delivery Applications

The option of using external food delivery services has contributed to many restaurants being able to gain some revenue during the pandemic as people refused or were not allowed to leave their homes (Kumar & Shah, 2021). Food delivery apps are digital platforms that allow consumers to order food online through a smartphone app and have it delivered to their location of choice, including their homes or hotels and other temporary holiday accommodations (Kumar & Shah, 2021; Ray et al., 2019; Wang et al., 2019). The technological solution can be further divided into two groups, although both categories are dependent on mobile applications

(Zhao & Bacao, 2020). The first group involves eateries and restaurant that develop their own apps that accept online food orderings (Kumar & Shah, 2021). These consist mainly of major enterprises and companies as such technology is rather costly to develop and maintain for hospitality MEs. It was also difficult to develop such technology in a short span of time when the pandemic and subsequent lock-downs came suddenly. The second category includes third-party intermediaries, such as Uber Eats, which act as a liaison between consumers and restaurants or catering services (Roh & Park, 2019).

However, such third-party services have not necessarily been a positive solution for many restaurants and especially MEs with already a tight profit margin. Depending on which food delivery company and the condition of the contract, they might charge restaurants a commission fee ranging from 15 per cent to 30 per cent per order (Snyder, 2020). Moreover, by leaving the ordering and delivery of orders to third parties, the restaurants themselves are losing a certain level of control. For instance, problems with payments, wrong orders, and deliveries as well as delays of deliveries, cancellation of the order without notice, and other problems caused by the third-party company (Chandrasekhar et al., 2019). These issues impact customers' overall experience in a negative manner. Another issue which has received less attention is the sustainability of such types of services. Li et al. (2020) analyse such technology using the three pillars of sustainability and found that in terms of economy, criticism due to the high commission fees charged to restaurants as discussed as well as poor working conditions for delivery workers have been raised. Hospitality MEs and other smaller restaurants that do not have the bargaining power of the larger businesses may suffer further reduction in profit (Neville, 2020; Snyder, 2020). From an environmental point of view, an increase in delivery works and the following increase in motorised vehicles lead to a high carbon footprint and a large amount of waste. Finally, from a social standpoint, this impacts the natural interaction and relationship between customers and restaurants as well as between customers and their food. This also naturally changes customer behaviour and experiences. Furthermore, such development may lead to an adverse effect on public health (Li et al., 2020). On the other hand, hospitality MEs and other smaller eateries would evidently be disadvantaged when choosing not to use such third-party solutions.

Mobile Payment Applications

Another type of service due to technological advancement over the year is mobile payment apps. Such systems are attributed to technological advancement along with the fierce competition in the banking industry where innovation in service delivery is the top priority in order to be ahead of competitors (Chung & Liang, 2020; Kong & Ibrahim, 2019). Thus, further development of payment technologies based on Internet-based solutions will continue to expand. In China, for instance, there is WeChat, a social media platform which also offers mobile payment through quick response (QR) codes, and worldwide there are both Apple Pay and Google Pay mobile payment systems (Chung & Liang, 2020; Singu & Chakraborty, 2022).

Numerous other similar mobile payment systems in different countries are developed by the banks in that particular country, indicating that there are abundant solutions and systems available.

Such systems offer immense flexibility and potential either as an addition to the traditional card and cash payment solutions or as a replacement, especially for MEs, home-based businesses, various stalls, or temporary pop-up stores. This is because to set up card payment systems, for instance, there is often a requirement for specific tools, fixed high-speed Internet systems, and commission and surcharge by the card issuer (Sorensen, 2022). Such a process may be costly and hassle for MEs and temporary businesses such as food stalls. Whereas a mobile payment system would usually only require the business to be registered with a business profile and for the customer, a smartphone with access to the Internet and with the app downloaded. Due to the many benefits that they provide customers and businesses, such as convenience, fast processing times, cashless and ubiquitous transactions, and bulk transactions, mobile payment apps can be considered superior payment systems (Verkijika & Neneh, 2021). More importantly, when the systems are working efficiently, they contribute to enhanced consumer experiences (Karimi & Liu, 2020).

With every digital tool nevertheless, there are bound to have some disadvantages. Despite their ease of use and popularity, mobile payment apps are not necessarily used by all types of customers as some may still prefer the traditional payment options. This may be due to trust issues and perceived security (Singu & Chakraborty, 2022), elderly people who might not be comfortable with technology, and the problem with the Internet as this is still an issue in many parts of the world (Verkijika & Neneh, 2021). Moreover, maintenance and downtime due to technical glitches are also to be expected, which can lead to negative consumer experiences should they occur at an unplanned and inconvenient time. The vast growth and potential of mobile payment systems indicate that the technology is here to stay, and it will continue to gain importance when the Internet system is also improving in many parts of the world.

- Thought point: COVID-19 has had a profound effect on the way restaurants operate. How will this continue to shape the industry for years to come or will restaurant go back to how it was pre-COVID?

Case Study – Vipps and Food Delivery Apps in Norway

Third-Party Food Delivery Services

In Norway, depending on the geographical locale, the available food delivery services through apps consist of larger and international companies such as Just Eat, Wolt, and Foodora. There are also smaller establishments including Delivia that focus on smaller cities and the local market, where many MEs are located. Using Delivia as an example, the system works in such a way:

1 The customer enters their address in the Delivia app (or any other food delivery apps) and selects a restaurant in their area.

2 The restaurant accepts the order through a tablet provided by Delivia, then the restaurant prepares the food for the specified pick-up time. It is also possible for the restaurants to close for any orders at a given time should there be too many orders to manage.
3 A Delivia driver then collects the order at the specified time and delivers the food orders to the customer.
4 The restaurant receives payment from Delivia every other week for completed orders (Delivia, 2021).

Other food ordering services have similar processes as the above Delivia example. The differences will be the percentage that they charge in commissions, the radius of delivery options, the number of partner restaurants, and the initial set-up costs (Cruzotec, 2023; Snyder, 2020). Another thing that differentiates some food delivery companies from others is that while a majority of such companies used motorised vehicles for deliveries, Foodora uses bicycle couriers as an approach of environmentally friendly delivery (Foodora, 2022).

Such services have enabled people to be able to order foods and restaurants are still able to gain income during quarantine and lockdowns due to COVID-19. While such services have existed before the pandemic, it was perhaps during the pandemic that many MEs choose to integrate such delivery services in their business operation as part of service innovation. Many may have been the fence pre-COVID but were left with little other choices in order to sustain their businesses. For many hospitality MEs that did not have any digital ordering system or be able to offer food delivery on their own, such apps also help MEs to reach out to more customers. While this has changed the playing field for hospitality MEs, some negative experiences have been reported by customers using the apps. For instance, there are customers reportedly not receiving their food orders after more than an hour and the food arriving cold as well as orders suddenly cancelled without any explanation (Dhale, 2023). Other complaints include no refunds when food is not delivered and lousy customer service (Fosse, 2021). Based on online reviews on Facebook, TripAdvisor and Google Reviews and news reports, some food delivery services have mostly received positive feedback, while others have gained more negative feedback and complaints than others. The common issues seem to be cold food and late with deliveries. Other issues include less control by the restaurants on food quality, hereby cold food upon arrival as discussed as well as lack of direct personal interaction between the restaurants and customers. This has arguably changed customer experiences. Since many are still using such services now that the world is slowly returning to its pre-COVID stage, such technological solutions are here to stay as the benefits clearly outweigh the drawbacks.

Mobile Payment System – Vipps

Vipps is a mobile app designed for consumers to make payments for bills, goods, and services, as well as send money to other Vipps users. For businesses, the solution provides a secure and convenient alternative to handling cash transactions as customers can pay and transfer money from their Vipps account straight to the business using a designated code of six digits for each business. As Vipps only required the user's mobile phone number to create an account, it provides ease of use as no lengthy bank details such as bank account and other bank information are needed to transfer money. The user needs, however, to register his or her bank account or card number when the profile is first created in order to pay and receive money. For any payment to businesses such as restaurant purchases, the transaction is completely free for users with no limitation in amount (Vipps, 2022). The solution makes it worry-free and ease of use for diners and customers if they want a contactless payment system should they not have their physical payment cards available at the time. While other similar systems exist in Norway such as Apple Pay, Vipps is far superior as it does not require a specific type of smartphone or operating system. The significance of Vipps is also illustrated when the word 'Vipps' has now become a well-accepted verb in the Norwegian language where 'to vipps' (å vippse) someone means to pay someone or to transfer money to someone or a business using the app (Dalsbø, 2018).

During the COVID-19 lockdowns, many hospitality MEs in Norway only offered takeout. While some used third-party food delivery services as listed in the above section, others choose not to do so due to the hefty commission charges as well as to have better quality control over the food provided to the customers. In many peripheral regions, such third-party delivery companies were also not established yet. Instead, some hospitality MEs used low threshold solutions where customers order food on the phone through normal phone calls and then made the payment on Vipps. When the food was ready to be collected, it was placed on a table which was located right outside the front door of the restaurants. The food was only placed outside when the customer arrived outside at the premises. The restaurant venue itself was closed and no customers were able to enter inside the premises. Food order sheets were placed on the windows facing the front door so that customers could just point out their orders with their names when they arrived. Otherwise, the customer could also call on the phone to notify the restaurant that he or she has arrived at the premises. In such a way, direct physical contact between the customer and employee was limited to a minimum, providing safety for both parties. Cash payments were not possible to limit the spread of the virus. The disadvantage of this solution was that it excluded some customers, especially those who did not have Vipps or did not want to use such a payment system. For many restaurants and especially MEs, this was a quick and uncomplicated solution that was necessary to implement in response to the challenges at hand. While the restaurants did not invent Vipps themselves, as they rather used existing technology and integrate that into their business operation. This indicates that this is a type of incremental innovation due to changes to their service interaction and process (Schumpeter, 1934; Steele, 1975) that kept their businesses afloat during the pandemic.

Conclusion

Customer experiences are constantly changing along with various technological advancements leading to many creative digital tools and solutions. Such development will keep fuelling further progression of the experience economy. For hospitality MEs that are faced with resource scarcity compared with their larger counterparts, integrating existing technologies and digital tools that are available at their disposal has been important to survive the crisis. Food delivery apps and mobile payment apps such as Delivia and Vipps have been important contributors, but it is the MEs themselves that must figure out how to integrate such solutions in order to enhance customer experiences. Moreover, during the lockdowns, it was important to integrate these systems in the sense that they ensure safety for both the customers and the employees. In that regard, the service process and delivery were transformed leading to service innovation in form of incremental changes.

As the world has slowly returned to its pre-COVID stage, normal physical contact between customer and hospitality staff and among customers themselves has been resumed. Some solutions that have been adapted during the lockdowns are still being used as customers have found the solution to be positive for their overall restaurant and dining experience. While others are no longer necessary as dining experiences through personal interactions with the restaurant employees at the premises rather than merely takeout are possible again. At least many hospitality MEs are prepared for such type of crisis, should a similar situation occur again. Regardless of COVID-19, the ease of use and the digital tools as discussed are changing customer experiences to mostly positive ones. It is however also important to take into consideration the negative sides of such tools and investigate how these can be minimised in order to ensure an overall positive customer experience in the long run.

Further Questions

- Think about the negative sides of the digital tools that have been raised in this chapter and discuss how they can be tackled. As more and more people will continue to use these tools, what can be additional disadvantages that may occur as a result?
- Tourism and hospitality MEs are often the backbones of many regions, and it is important to sustain such businesses. Beside the digital tools of food delivery apps and mobile payment apps, are there any other advancement in technology can that assist such businesses in becoming more innovative and resilient?

Further Readings

Hong, C., Choi, E.-K., & Joung, H.-W. (2023). Determinants of customer purchase intention toward online food delivery services: The moderating role of usage frequency. *Journal of Hospitality and Tourism Management*, 54, 76–87. https://doi.org/10.1016/j.jhtm.2022.12.005

Talwar, M., Talwar, S., Kaur, P., Tripathy, N., & Dhir, A. (2021). Has financial attitude impacted the trading activity of retail investors during the COVID-19 pandemic?. *Journal of Retailing and Consumer Services*, 58, 102341. https://doi.org/10.1016/j.jretconser.2020.102341

Verkijika, S. F. (2020). An affective response model for understanding the acceptance of mobile payment systems. *Electronic Commerce Research and Applications*, 39, 100905. https://doi.org/10.1016/j.elerap.2019.100905

References

Ates, A., & Bititci, U. (2011). Change process: A key enabler for building resilient SMEs. *International Journal of Production Research*, *49*(18), 5601–5618. https://doi.org/10.1080/00207543.2011.563825

Baláž, V. (2004). Knowledge-intensive business services in transition economies. *The Service Industries Journal*, *24*(4), 83–100. https://doi.org/10.1080/0264206042000275208

Baluku, M. M., Kikooma, J. F., Bantu, E., & Otto, K. (2018). Psychological capital and entrepreneurial outcomes: The moderating role of social competences of owners of micro-enterprises in East Africa. *Journal of Global Entrepreneurship Research*, *8*(1), 26. https://doi.org/10.1186/s40497-018-0113-7

Camilleri, M. A., & Valeri, M. (2021). Thriving family businesses in tourism and hospitality: A systematic review and a synthesis of the relevant literature. *Journal of Family Business Management*, https://doi.org/10.1108/JFBM-10-2021-0133

Camisón, C., & Monfort-Mir, V. M. (2012). Measuring innovation in tourism from the Schumpeterian and the dynamic-capabilities perspectives. *Tourism Management*, *33*(4), 776–789. https://doi.org/10.1016/j.tourman.2011.08.012

Chandrasekhar, N., Gupta, S., & Nanda, N. (2019). Food delivery services and customer preference: A comparative analysis. *Journal of Foodservice Business Research*, *22*(4), 375–386. https://doi.org/10.1080/15378020.2019.1626208

Chung, K. C., & Liang, S. W.-J. (2020). Understanding factors affecting innovation resistance of mobile payments in Taiwan: An integrative perspective. *Mathematics*, *8*(10), 1841. https://www.mdpi.com/2227-7390/8/10/1841

Coad, A., Grassano, N., Hall, B. H., Moncada-Paternò-Castello, P., & Vezzani, A. (2019). Innovation and industrial dynamics. *Structural Change and Economic Dynamics*, *50*, 126–131. https://doi.org/10.1016/j.strueco.2019.06.008

Cruzotec. (2023). *What's the difference between food delivery apps and food delivery aggregator app*. Retrieved February 7 from https://cruzotec.com/whats-the-difference-between-food-delivery-apps-and-food-delivery-aggregator-apps/

Dalsbø, V. K. (2018). *Å vippse – vippser – har vippset*. DNB. from https://www.dnb.no/dnbnyheter/no/din-okonomi/a-vippse-vippser-har-vippset

Delivia. (2021). *Bli* Delivia *partner [become Delivia partner]*. https://www.delivia.no/bli-restaurantpartner

Dhale, C. J. (2023). *Raser mot Foodora: Kommer aldri til å bestille derfra igjen [Rage against Foodora: Will never order from there again]*. https://www.tv2.no/nyheter/forbruker/kommer-aldri-til-a-bestille-derfra-igjen/15258805/

European Commission. (2021). *Annual report on European SMEs*. European Union.

Foodora. (2022). *What you need, delivered in minutes*. https://www.foodora.no/en/?ax=139669170633&tx=kwd-128078778569&ap=&dv=c&nt=g&mt=p&pm=1010832&pi=&cr=607051110936&fi=&bc=7513&gclid=CjwKCAiA0JKfBhBIEiwAPhZXD4_KEx-yfaal4nHPzWosSg52Qn2Igp4VXaOqBOm_XqZZGSODcG3xoAhoCeAkQAvD_BwE

Fosse, A. L. (2021). *Raser mot Foodora: – Skikkelig ekkelt [Rage against Foodora – Really disgusting]* Nettavisen. https://www.nettavisen.no/okonomi/raser-mot-foodora-skikkelig-ekkelt/s/12-95-3424078095

Gallouj, F., & Weinstein, O. (1997). Innovation in services. *Research Policy*, *26*(4–5), 537–556. https://doi.org/10.1016/S0048-7333(97)00030-9

Hall, C. M., & Williams, A. M. (2008). *Tourism and innovation*. Routledge.

Karimi, S., & Liu, Y.-L. (2020). The differential impact of "mood" on consumers' decisions, a case of mobile payment adoption. *Computers in Human Behavior*, *102*, 132–143. https://doi.org/10.1016/j.chb.2019.08.017

Kong, Y., & Ibrahim, M. (2019). Service innovation, service delivery and customer satisfaction and loyalty in the banking sector of Ghana. *International Journal of Bank Marketing, 37*(5), 1215–1233. https://doi.org/10.1108/IJBM-06-2018-0142

Korres, G. M. (2007). The role of innovation activities in tourism and regional growth in Europe. *Tourismos: An International Multidisciplinary Journal of Tourism, 3*(1), 135–152.

Kumar, S., & Shah, A. (2021). Revisiting food delivery apps during COVID-19 pandemic? Investigating the role of emotions. *Journal of Retailing and Consumer Services, 62*, 102595. https://doi.org/10.1016/j.jretconser.2021.102595

LaPiere, R. T. (1965). *Social change*. Ann Arbor: McGraw-Hill.

Li, C., Mirosa, M., & Bremer, P. (2020). Review of online food delivery platforms and their impacts on sustainability. *Sustainability, 12*(14), 5528. https://www.mdpi.com/2071-1050/12/14/5528

Mansfield, E. (1963). Size of firm, market structure, and innovation. *Journal of Political Economy, 71*(6), 556–576. http://www.jstor.org/stable/1828440

Mei, X. Y. (2022). The impact of negative online reviews (NORs) on hospitality micro enterprise (ME) owners. *Anatolia*, 1–3. https://doi.org/10.1080/13032917.2022.2119592

Meta. (2023). *Facebook ads: Social media advertising for your business*. Retrieved February 28 from https://www.facebook.com/business/ads

Muske, G., & Woods, M. (2004). Micro businesses as an economic development tool: What they bring and what they need. *Journal of the Community Development Society, 35*(1), 97–116. https://doi.org/10.1080/15575330409490124

Neville, A. (2020). *Not a level playing field: NZ restaurants speak out on Uber Eats*. The Spinoff. Retrieved January 31 from https://archive.is/0hpR5#selection-1221.1-1221.66

Norwegian Government Security and Service Organisation. (2002). *Prosjekt – DIFFERENSIERT regelverk for mikrobedrifter og nyetablert [Project – DIFFERENTIATED regulations for micro-enterprises and newly established]*.

OECD. (2021). *OECD SME and entrepreneurship outlook 2021*. OECD.

Price, S., Wilkinson, T., & Coles, T. (2022). Crisis? How small tourism businesses talk about COVID-19 and business change in the UK. *Current Issues in Tourism, 25*(7), 1088–1105. https://doi.org/10.1080/13683500.2021.2023114

Ray, A., Dhir, A., Bala, P. K., & Kaur, P. (2019). Why do people use food delivery apps (FDA)? A uses and gratification theory perspective. *Journal of Retailing and Consumer Services, 51*, 221–230. https://doi.org/10.1016/j.jretconser.2019.05.025

Roh, M., & Park, K. (2019). Adoption of O2O food delivery services in South Korea: The moderating role of moral obligation in meal preparation. *International Journal of Information Management, 47*, 262–273. https://doi.org/10.1016/j.ijinfomgt.2018.09.017

Saleh, A. S., & Ndubisi, N. O. (2006). An evaluation of SME development in Malaysia. *International Review of Business Research Papers, 2*(1), 1–14.

Schaper, M., & Volery, T. (2007). *Entrepreneurship and small business* (2nd ed.). John Wiley & Sons.

Schön, D. (1982). The fear of innovation. In B. Barnes and D. Edge (Eds.), *Science in Context: Readings in the Sociology of Science* (pp. 290–302), Open University Press.

Schumpeter, J. A. (1934). *The theory of economic development: An inquiry into profits, capital, credit, interest, and the business cycle*. Harvard University Press.

Singu, H. B., & Chakraborty, D. (2022). I have the bank in my pocket: Theoretical evidence and perspectives. *Journal of Public Affairs, 22*(3), e2568. https://doi.org/10.1002/pa.2568

Skuras, D., Tsegenidi, K., & Tsekouras, K. (2008). Product innovation and the decision to invest in fixed capital assets: Evidence from an SME survey in six European Union member states. *Research Policy, 37*(10), 1778–1789. https://doi.org/10.1016/j.respol.2008.08.013

Snyder, G. (2020, December 19). Food delivery apps are more popular than ever. But can they help restaurants survive? *Los Angeles Times.* https://www.latimes.com/food/story/2020-09-19/the-state-of-food-delivery

Sorensen, E. (2022). *Card machine charges and fees explained.* Mobiletransaction.org. https://www.mobiletransaction.org/card-machine-charges-and-costs-explained/

Statistics Norway. (2022). *Establishments.* https://www.ssb.no/en/bedrifter

Steele, L. W. (1975). *Innovation in big business*. Elsevier Publishing Company.

Sundbo, J., Orfila-Sintes, F., & Sørensen, F. (2007). The innovative behaviour of tourism firms—Comparative studies of Denmark and Spain. *Research Policy*, *36*(1), 88–106. https://doi.org/10.1016/j.respol.2006.08.004

UNWTO. (2020). *Impact assessment of the COVID-19 outbreak on international tourism*. https://www.unwto.org/impact-assessment-of-the-covid-19-outbreak-on-international-tourism

Verkijika, S. F., & Neneh, B. N. (2021). Standing up for or against: A text-mining study on the recommendation of mobile payment apps. *Journal of Retailing and Consumer Services*, *63*, 102743. https://doi.org/10.1016/j.jretconser.2021.102743

Vipps. (2022). *Vipps terms and conditions*. https://vipps.no/vilkar/vipps-terms-and-conditions/

Wang, Y.-S., Tseng, T. H., Wang, W.-T., Shih, Y.-W., & Chan, P.-Y. (2019). Developing and validating a mobile catering app success model. *International Journal of Hospitality Management*, *77*, 19–30. https://doi.org/10.1016/j.ijhm.2018.06.002

Zhao, Y., & Bacao, F. (2020). What factors determining customer continuingly using food delivery apps during 2019 novel coronavirus pandemic period? *International Journal of Hospitality Management*, *91*, 102683. https://doi.org/10.1016/j.ijhm.2020.102683

11 The Influence of Social Media in Overcrowded Destinations and the Re-Emergence of Slow Travel in Gen Z

Expectations versus Reality

Lena Wistveen

Introduction

Documenting memorable vacations, stunning nature encounters and historical buildings and sharing them with family and friends has always been part of the travel experience. Although smartphones and social media have replaced analogue cameras and photo albums, the practice remains the same. Social media plays an essential part in destination management in terms of branding and image building, as well as the co-creation of experiences (Cavagnaro et al., 2021; Melati et al., 2022). Social media can also provide visual information and support, travel information, planning itineraries, making decisions and projecting expectations on a destination (Skavronskaya et al., 2020). Hence, social media provides valuable information about tourists' experiencescapes and contributes to experience innovation processes at tourism destinations (Åstrøm, 2022).

However, advances in social media and related technologies are not without complications. Although previous studies have mostly focused on the benefits that social media can provide to tourism management, there is increasing recognition of the possible downsides that can lead to co-destructive processes (Dolan et al., 2019). In fact, social media apps are powerful tools for destinations and marketing, and one must be aware of the responsibilities involved in the use of these tools (Huerta-Álvarez et al., 2020). For example, it is important to create a destination image that is both enticing and realistic – that is, capable of meeting visitors' projected expectations and experiences (Reisinger et al., 2019). However, destination image, management and marketing can be difficult to handle due to the complexity and diversity of tourism destinations (Palmer, 2010). Projected expectations that do not concur with perceived experiences are misleading and can ultimately damage the image of a destination. Factors such as overcrowding, poor visitor management and low resiliency can result in unsustainable experiences and destinations, thus producing overtourism and damaging sustainability (see Cheung & Li, 2019; Oklevik et al., 2019).

Increasing overtourism and the normalisation of the 'fast society' – for example, fast travel, fast food and fast fashion – in addition to the COVID-19 pandemic have led to a counterreaction in touristic travelling trends, also known as slow travel, that emphasises values such as quality of life, local culture and food. This trend

DOI: 10.4324/9781003335924-15

appears to be particularly attractive to Gen Zers in post-COVID-19 tourism. Gen Zers are the first true digital natives, accustomed to communicating and interacting in the digitally connected world; thus, they expect experiences and transactions to be available through their phones (Olson & Ro, 2021; Priporas et al., 2017). As travellers, Gen Zers crave authenticity, escapism, safety and memorability and exhibit an awareness of social issues, the environment and sustainability (Wood, 2013). Gen Z brings new and exciting perspectives, challenging established norms and habits in the tourism and hospitality sector with their constant social and environmental awareness and social media presence.

This chapter explores Gen Z's use of social media and the changing trends of tourism and hospitality in the post-COVID-19 era. The goal is to determine what factors contribute to the co-creation or co-destruction of a destination and its experience value. In addition, this chapter discusses case studies of popular social media destinations, including Lofoten (Norway) and Venice (Italy), from the perspectives of co-creation and co-destruction processes and experience innovation.

Literature Review

The following section is written with Gen Z in mind, which refers to the demographics of people born between 1997 and 2012. Gen Z is different from its peers, such as millennials and Gen X, having grown up with social media, technology and societal and economic uncertainties. In tourism studies, Gen Z is described as a demographic that exhibits low brand loyalty, embraces social justice and environmental consciousness and insists on technological accessibility (Olson & Ro, 2021; Priporas et al., 2017; Tseng et al., 2021). These characteristics make Gen Z a complex and challenging demographic, both to understand and to please.

This chapter uses the terms tourist, user and consumer interchangeably. Given the interconnectivity of the topics, the term 'user' will usually be employed in the contexts of social media and service use in destinations, which turns users into consumers. At the same time, a tourist is someone who travels for the pleasure of travelling (Harrison, 2003, pp. 4–5). A tourist can be a consumer and vice versa, but the term is used as to what fits the context.

Co-Creation and Co-Destruction of Tourism Experiences

The role, use and impact of social media in relation to the tourism system, decision-making processes, tourism operations and management are widely discussed topics in tourism and hospitality research (Leung et al., 2013). An essential feature of social media is its capacity to facilitate dynamic relations between consumers and service providers, whereby expectations, information and opinions can significantly affect consumer choices (Zeng & Gerritsen, 2014). Social media is a tool that allows tourists and users to become co-creators in the production and consumption of travel information, challenging service providers regarding trends, sustainability and travelling habits. In other words, social media can empower consumers to participate in the co-creation and value formation of tourist experiences.

A large body of research has considered the positive effects of social media on tourism marketing, decision-making, experiences and destination branding and how these effects contribute to processes of co-creation and value formation (Cuomo et al., 2021; Huerta-Álvarez et al., 2020). Salem and Twining-Ward (2018, p. 18) stated that social media helps create valuable travel information, as people share personal insights and preferences without being asked. In fact, uploading content has become an ingrained habit, and tourists find information on social media highly reliable because it is independently generated, which makes it more trustworthy than advertisements and marketing campaigns (Sigala et al., 2012).

However, increasing attention has been directed towards the negative impacts of social media on tourist destinations, which can lead to processes of co-destruction rather than co-creation (Dolan et al., 2019; Lund et al., 2020). Whereas co-creation fosters user involvement and contributes to product development and marketing, co-destruction refers to the negative effects stemming from customer interactions and the failure to arrive at expected value (Järvi et al., 2018; Prahalad & Ramaswamy, 2004). The challenges related to overtourism have also contributed to more attention being given to undesirable outcomes resulting from the influence of social media. Processes of co-destruction involve various dimensions. Echeverri and Skålén (2011, p. 359) pointed out that incompatible comprehensions of procedures lead to the co-destruction of value. The creation of value, for example, in destinations, is related to different expectations towards practices: if expectations of experience are met, this leads to co-creation, but if not, co-destruction may occur. These anticipations have to do with social media's central role in everyday life and the fact that we project what we see on social media into real life. Social media causes a gap between the projected expectations and the perceived reality of a destination, potentially ruining the perceived experience value and producing negative associations, impacts and reviews in relation to the destination and associated companies.

- Thought point: How can social media turn from a good tool to a destructive process for a destination in terms of management, experiences and reputation? Find destinations online and discuss whether these destinations match the criteria of co-creation/co-destruction.

Experience Innovation

The experience economy concerns activities that emphasise the fulfilment of people's needs for experiences and address how users react to and practise experiential elements (Sundbo & Sørensen, 2013). The experience economy involves the concept of consumerism, experiences and economy and studies what elements motivate the need for experiences. Such elements include anything from money and emotional needs to changing morals (Holbrook & Hirschman, 1982). Innovation and co-creation are fundamental aspects of the experience economy, which focuses on customers and their involvement in innovation processes. In experience innovation processes, co-creation does not necessarily involve physical artefacts or services; rather, the emphasis falls on the experiencescape, an environment that contributes to staging an experience, often enhanced by technology (Åstrøm, 2022). The experiencescape describes physical settings in which the goal of companies and service providers is to facilitate memorable experiences using different elements to enhance visitors' feelings and values (Mei et al., 2020).

Sundbo (2009) identified three critical concerns that contribute to the theoretical framework for understanding the experience economy: society's demand for experiences, companies' efforts to facilitate innovations and technology. Toffler (1970) and Holbrook and Hirschman (1982) pointed out that society's need for experiences, adventures and something that contrasts with everyday life is rooted in emotions. Therefore, one's experiences can soothe or fulfil one's emotional needs. Experience innovation is rooted in a company's understanding of what is unique and memorable for its customers' experiences and thus involves constantly improving the knowledge of customer needs (Sipe, 2021). The components that make experiences memorable, such as escapism, novelty and engagement, can act as initiators of innovation (Egger & Bulencea, 2015).

For example, slow travel can act as an initiator of innovation because it is different from mass tourism, offering new, and for some users improved, approaches to existing experiences. Technology can play an essential role in designing an experience as a social construct and technological possibility. Social media can contribute to improving services, feedback and user understanding, as well as serving as a system that provides travel suggestions through visual content and geotags – for example, regarding culture, food and experiences. Gen Z travellers can function as actors of innovation because they demand novelty, sustainability, escapism, accessibility and digital solutions (Martínez-Pérez et al., 2018; Robinson & Schänzel, 2019). As companies strive to understand and accommodate the needs of their customers, Gen Zers contribute to the development and implementation of solutions for more sustainable tourism, thus helping to improve the holistic experience of a destination. Social media, slow travel and Gen Z are discussed in detail in the following sections.

External and internal drivers of innovation need to be considered because they push the tourism industry and experience economy forward, helping generate new ideas, experiences and perspectives. External drivers involve technology, markets, competition and consumer needs. One example is social media: as an external driver of innovation, social media provides opportunities in terms of planning, exploring, visual context and information regarding destinations for both tourists and service providers. This, in turn, can affect internal drivers, such as tourist organisations, destination management and businesses and their business models. However, one challenge with social media is that it has made the tourism industry more information intense (Narangajavana et al., 2017), which can make it difficult for destination management to control what kind of information is spreading and to verify whether it is reliable.

- Thought point: How is experience affected by social, cultural and emotional sustainable dimensions, and why is this important to understand experience innovation?

The Role of Social Media

Social media and its users can play an essential role in improving services and experiences and contribute to a better understanding of customers' needs. However, social media can also significantly influence the value co-destruction of a destination and related experiences. Scholars have argued that social media, its networks and the data it generates act as accelerators of destination overcrowding (Alonso-Almeida et al., 2019), which affects the perceived experiences and values connected to such destinations. A poor understanding of tourists' discrepancies produces misinformation, and the misuse of resources impacts destinations as well as their images and sustainability (Sun et al., 2021), thus leading to processes of co-destruction. In such cases, it is important to understand how society and technology influence each other. As technology is perceived subjectively, different social groups have different understandings of what technology is, what it can do and how it should be used (Ryghaug & Toftaker, 2014). These different perceptions of technology generate diverse understandings, which may result in gaps between expectations and reality.

Moreover, social media contributes to the societal pressure to have positive experiences while travelling, but projected destination images may not concur with perceived reality. Therefore, everyone can become a victim of the 'Paris syndrome', a condition whereby the idealised idea of Paris and the derealisation of the city clash and produce confusion (Lyons, 2015). This causes an internal crisis because the picture in one's head does not match what one's eyes can see. Tourists become trapped in their own 'tourist gazes', where too much emphasis is put on the visual aspects of being a tourist rather than the whole experience (Benenti & Giombini, 2020).

Experiences should not only function as sources of individual satisfaction but also fulfil the need for social and cultural values, stimuli and challenges. This is the very core of the experience economy: experiences form the basis for value creation and innovation, as experiences give high enjoyment that consumers can attain with money (Mehmetoglu & Engen, 2011; Pedersen, 2012). Therefore, bad experiences are bad business because appealing to customers' emotions and staging experiences is crucial in a market dominated by the demand for pleasure. However, pleasure is subjective, and what appears alluring to some can be a nightmare for others. As Mark Manson (2016, p. 9) described it, 'The desire for more positive experience is itself a negative experience. And, paradoxically, the acceptance of one's negative experience is itself a positive experience'. An example of this is hiking. For some, hiking is a thrilling and pleasurable leisure activity that provides nature experiences and picturesque views. While for others, it can be related to fear, being cold and going to desolate areas, a popular activity that puts certain users outside of their comfort zone. This example shows that people immerse themselves in experiences to such degrees that they become physical parts of the experiences themselves (Pine & Gilmore, 1999). Therefore, unsatisfactory experiences can affect one's state of mind or physical well-being. Other examples of such experiences include cruise ships, tour buses, sports events, passive travel arrangements, physical adventures and so on. Slow travel versus fast travel is another element of travel that emphasis on physical experiences and emotions. There are those who prefer getting to know local cultures and cuisines, while others may simply cruise through, ticking it off the bucket list and moving on to the next experience or destination to fulfil their needs. In recent years, experience quality in terms of social and cultural considerations has become more significant to younger generations, such as Gen Z. Furthermore, the COVID-19 pandemic produced new perspectives on consumerism and travel, prompting habits and behaviours to be more focused on sustainability and awareness.

A Change in Demographics and Travel Trends – Slow Travel and Gen Z

Dating back to the late 1980s and inspired by the slow food movement (see Petrini, 2003), slow travel focuses on quality of life, culture and sustainability – the journey rather than the destination is the goal (Dickinson & Lumsdon, 2010). The increasingly speedy lifestyles that people end up adopting have affected various aspects of life, such as travelling, consumption and experiences. Fast travel and consumerism lead to prioritising quantity over quality: food is perceived as a means, or fuel, rather than cultural cuisine, and destinations become mere backdrops for pictures instead of serene experiences. These elements are the usual characteristics of mass tourism. Therefore, slow tourism can be considered a counterreaction to mass tourism, where you enjoy quality food, slow down, take in all the impressions and focus on the local culture and traditions (Ernszt & Marton, 2021).

It appears that Gen Z has jumped off the hedonistic treadmill, emphasising convenience and escapism (Wood, 2013) in contrast to the earlier demand for travel, whereby pleasures could be bought with money. In this regard, Gen Zers' drastic shifts in values, popular culture, morals and social norms exhibit similarities with the generation of 1968. The flower power movement of the 1960s, in which individualism emerged as a new ethical, political and social philosophy, initiated what we today understand as the experience market (Schulze, 2013). In fact, some scholars have claimed that we have been riding on the wave of individualism for more than 40 years (Jantzen et al., 2011), but the COVID-19 pandemic produced a clear interruption of the existing excessive consumption patterns, once again challenging bourgeois values. Gen Z has managed to break away from the tourist gaze, developing the ability to discern and dissect its role in tourism (Wee, 2019), which makes Gen Zers more influential than their predecessors and more difficult to accommodate. Therefore, the shift in consumer values makes it important for the tourism industry to understand this social and demographic change and how it influences the expectations and projected image of destinations.

The rest of this chapter discusses relevant case studies of the destinations of Lofoten and Venice. These cases were chosen because tourism was the core industry of the local communities. In addition, these destinations have experienced challenges related to the negative dimensions of social media in tourism, leading to residents' resistance to tourism activities and overcrowding.

Case Studies – Expectations versus Reality

Lofoten Islands, Norway

The Lofoten archipelago in Northern Norway is a world-class destination for nature-based tourism experiences and cultural heritage. The archipelago consists of six municipalities inhabited by roughly 24,000 residents that accommodated 1.1 million overnight stays per year pre-COVID-19, generating an annual revenue of 56 million euros (Menon Economics, 2019). Both domestic and international tourists flock to Lofoten to experience the northern lights, midnight sun, wildlife, fishing villages and breath-taking hikes. Well known for its picturesque mountains, deep fjords and recreational opportunities, this location is a social media paradise where visitors can create and share Instagram-friendly content, experiences and pictures. However, the archipelago is not adapted to receive massive numbers of visitors throughout the year, which has caused conflicts among tourist management, public administration, residents and visitors (Nordland County Municipality, 2019). The constant stream of visitors affects residents' quality of life, who plead for a more restrictive system for tourism. In other words, processes of co-destruction have begun, as is apparent to both visitors and residents in Lofoten. For example, insufficient or expensive accommodations lead to camping in restricted or vulnerable areas, which irritates the local community. Social media hotspots that are not adapted for high visitor numbers and lack parking, trails and restrooms may produce long-term and irreversible effects on nature. These impacts lead to undesirable outcomes that affect the destination image, thus impacting the perceived experience, value and sustainability of the destination. Such developments make tourism and related activities unsustainable for everyone involved. Therefore, how can this volume of visitors be turned into something of value, for both visitors and residents?

The focus should not be on the number of visitors but on the value that visitors provide to the host community. This is one of the principles of slow travel. Slow travel offers possibilities for the sustainability and security of vulnerable destinations (Mavric et al., 2021) affected by overtourism and social media. It emphasises sustainability and co-creation to draw attention to experiences that contribute to the local economy and the social sustainability of the residents of a destination. Moreover, encouraging positive attitudes towards tourism enhances perceived experience value (Breiby et al., 2020), which helps create sustainable experiences. The surfers of Lofoten are an example of how younger generations contribute to more activity in smaller communities, environmental awareness and support sustainable experiences. Surfers are characterised by similar values to Gen Z, a nature-friendly lifestyle and being environmentally conscious. Involving younger generations like surfers, who are both visitors and seasonal residents in Lofoten, can contribute to developing low-cost activities that have a low impact on nature yet at the same time allow mindfulness towards sustainability (Langseth & Vyff, 2021).

Social media, alongside visitors and residents, can help spread awareness and information related to vulnerable areas. This is beneficial because many members of the younger generations find most of their information related to travel through social media rather than traditional search engines, such as Google (Nilashi et al., 2021). In addition, social media can be a valuable tool for providing feedback via texts and pictures and insights into trends and needs. A fitting and attentive social media presence from tourism organisers and destination management can positively impact destinations and related experiences. Social media can also be crucial in users' choices of which destination to visit, thus impacting organisers' decision-making processes and competitiveness. Humans are visual creatures and are highly receptive to visual content, such as images and videos, preferably with colours pleasing to the eye (McAndrew, 2004, p. 1). Consequently, social media plays an essential role in directing consumer behaviours, promoting destinations and building expectations.

It is safe to say that Gen Z is breaking stereotypes and creating changes in tourism trends. Unlike their predecessors, Gen Zers are focused on being genuine and true to their values, and social media is not necessarily a place to show off. Rather, social media can be used to express yourself rather than conform to the norms of society. Moreover, Gen Z is well aware of the negative implications that social media produced for their millennial predecessors, which has allowed them to break previous norms and stereotypes. On social media, the common rule is that when you go on holiday, you stage the experience you (believe) have and share it on social media. However, recently, it has become more common and accepted (likely thanks to Gen Z) to show behind-the-scenes mishaps during holidays. Users usually perform such behind-the-scenes moments in a sarcastic manner, making fun of themselves for believing that they could have a picture-perfect Instagram holiday. However, for uncomprehending social media users, this might appear as criticism and can lead to a destructive perception of a destination (see Figures 11.1 and 11.2)

Venice, Italy

Venice is a destination on many people's bucket lists. Located in Northeast Italy, Venice is a city full of architecture, Italian cuisine, history, art and culture. Despite its status as a UNESCO World Heritage site, the city has become a candidate for the 'heritage in danger' category. The reasons involve overtourism, cruise ships and an imbalanced relationship between residents' quality of life and tourism demands (Seraphin et al., 2018). Although Venice has made itself, along with its services, experiences and economy, dependent on tourism, the economic contributions of tourists to local businesses are limited. The negative effects and lack of regulation have pushed locals to migrate to the mainland. Drawing a comparison with the last time this happened – namely, during the bubonic plague – one can get the impression that tourism in Venice functions like a pandemic (González, 2018). Overtourism has resulted in Venice losing its authenticity, affecting visitors' satisfaction and residents' sense of belonging.

The differences among pre-, during- and post-COVID-19 Venice are quite sensational. Before the pandemic, the city had almost reached breaking point. Cruise

Figure 11.1 Scan the QR codes to see the expectations versus reality

Source: Author's own graphics

ships threatening the fragile foundations of the city produced tensions among local authorities, creating a collision between the need to manage traffic flow and to ensure that tourists remained in the city centre. Massive daily visits reduced the possibilities for value creation and interaction with locals. This situation was the epitome of modern mass tourism, with profit conquering sustainability. However, the COVID-19 pandemic provided Venice with a much-needed break, pausing all tourist-related activities, which made the tourism impact on the city even more apparent. However, although the pollution and visitor numbers went down, the economic consequences of the lockdown were enormous, prompting the need to get the tourism industry up and running as soon as possible. Once again, the greed for profit came back. As a surprise to many, the lockdown and travel restrictions lasted longer than anticipated. Nowadays, as the world opens up, places like Venice face renewed challenges related to the magnitude and flow of visitors, which became a pressing matter during times of social distancing. However, the post-COVID-19 development has moved towards a more sustainable tourism approach that involves actively averting and taking countermeasures to prevent the negative impacts of mass tourism. Venice has started making measures against overtourism by implementing visitor management through an entry ticket system, as well

Figure 11.2 Scan the QR codes to view behind the scenes of social media

Source: Author's own graphics

as banning cruise ships to enter the central harbour (Bertocchi & Camatti, 2022), allowing Venice to focus on the slow and authentic experiences.

In theory, Venice may appear to be an ideal destination for Gen Zers in terms of authenticity and novelty by providing culturally enriching experiences. However, in practice, Venice is likelier to intimidate Gen Zers and the younger generations of travellers. Gen Z advocates social justice and environmental rights and is a group with low loyalty, which means its members have no problem boycotting a destination if it has negative connotations (Olson & Ro, 2021). Therefore, Gen Z is a powerful constituency of consumers and tourists that can affect the demand for services and experiences, along with their organisation, across the tourism sector. For example, the rise of concepts such as slow travel shows that the tourism industry has not managed popular destinations well enough, jeopardising cultural sites and causing local inflation and the co-destruction of value. Consumers such as Gen Zers are socially aware of the negative effects of these destructive trends in tourism. Consequently, a destination is not just a geographical unit but also a subject for judgement and evaluation (Chen & Šegota, 2015). In other words, tourists consider not only the physical features of destinations but also their abstract and subjective elements.

Conclusion

The tourism industry and destinations that are marked by overtourism are at a crossroads. On one hand, it is only the profit and amount of visits that matter. On the other hand, the environmental and social sustainability and quality desired by residents, tourists and society are key. The world is moving forward towards a more balanced, sustainable approach, regardless of industries, experiences and demands. One can go so far as to say that sustainability has become 'a must' for most businesses. However, if the industry does not comply with this emerging reality and continues promoting mass tourism, it will likely be abandoned by younger generations, such as Gen Z. Struggling to keep the old norms of capitalism and mass consumerism is simply a denial of reality.

The impact of social media, the demographic changes brought about by Gen Z and the re-emergence of slow travel represent remarkable opportunities in tourism and hospitality for the industry, providers and users. There is greater awareness of environmental and societal issues and concerns about sustainability. The industry must embrace change and value co-creation processes that can contribute to better services, products and sustainable experiences. Social media and consumers such as Gen Zers act as agents of innovation, putting tourism challenges on the socio-political agenda. Social media allows everyone to see what it is like to experience destinations such as Venice in diverse forms: from the more appealing dimensions, such as architecture, canals and history, to the more unappealing ones, such as visitor numbers and a lack of destination management.

It is evident that there is a need for information administration and accommodation of the needs of new emerging user trends, such as slow travel and social media hotspots. Travel behaviour differs significantly from generation to generation, which makes it even more important to understand generational preferences as well as what makes users feel fulfilled and how to implement such measures in travel experiences. The demographic changes that Gen Z represents allow for changes in supply and demand. The future growth of tourism depends on whether the industry understands how social trends and demographic changes affect travel behaviours. It is essential for the tourism industry to develop the ability to recognise and deal with changes in a broad manner (Dwyer et al., 2009).

In this context, social media can be both a tool of co-creation and co-destruction, depending on how companies and actors manage destinations and how the latter are perceived by visitors. Social media allows tourists and users to become co-creators in producing and consuming travel information and challenging service providers regarding trends, sustainability and consumption. Therefore, social media serves as an external driver of innovation, pushing the tourism industry and consumers towards sustainable and creative solutions, services and experiences. New user trends, the increasing demand for sustainability and changing demographics imply that changes will continue and intensify over the years to come. One can only hope that the pandemic has made people more aware of their impact on nature and destinations, emphasising the need to find a careful balance between exploring and preserving the world.

Further Questions

- How do demographic factors affect the tourism industry and its related services and experiences?
- From the perspective of experience innovation, how can Gen Zers travel behaviours contribute to a more sustainable and less consumerist direction in the tourism industry?
- What consequences do destinations and related actors face due to a limited understanding of travel trends and users, and how does this affect destinations' resilience and co-creation processes?

Further Readings

Barbe, D., & Neuburger, L. (2021). Generation Z and digital influencers in the tourism industry. In N. Stylos, R. Rahimi, B. Okumus, & S. Williams (Eds.), *Generation Z marketing and management in tourism and hospitality: The future of the industry* (pp. 167–192). Springer International Publishing. https://doi.org/10.1007/978-3-030-70695-1_7

Dickinson, J., & Lumsdon, L. (2010). *Slow travel and tourism*. Routledge.

Gon, M. (2021). Local experiences on Instagram: Social media data as source of evidence for experience design. *Journal of Destination Marketing & Management*, *19*, 1–11. https://doi.org/10.1016/j.jdmm.2020.100435

Sundbo, J., & Sørensen, F. (2013). Introduction to the experience economy. In Sundbo, J., & Sørensen, F. (Eds.) *Handbook on the experience economy* (pp. 1–18). Edward Elgar Publishing.

References

Alonso-Almeida, M.-d-M., Borrajo-Millán, F., & Yi, L. (2019). Are social media data pushing overtourism? The case of Barcelona and Chinese tourists. *Sustainability*, *11*(12), 33–56. https://www.mdpi.com/2071-1050/11/12/3356

Åstrøm, J. K. (2022). *Theming in experience-based tourism: Visitor and provider perspectives*. (Publication No. 23) [Doctoral dissertation, Inland Norway University of Applied Sciences]. https://hdl.handle.net/11250/3012286

Benenti, M., & Giombini, L. (2020). The aesthetic paradox of tourism. *Proceedings of the European Society for Aesthetics*, *12*, 1–31.

Bertocchi, D., & Camatti, N. (2022). Tourism in Venice: Mapping overtourism and exploring solutions. In J. v. d. Borg (Ed.), *A research agenda for urban tourism* (pp. 107–125). Edward Elgar Publishing.

Breiby, M. A., Duedahl, E., Øian, H., & Ericsson, B. (2020). Exploring sustainable experiences in tourism. *Scandinavian Journal of Hospitality and Tourism*, *20*(4), 335–351. https://doi.org/10.1080/15022250.2020.1748706

Cavagnaro, E., Michopoulou, E., & Pappas, N. (2021). Revisiting value co-creation and co-destruction in tourism. *Tourism Planning & Development*, *18*(2), 121–124. https://doi.org/10.1080/21568316.2021.1879924

Chen, N. C., & Šegota, T. (2015). Resident attitudes, place attachment and destination branding: A research framework. *Tourism and Hospitality Management*, *21*(2), 145–158.

Cheung, K. S., & Li, L.-H. (2019). Understanding visitor–resident relations in overtourism: Developing resilience for sustainable tourism. *Journal of Sustainable Tourism*, *27*(8), 1197–1216. https://doi.org/10.1080/09669582.2019.1606815.

Cuomo, M. T., Tortora, D., Foroudi, P., Giordano, A., Festa, G., & Metallo, G. (2021). Digital transformation and tourist experience co-design: Big social data for planning cultural tourism. *Technological Forecasting and Social Change*, *162*, 1–9. https://doi.org/10.1016/j.techfore.2020.120345

Dickinson, J., & Lumsdon, L. (2010). *Slow travel and tourism*. Routledge.

Dolan, R., Seo, Y., & Kemper, J. (2019). Complaining practices on social media in tourism: A value co-creation and co-destruction perspective. *Tourism Management*, *73*, 35–45. https://doi.org/10.1016/j.tourman.2019.01.017

Dwyer, L., Edwards, D., Mistilis, N., Roman, C., & Scott, N. (2009). Destination and enterprise management for a tourism future. *Tourism Management*, *30*(1), 63–74.

Echeverri, P., & Skålén, P. (2011). Co-creation and co-destruction: A practice-theory based study of interactive value formation. *Marketing Theory*, *11*(3), 351–373.

Egger, R., & Bulencea, P. (2015). *Gamification in tourism: Designing memorable experiences*. BoD–Books on Demand.

Ernszt, I., & Marton, Z. (2021). An emerging trend of slow tourism: Perceptions of Hungarian citizens. *Interdisciplinary Description of Complex Systems: INDECS*, *19*(2), 295–307.

Gon, M. (2021). Local experiences on Instagram: Social media data as source of evidence for experience design. *Journal of Destination Marketing & Management*, *19*, 1–11. https://doi.org/10.1016/j.jdmm.2020.100435

González, A. T. (2018). Venice: The problem of overtourism and the impact of cruises. *Investigaciones Regionales = Journal of Regional Research* (42), 35–51.

Harrison, J. D. (2003). *Being a tourist: Finding meaning in pleasure travel*. uBC Press.

Holbrook, M. B., & Hirschman, E. C. (1982). The experiential aspects of consumption: Consumer fantasies, feelings, and fun. *Journal of Consumer Research*, *9*(2), 132–140.

Huerta-Álvarez, R., Cambra-Fierro, J. J., & Fuentes-Blasco, M. (2020). The interplay between social media communication, brand equity and brand engagement in tourist destinations: An analysis in an emerging economy. *Journal of Destination Marketing & Management*, *16*, 1–12.

Jantzen, C., Vetner, M., & Bouchet, J. (2011). *Oplevelsesdesign [Experience design]*. Samfundslitteratur.

Järvi, H., Kähkönen, A.-K., & Torvinen, H. (2018). When value co-creation fails: Reasons that lead to value co-destruction. *Scandinavian Journal of Management*, *34*(1), 63–77.

Langseth, T., & Vyff, A. (2021). Cultural dissonance: Surfers' environmental attitudes and actions [Original research]. *Frontiers in Sports and Active Living*, *3*. https://doi.org/10.3389/fspor.2021.695048

Leung, D., Law, R., van Hoof, H., & Buhalis, D. (2013). Social media in tourism and hospitality: A literature review. *Journal of Travel & Tourism Marketing*, *30*(1–2), 3–22. https://doi.org/10.1080/10548408.2013.750919

Lund, N. F., Scarles, C., & Cohen, S. A. (2020). The brand value continuum: Countering co-destruction of destination branding in social media through storytelling. *Journal of Travel Research*, *59*(8), 1506–1521.

Lyons, S. (2015). In search of lost cities. Imagined geographies and the allure of the fake. *Diffractions*, (5), 1–20. https://doi.org/10.34632/diffractions.2015.506

Manson, M. (2016). *The subtle art of not giving a F* ck: A counterintuitive approach to living a good life*. Macmillan Publishers Aus.

Martínez-Pérez, Á, Elche, D., García-Villaverde, P. M., & Parra-Requena, G. (2018). Cultural tourism clusters: Social capital, relations with Institutions, and radical innovation. *Journal of Travel Research*, *58*(5), 793–807. https://doi.org/10.1177/0047287518778147.

Mavric, B., Öğretmenoğlu, M., & Akova, O. (2021). Bibliometric analysis of slow tourism. *Advances in Hospitality and Tourism Research (AHTR)*, *9*(1), 157–178.

McAndrew, A. (2004). *An introduction to digital image processing with Matlab notes for SCM2511 image processing 1 semester 1*. School of Computer Science and Mathematics, University of Victoria, 2004. Retrieved from https://www.hlevkin.com/hlevkin/49octaveImageProc/Books/McAbdrew-An%20Introduction%20to%20Digital%20Image%20Processing%20with%20Matlab.pdf

Mehmetoglu, M., & Engen, M. (2011). Pine and Gilmore's concept of experience economy and its dimensions: An empirical examination in tourism. *Journal of Quality Assurance in Hospitality & Tourism*, *12*(4), 237–255. https://doi.org/10.1080/1528008X.2011.541847

Mei, X. Y., Hågensen, A.-M. S., & Kristiansen, H. S. (2020). Storytelling through experiencescape: Creating unique stories and extraordinary experiences in farm tourism. *Tourism and Hospitality Research*, *20*(1), 93–104.

Melati, N. L. P. K., Fathorrahman, F., & Pradiani, T. (2022). The influence of Instagram, Tiktok travel influencers and city branding on the decision to choose a tourist destination. *Journal of Business on Hospitality and Tourism*, *8*(1), 267–289.

Menon Economics. (2019). *Ringvirkningsanalyse av reiselivet i Lofoten og Vesterålen*. M. Economics (Ripple effects of tourism in Lofoten and Vesteråen). https://www.menon.no/publication/ringvirkningsanalyse-reiselivet-lofoten-vesteralen/

Narangajavana, Y., Callarisa Fiol, L. J., Moliner Tena, M. Ángel, Rodríguez Artola, R. M., & Sánchez García, J. (2017). The influence of social media in creating expectations. An empirical study for a tourist destination. *Annals of Tourism Research*, *65*, 60–70. https://doi.org/10.1016/j.annals.2017.05.002

Nilashi, M., Asadi, S., Minaei-Bidgoli, B., Ali Abumalloh, R., Samad, S., Ghabban, F., & Ahani, A. (2021). Recommendation agents and information sharing through social media for coronavirus outbreak. *Telematics and Informatics*, *61*, 101597. https://doi.org/10.1016/j.tele.2021.101597

Nordland County Municipality. (2019). *Underveisrapport – pilotprosjektet på besøksforvaltning [Report along the way – the pilot project on visitor management]*. https://www.nfk.no/besoksforvaltning/_f/p31/i75cb6d4c-f7d7-4939-8f29-9fa9afa07f53/underveisrapport-pilotprosjekt-besoksforvaltning.pdf

Oklevik, O., Gössling, S., Hall, C. M., Steen Jacobsen, J. K., Grøtte, I. P., & McCabe, S. (2019). Overtourism, optimisation, and destination performance indicators: A case study of activities in Fjord Norway. *Journal of Sustainable Tourism*, *27*(12), 1804–1824. https://doi.org/10.1080/09669582.2018.1533020

Olson, E. D., & Ro, H. (2021). Generation Z and their perceptions of well-being in tourism. In N. Stylos, R. Rahimi, B. Okumus, & S. Williams (Eds.), *Generation Z marketing and management in tourism and hospitality: The future of the industry* (pp. 101–118). Springer International Publishing. https://doi.org/10.1007/978-3-030-70695-1_4

Palmer, A. (2010). The internet challenge for destination marketing organizations. In N. Morgan, A. Pritchard, & R. Pride (Eds.), *Destination branding* (pp. 128–140). Routledge.

Pedersen, A.-J. (2012). *Opplevelsesøkonomi: Kunsten å designe opplevelser [Experience economy: The art of designing experiences]*. Cappelen Damm akademisk.

Petrini, C. (2003). *Slow food: The case for taste*. Columbia University Press.

Pine, B. J., & Gilmore, J. H. (1999). *The experience economy: Work is theatre & every business a stage*. Harvard Business Press.

Prahalad, C. K., & Ramaswamy, V. (2004). Co-creating unique value with customers. *Strategy & Leadership*, *32*(3), 4–9.

Priporas, C.-V., Stylos, N., & Fotiadis, A. K. (2017). Generation Z consumers' expectations of interactions in smart retailing: A future agenda. *Computers in Human Behavior*, *77*, 374–381. https://doi.org/10.1016/j.chb.2017.01.058

Reisinger, Y., Michael, N., & Hayes, J. P. (2019). Destination competitiveness from a tourist perspective: A case of the United Arab Emirates. *International Journal of Tourism Research, 21*(2), 259–279.

Robinson, V. M., & Schänzel, H. A. (2019). A tourism inflex: Generation Z travel experiences. *Journal of Tourism Futures, 5*(2), 127–141.

Ryghaug, M., & Toftaker, M. (2014). A Transformative Practice? Meaning, Competence, and Material Aspects of Driving Electric Cars in Norway. *Nature and Culture, 9*(2), 146–163. https://doi.org/10.3167/nc.2014.090203

Salem, T., & Twining-Ward, L. (2018). *The voice of travelers: Leveraging user-generated content for tourism development 2018*. World Bank.

Schulze, G. (2013). The experience market. In J. Sundo, & F. Sørensen (Eds.), *Handbook on the experience economy* (pp. 98–121). Edward Elgar Publishing.

Seraphin, H., Sheeran, P., & Pilato, M. (2018). Over-tourism and the fall of Venice as a destination. *Journal of Destination Marketing & Management, 9*, 374–376. https://doi.org/10.1016/j.jdmm.2018.01.011

Sigala, M., Christou, E., & Gretzel, U. (2012). *Social media in travel, tourism and hospitality: Theory, practice and cases*. Ashgate Publishing, Ltd.

Sipe, L. J. (2021). Towards an experience innovation canvas: A framework for measuring innovation in the hospitality and tourism industry. *International Journal of Hospitality & Tourism Administration, 22*(1), 85–109. https://doi.org/10.1080/15256480.2018.1547240.

Skavronskaya, L., Moyle, B., Scott, N., & Kralj, A. (2020). The psychology of novelty in memorable tourism experiences. *Current Issues in Tourism, 23*(21), 2683–2698.

Sundbo, J. (2009). Innovation in the experience economy: A taxonomy of innovation organisations. *The Service Industries Journal, 29*(4), 431–455. https://doi.org/10.1080/02642060802283139

Sundbo, J., & Sørensen, F. (2013). Introduction to the experience economy. In J. Sundbo, & F. Sørensen (Eds.), *Handbook on the experience economy* (pp. 1–18). Edward Elgar Publishing.

Sun, W., Tang, S., & Liu, F. (2021). Examining perceived and projected destination image: A social media content analysis. *Sustainability, 13*(6), 1–16. https://www.mdpi.com/2071-1050/13/6/3354

Toffler, A. (1970). *Future shock.* Bantam.

Tseng, L.-Y., Chang, J.-H., & Zhu, Y. L. (2021). What drives the travel switching behavior of Chinese Generation Z consumers. *Journal of Tourism Futures*. 1–16

Wee, D. (2019). Generation Z talking: Transformative experience in educational travel. *Journal of Tourism Futures, 5*(2), 157–167.

Wood, S. (2013). Generation Z as consumers: Trends and innovation. *Institute for Emerging Issues: NC State University, 119*(9), 7767–7779.

Zeng, B., & Gerritsen, R. (2014). What do we know about social media in tourism? A review. *Tourism Management Perspectives, 10*, 27–36. https://doi.org/10.1016/j.tmp.2014.01.001

12 Smart Tourism in Developing Smart Destinations

Cases from Borneo Island

Xiang Ying Mei

Introduction

The growth of Information Communication Technology (ICT) has revolutionised the world, including the tourism industry. With the emphasis on the Internet and the World Wide Web and the dependence on smartphones and mobile apps, it is not surprising that travel behaviour and thereby experiences need to be reinvestigated and reframed in the Smart Tourism context. People depend on various digital tools and the Internet in their everyday life; this is not an exception when travelling (Wang et al., 2016). As a result, it is believed that more smart services will be developed to respond to such a trend. Destinations that manage to integrate various ICT and digital tools into providing seamless services would gain major advantages in providing the overall smart tourism experiences and contribute to the experience economy. Naturally, the impact of smart technologies leads to the transformation of tourist experiences and the roles played by tourists themselves (Mehraliyev et al., 2020). Research on smart tourism and Smart Tourism Destinations is still in its infancy and many topics remain to be explored particularly in developing countries, regions, and island destinations.

This chapter aims to explore the notion of Smart Tourism Destinations in the context of the island of Borneo, the largest island in Asia. Due to its size, history, and political interests, the island does not consist of one single destination. It is politically controlled by three countries: Indonesia, Malaysia, and Brunei. Thus, there are vast destinations, cities, and areas with their uniqueness and culture that together form unique tourism experiences that the island offers. All three countries have shown some interest in developing smart solutions for tourism at least at the micro level among tourism providers (Halim, 2022; Lopes et al., 2019). However, the national government in Malaysia has specifically announced The Malaysia Smart Tourism 4.0 initiative. This initiative was launched by Tourism Malaysia on 5 April 2018 to bring the industry to the next level and take advantage of opportunities of digital technology (Malaysian Investment Development Authority [MIDA], 2021). While this was put on hold due to the pandemic, it is believed that further development of this strategy is even more important in helping to recover the tourism industry. Within Borneo, the Malaysian state of Sabah is one of the popular

DOI: 10.4324/9781003335924-16

tourist destinations on the island. The case study thus concentrates on the state of Sabah and Kota Kinabalu as its capital city.

Smart Tourism

The development of technology and digitalisation has changed the life of many people. The tourism industry has also evolved in line with ICT development leading to the concept of smart tourism. Smart tourism evidently changes and impacts tourist activities and thereby tourism experiences. Academic attention on smart tourism was initiated by Wang et al. (2013) and Buhalis and Amaranggana (2015) when the concept of Smart Cities was expanded to understand Smart Tourism Destinations (Mehraliyev et al., 2020). The original notion of Smart Cities was an initiative in response to environmental concerns related to climate change and other societal difficulties. As a result, many cities and regions that are looking for novel ways to deal with such challenges turned to innovation and smart solutions. Smart Cities were not initiated with tourism in mind, at least not as the focal point as the emphasis was to improve the lives of the citizens through a smart solution that communicates with each other seamlessly. Nevertheless, the logic is that a city that is good to live in is also a city that is good to visit for tourists where memorable and unique experiences are facilitated and gained.

In Europe through the European Union (EU), large resources have been committed to promoting 'smart' urban development in its metropolitan areas (Caragliu et al., 2011). As with any other concept, there are various definitions of 'smart'. 'Smart' is understood as 'quick intelligence' (Dictionary, 2012) and the term is now commonly utilised to explain the features and elements of particular technologies (Mehraliyev et al., 2020). Based on such knowledge and moving its understanding to describe Smart Cities, a common definition is an emphasis on the integration of ICT systems and technological innovation. This also includes investment in human and social capital, and communication infrastructures in conjunction with sustainable developments (Caragliu et al., 2011; Mei & Slettli, 2022). In the context of smart tourism, it may simply be defined as a 'ubiquitous tour information service received by tourists during a touring process' (Li et al., 2017, p. 297).

Smart Tourism Destination

From smart tourism, the notion of a Smart Tourism Destination emerged. The difference between smart tourism and Smart Tourism Destination is explained by Bouchon (2022). Smart tourism is about changing tourism experiences in a digital environment. On the other hand, Smart Tourism Destination emphasises the changing of a place's tourism system by emphasising the digital environment. Thus, transforming into a Smart Tourism Destination is a much more complex process as the entire tourism ecosystem has to be changed. Developed economies and the EU in particular have placed much emphasis on developing Smart Tourism Destinations. As discussed, since the notion of smart tourism and thereby Smart Tourism Destination derive from Smart Cities, such emphasis by the EU is quite natural. According to the EU and the European Capital of Smart Tourism, which is an initiative founded in 2019 that aims to raise awareness about smart tourism, a Smart Tourism Destination is:

> A destination facilitating access to tourism and hospitality products, services, spaces, and experiences through ICT-based tools. It is a healthy social and cultural environment, which can be found through a focus on the city's social and human capital. It also implements innovative, intelligent solutions and fosters the development of entrepreneurial businesses and their interconnectedness.
>
> (European Union [EU], 2019, p. 3)

Reflecting on such a definition, the four categories of accessibility, sustainability, digitalisation, and cultural heritage and creativity (see Table 12.1) are emphasised in developing a Smart Tourism Destination.

Accessibility and being able to access the destination are key in getting tourists to visit a certain destination in the first place (Kastenholz et al., 2012). Once arrived at the destination, there must be ways to get to its surrounding activities and attractions. Not being able to access such activities and attractions or if the mode of transport is limited and unreliable, frustration and stress might arise. On the other hand, when the mode of transport is at ease and is available and accessible to all types of tourists regardless of possible language barriers and other physical barriers, the overall experience of the destination will be positive.

As a term coined from Smart City initiatives, **sustainability** is a key principle in Smart Tourism Destination development. Smart solutions contribute to sustainability and improved quality of life for all stakeholders. These include the citizens of the destination and also temporary citizens such as tourists when the services provided through smart technology are used to support collaborative decision-making (Buhalis, 2022). Data that are gathered through smart technologies can be used to inform people about the validity and usage of certain attractions and facilities. For example, data can be analysed to understand people's usage of airports, museums, public transport, national parts, etc. Such information can then be distributed to the public through various apps and platforms to prevent a large number of people from using the same facilities at one given time and prevent overcrowding and queues.

Smart Tourism Destinations derive from technological innovations. Such innovations focus on the **digitalisation** and the development of digital data and artificial intelligence in a tourism context (Bouchon, 2022). Logically, there is a heavy emphasis on the technology and digitalisation of services to simplify, automatise, and increase efficiency. Closely related to the discussion about sustainability, digital technology must be able to provide key information up-to-date and in real time for the communication to be relevant. Digitalisation also contributes to revitalising destinations and creating attractive cities to live in and visit. In addition, the obtained data provides an exact understanding of the destination's many spatial components and such information can be used for optimisation (Bouchon, 2022).

Table 12.1 The four principles of a Smart Tourism Destination

Accessibility **Reachability** through different modes of transport	• What does the infrastructure look like? • How accessible is the city? • How can tourism offers be made barrier-free, physically, and psychologically? • How can multilingual services be provided? • How can services be digitally provided to all tourists and visitors?
Sustainability Managing and protecting the natural resources in the city, and also reducing seasonality and including the local community	• What opportunities does a city have to preserve and enhance the natural environment resources? • How can economic and socio-cultural efforts be developed in a balanced way? • How are natural resources such as innovative environmentally friendly measures managed in a tourism destination? • How can cities as tourism destinations contribute to local employment and diversification of local economies?
Digitalisation Innovative tourism and hospitality information, products, services, spaces, and experiences adapted to the needs of the consumers through ICT	• How can the city support tourism businesses in the development and use of digital skills and tools? • How does the city support and encourage the digitalisation of tourism services?
Cultural Heritage and Creativity Protecting and capitalising on the local heritage as well as cultural and creative assets for the benefit of the destination, the industry, and tourists	• How can the city make resourceful use of its cultural heritage and creative industries for an enriched tourism experience? • What actions are implemented to render recognition and to incorporate the tangible and intangible heritage of art, history, and culture in its centre and surroundings, in the enhanced tourism offer? • How are cultural heritage and creativity used to attract tourists and exploit synergies between tourism and cultural and creative industries?

Source: Adapted from EU (2019).

Cultural heritage and creativity are some of the key attractions in destinations due to their ability to enrich the uniqueness of tourism experiences. Sustainability is more than just the environment as the socio-cultural efforts along with the economy are equally vital. Smart tourism can be used to revive traditions and cultural heritage sustainably, improve communal infrastructures, and use cultural heritage for new creativity. For instance, the National Museum of Copenhagen, Denmark developed a chatbot in assisting visitors to experience the museum in a new way by giving an overview of the many possibilities that the museum offers, which was previously unknown. In addition to answering questions, the chatbot also serves as an interactive and digital guide (EU, 2022). Another example is the 'This is Athens with a Local', which is a digital open platform that aims to connect tourists with a community of local volunteers. The purpose is to introduce Athens to tourists in a new way and to new places that are not presented in official tourist guides. In the process, the locals and the tourists can learn from each other while taking a stroll around the locals' neighbourhood (Athens Development and Destination Management Agency SA, 2022; EU, 2022).

Furthermore, González-Reverté (2019) stresses that Smart Tourism Destination seeks to transform the tourism experiences, facilitate the co-creation process of communication in the destination, and enhance the competitiveness of a destination. It is therefore not surprising that much attention on Smart Tourism Destinations has been devoted to developed economies due to the availability of ICT facilities and technologies to facilitate such a process. Thus, many destinations particularly in developing economies have yet to fully explore the benefits of smart tourism. At the same time, many have realised that this is a way to build a more resilient and sustainable future, particularly due to the blow that tourism has suffered from the pandemic.

- Thought points: What are some of the challenges in developing destinations into Smart Tourism Destinations? Evaluate whether there are some destinations or cities that would benefit more from the smart tourism initiative than others.

Smart Tools and Tourism Experiences

Buhalis (2022) argues that the need for smart tourism technologies and the digitalisation of the industry is much attributed to the desire for memorable experiences. The digital tools thus help tourists to view their experiences in multiple ways and assist them to personalise and access content and information with ease. With the help of various ICT tools, including smartphones and wearable devices such as smartwatches and other equipment that are either used on a daily based or easily accessible, tourism experiences are transformed (Bouchon, 2022). According to Buonincontri and Micera (2016), the usage of smart tourism-related technologies improves the entire tourist experience by encouraging active engagement, interactions among tourists, between the tourist and the tourism provider as well as the sharing of experiences. For instance, tourism providers that integrate smart technologies and solutions, such as virtual reality (VR) and augmented reality (AR) to capture tourism destinations uniquely, play an important role in this context. Previous studies on VR tourism have centralised on providing memorable and unique experiences without tourists being physically present at the destination (Merkx & Nawijn, 2021). This is particularly relevant during the pandemic or for some reason travellers are unable to physically travel to a destination, including people with disabilities or senior citizens with mobility issues. In such a sense, such smart solutions remove physical barriers and promote inclusiveness and accessibility for all travellers regardless of their physical state and impairments such as mobility, visual, auditory, and cognitive challenges (Buhalis, 2022). Thus, due to technological development, the development of tourism activities and products is now intertwined with space usage and the digitalisation of space (Bouchon, 2022).

Moreover, VR can also be used as an effective marketing tool for tourism destinations and companies. With tourism being essentially a service industry where service is a performance and not an object or goods, which can be seen, felt, tasted, touched, or tested (Kandampully, 2007) before the actual purchase, VR has opened up many possibilities. This is especially useful when potential travellers wish to explore the destination and its amenities such as hotels, restaurants, and other activities before physically arriving at the location. Moreover, during and post-visits, Chung et al. (2018) stress that the perceived advantages and aesthetics of VR and AR technology impact consumers' satisfaction with its usage when the experiences with the smart tourism technologies are positive. This leads to influencing their attitude in a positive way towards a destination and increasing the intention to revisit a destination in the future as well as positive word-of-mouth. Other than VR and AR, it is also important to have the right technological equipment to capture high-quality images and High-Definition videos. This is where drones come into play as they are considered some of the greatest technologies and solutions to present tourism attractions on aerial video and photographs to intensify emotions when special view and unusual perspective are captured (Ilkhanizadeh et al., 2020; UASLogic, 2016). Drones can also be used to provide live-stream experiences for tourists (Ilkhanizadeh et al., 2020).

In addition, the rise of sharing economy has also undoubtedly increased many 'new' types of services in a destination. The most prominent ones include Uber and Airbnb. Such services have evidently promoted smart tourism at a destination level, which all contribute to the overall satisfaction and experience with the destination. That is, however, when the technology is working as it should and tourists feel that they can use the technology with ease and enjoyment.

- Thought points: What are other digital games using VR and AR technologies that can change tourism experiences? In what other ways can digital games influence the tourism experience?

Is It All Fun and Game?

(Over-) Reliance on Technology

Smart tourism is dependent on the Internet and the Internet of Everything (IoE) to work. IoE is understood as a digital ecosystem consisting of networked connection of devices, people, data, processes, applications, and things (Porter & Heppelmann, 2014). For this to work seamlessly, smart systems need to be able to communicate with each other. Challenges during this Internet of Things (IoT) era are that numerous smart solutions are developed and created by many different providers and actors. These systems often do not communicate with each other (Mei & Slettli, 2022). This leads to multiple technologies and solutions available but there are difficulties in integrating these by creating positive synergy. Resource wastages are thus created while not achieving the ideal efficiency. As with all technologies in general as well as with the Internet in general, not everything is positive. While the negative sides of smart solutions are raising, including the loss of privacy and surveillance issues, Mehraliyev et al. (2020) argue that these are often downplayed. Moreover, another negative impact of smart tourism tools includes the promotion of addiction and isolation thereby self-estrangement (Merkx & Nawijn, 2021; Tribe & Mkono, 2017). This challenges the whole purpose of experiencing positive and hedonic feelings whilst on holiday. As discussed previously, should the tourists using the technology not finding it to be easy to use or have a sense of control leading to stressfulness, it will negatively affect their satisfaction and experience. When technology is no longer able to significantly enhance both peoples' daily lives and tourism experiences, smart tourism may be questioned (Kontogianni & Alepis, 2020).

Impact on Other Stakeholders

Buhalis (2022) argues that although there is great potential due to the development and the importance of such technological advancement in developing smart tourism, not everyone can benefit from this. Tourists as one of the major stakeholders will be able to transform their experiences through smart solutions as agents. It is, however, not sure how all stakeholders at the destination can benefit from such development. Moreover, when digital technologies provided the platforms for the introduction of 'new' economies such as Airbnb and Uber as discussed, so were many social consequences. Related to Airbnb and other similar online accommodation platforms, competition in the local real estate market leads to the feeling of over-tourism (Pasquinelli & Trunfio, 2020) as well as driving up the real estate prices in the destination. Similarly, Uber and car booking services have been criticised for the adverse effects on the earnings of traditional workers in the taxi industry as well as increased pollution and road congestion (Berger et al., 2018). Other social aspects include the role played by technology in changing the relationship between tourists, residents, and the destination itself have also received less attention (Bouchon, 2022). Moreover, while one of the aims of a Smart Tourism Destination is sustainability, the balance of such is difficult to achieve. The usage of social media to share tourism experiences has become a norm in the digital age. Some destinations may face unexpected fame and instant attention and the following consequences and issues of over-tourism and carrying capacity, leading to tension between the residents and tourists (Wall, 2020).

- Thought points: With this heavy reliance on technology and the Internet, what other issues may arise apart from the points discussed above? How can smart tourism and Smart Tourism Destinations be further developed to benefit all stakeholders beyond tourists?

Case Study of the Island of Borneo and the State of Sabah

As discussed, studies on Smart Tourism Destinations are still in their infancy and the majority of the development has been initiated in developed economies where smart tourism initiatives are supported and encouraged by the EU. With the increased technological advancement in developing countries and the realisation of how smart tools can facilitate and enhance tourists' overall experiences in a destination in a seamless manner, many 'new' Smart Tourism Destinations can be created. The case study of this chapter centres on the island of Borneo, which is the third-largest island in the world and the largest one in Asia. Politically divided between three countries, Indonesia controls around 73 per cent of the island, whereas the East Malaysian states of Sabah and Sarawak make up around 26 per cent of the island in the north. Brunei, a sovereign state on Borneo's north coast, accounts for around 1 per cent of the island's land area. Whereas some collaboration between the three countries' tourism boards exists, the general tourism efforts are separated. Nevertheless, there are other types of collaborations such as The Brunei Darussalam–Indonesia–Malaysia–Philippines East ASEAN Growth Area (BIMP-EAGA). Although not specifically focused on tourism, the industry also benefits from such cooperation, which aims to develop remote and less-developed areas in the four participating Southeast Asian countries (Brunei Darussalam–Indonesia–Malaysia–Philippines East ASEAN Growth Area [BIMP-EAGA], 2022b).

Tourism in Sabah

The Malaysian state of Sabah with Kota Kinabalu as its capital city is located in north Borneo with a border with the Brunei and its capital city of Bandar Seri Begawan (refer to Figure 12.1). The state of Sabah is one of its most popular tourism destinations with approximately 4.2 million visitors (1.5 million international and 2.7 million domestic) in total pre-pandemic (Sabah Tourism, 2020). One of the reasons for its popularity is due to the iconic Mount Kinabalu, standing at 4,095 meters above sea level. Climbing Mount Kinabalu as well as taking on the Summit Trail are popular activities. Located merely 90 kilometres from Kota Kinabalu, the city with its international airport is thus used as the main starting point for those interested in Mount Kinabalu and surrounding attractions. Kota Kinabalu is nevertheless a popular and attractive destination by itself with its culturally diverse population, proximity to islands and beaches and notable national parks. In addition, its heritage and culture are showcased in museums and art galleries, cultural villages, local markets, and many notable landmarks such as the majestic floating mosque (Sabah Tourism, 2022).

Sabah and Smart Tourism

As discussed at the beginning of this chapter, Malaysia has put smart tourism on the Smart Tourism 4.0 agenda for tourism recovery post-pandemic and its future development. The purpose of such an initiative is to improve the industry by making use of technological innovations. The aim is to enhance tourist experiences, boost the countries' overall competitiveness, and also promoting sustainability through ecotourism (MIDA, 2021). While Smart Tourism 4.0 is not specifically focused on Borneo or Kota Kinabalu, the focus of such an initiative on a national level also leads to other states and cities in Malaysia being able to head in this

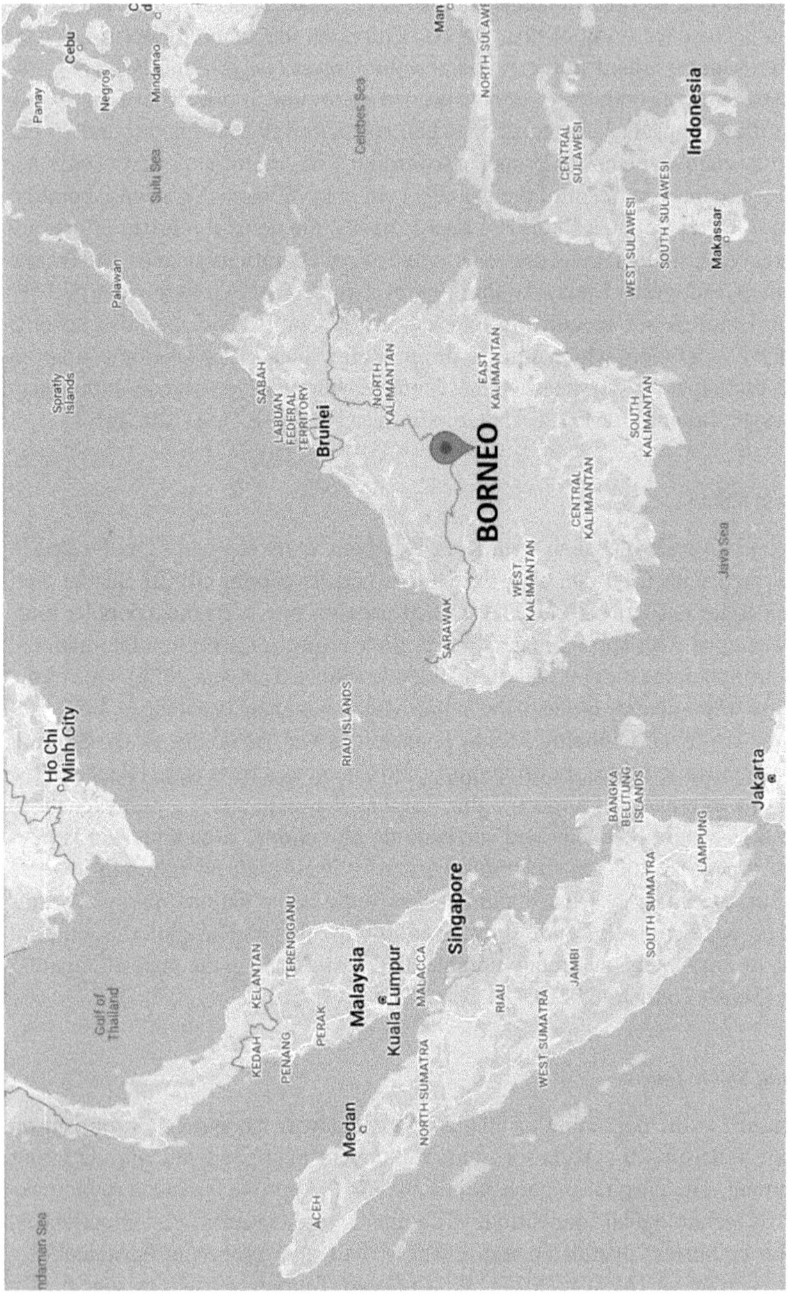

Figure 12.1 Map of Borneo Island

Source: Adapted from Google (2023)

direction. Moreover, Sabah also launched its Smart Sabah 2030 initiative in 2021 with the aim of digitalisation of Sabah (The State Government of Sabah, 2022). This indicates that digitalisation, smart solutions, innovation, and technology are on its agenda for the future development of the state. While the overall ecosystem of Smart Tourism is still in its infancy and the integration of smart technologies and solution remain to be developed, some key smart solutions already exist.

Car Booking Service

For any tourists visiting a destination, accessibility and transportation are vital. When Uber launched its services, it revolutionised the taxi and car transportation industry. Since then, many similar services and companies have established their foothold in respective countries and markets. In Southeast Asia and Sabah, it is Grab. Grab decided to launch its services in Kota Kinabalu in 2016 due to the city's significant number of both local and international tourists annually (Grab, 2016). From being a taxi booking service, Grab now also provides food, courier, and grocery delivery services much attributed to and fuelled by the pandemic where such services were highly sought after. Nevertheless, its taxi booking service remains the largest part of its operation. Tourists wishing to travel from one place to another can simply download the app, connect various payment types to the app, and then start the booking. The app shows in real time where the driver is located, the name and picture of the driver, registration number, make and model, and colour of the car.

In addition, the app also integrates a message function, and voice and video call options should the driver and customer need to communicate before the arrival of the driver. There is no cash involved and the price is fixed and pre-determined, providing additional comfort and control for the customer. Grab is now widely available throughout Sabah, but challenges are experienced in more remote areas where the Internet connection is poor. As other authors have discussed, such type of sharing economy has disrupted the tourism industry and changed tourism experiences (Berger et al., 2018). Tourists have now more options by assuming much of the control and reducing stressful situations related to mobility and accessibility to attractions and facilities in the destination. In such a sense, their time and spending can be redistributed to other parts of the destination's activities and experiences. At the same time, this also contributes to enhancing the experience economy in destinations, especially in places where the public transportation system is inefficient (Park et al., 2021). Moreover, such development also benefits the locals as this service is also largely used by residents. However, there are also some negative impacts related to such sharing economy as discussed previously in regard to Uber. Some additional challenges may include possible communication problems between the driver and tourists, and the accuracy of the locations as it is dependent on the GPS positioning. The ability of the driver to provide excellent services not only in form of bringing the passengers from point A to point B but also serving as a tour guide in promoting or informing about the destination will evidently impact the overall tourism experiences. However, there are some negative issues reported that are similar to other examples of services within the sharing economy, and additional challenges, including questionable data storage and privacy issues as well as sudden and additional surge charges on short rides (Gutierres, 2022). Overall, the popularity of the service indicates that many are still willing to use the service due to its significant benefits, especially in destinations where public transportation system is still challenged.

Nature Conservation through Drones

Digital innovation has changed how nature conservation takes place. Sabah has nine protected parks that sprawl over 1.21 million hectares in the northern part of Borneo. Managing these parks is a challenging task. Through BIMP-EAGA as mentioned previously, smart technology is being used to monitor Sabah's nature and its protected national parks (BIMP-EAGA, 2022a). Using satellites and drones, it is possible to prevent incidents, such as deforestation, illegal poaching, bush fire, and harmful algal blooms as well as using technology to monitor water quality. Moreover, such 'digital conservation' comprises five pivotal dimensions, including data on nature, data on people, data integration and analysis, communication and experience, and participatory governance (Arts et al., 2015). Such tools also contribute to monitor the carrying capacity of the protected areas and may serve as a guide to manage crowds should that become an issue. This is not only important for tourists but also to improve the life and livelihood of the locals living in and nearby the parks. Protecting and conserving nature for the future while improving the life of residents are some of the key goals of smart tourism (Mehraliyev et al., 2020). Nevertheless, as discussed above, while the initial goal of such technology has good intentions, such type of surveillance may also be misused and thus criticised by many. For instance, conservation surveillance technologies not only collect data on nature and its changes but also on human activities, which raises issues about the infringement of privacy and civil liberties (Simlai & Sandbrook, 2021). The usage of technologies, including data storage and security, must therefore be considered and evaluated when developing this further.

Conclusion

While various destinations have adopted smart technologies and smart tourism in various stages and ways, it is logical that all destinations have some elements of smartness. The question is how much innovation and technologies are used to improve the livelihood of the residents while creating attractive and competitive destinations for tourists sustainably. Smaller destinations with a fragile ecosystem that experience overnight fame may face significant challenges as well as larger destinations due to uncritical uses of destination spaces leading to carry capacity issues (Bouchon, 2022). Destinations, whether small or large, must thus be proactive and realise the impact of such smart solutions both positive and negative.

Borneo Island and Sabah still have a long way to go to be considered as 'smart' or a comprehensive Smart Tourism Destination. Since Smart Tourism Destination needs to have a sound digital ecosystem that links all IoE seamlessly and is accessible to all stakeholders, it is a complex process. Nevertheless, illustrated by the case of Kota Kinabalu and its surrounding cities and attractions as well as digital nature conservation, certain innovative and cutting-edge enterprises such as Grab and drone technology have opened many possibilities. There is evidence that much of the ICT development, services, and facilities that exist at present may well have already positively transformed tourism experiences. Such development is in line with the Malaysian national government's ambition of Smart Tourism 4.0, and The Government of Sabah's Smart Sabah 2023 initiative. The two cases demonstrate that Sabah has the facilities, the willpower, and the technology to further develop these elements that are essential in a Smart Tourism Destination in the future. As illustrated, integrating smart technologies can provide quality services such as accessibility through efficient transportation and effective management and conservation of protected nature areas. This in turn leads to positive and memorable experiences for tourists who visit the destination and is a great contributor to the experience economy in the long run and for future visitors. It can also be assumed that such development also benefits the locals by improving their quality of life and creating an excellent city for them to live in and a great destination for tourists.

Further Questions

- In what ways can the development of technology and smart solutions be negative for sustainability and the environment?
- What are some other additional negative impacts of smart tourism on tourism providers and tourists that may arise?
- How can developing economies use innovation and smart solutions to fast-pace their development into Smart Tourism Destinations?
- What are the elements that make some destinations more successful in adopting smart tourism than others?

Further Readings

Benckendorff, P., Xiang, Z. & Sheldon, P.J. (2019), *Tourism information technology* (3rd ed.). CABI.

Boes, K., Buhalis, D., & Inversini, A. (2016). Smart tourism destinations: Ecosystems for tourism destination competitiveness. *International Journal of Tourism Cities*, *2*(2), 108–124.

Della Corte, V., D'Andrea, C., Savastano, I., & Zamparelli, P. (2017). Smart cities and destination management: Impacts and opportunities for tourism competitiveness. *European Journal of Tourism Research*, *17*, 7–27.

Gretzel, U., Sigala, M., Xiang, Z. & Koo, C. (2015), Smart tourism: Foundations and developments. *Electronic Markets*, *25*(3), 179–188.

Shafiee, S., Rajabzadeh Ghatari, A., Hasanzadeh, A. & Jahanyan, S. (2019), Developing a model for sustainable smart tourism destinations: A systematic review. *Tourism Management Perspectives*, *31*, 287–300.

References

Arts, K., van der Wal, R., & Adams, W. M. (2015). Digital technology and the conservation of nature. *Ambio*, *44*(4), 661–673. https://doi.org/10.1007/s13280-015-0705-1

Athens Development and Destination Management Agency SA. (2022). *Experience the real Athens*. Athens Development and Destination Management Agency SA. Retrieved October 18 from https://www.thisisathens.org/withalocal/node/2

Berger, T., Chen, C., & Frey, C. B. (2018). Drivers of disruption? Estimating the Uber effect. *European Economic Review*, *110*, 197–210. https://doi.org/10.1016/j.euroecorev.2018.05.006

Brunei Darussalam–Indonesia–Malaysia–Philippines East ASEAN Growth Area (BIMP-EAGA). (2022a). *How Sabah is using smart technology to protect nature*. BIMP-EAGA. https://bimp-eaga.asia/article/how-sabah-using-smart-technology-protect-nature

Brunei Darussalam–Indonesia–Malaysia–Philippines East ASEAN Growth Area (BIMP-EAGA). (2022b). *What is BIMP-EAGA?* https://bimp-eaga.asia/index.php/about-bimp-eaga/what-bimp-eaga

Bouchon, F. (2022). Smart tourism destination. In D. Buhalis (Ed.), *Encyclopedia of tourism management and marketing* (pp. 127–130). Edward Elgar Publishing. https://doi.org/10.4337/9781800377486.smart.tourism.destination

Buhalis, D. (2022). Smart tourism. In D. Buhalis (Ed.), *Encyclopedia of tourism management and marketing* (pp. 124–127). Edward Elgar Publishing. https://doi.org/10.4337/9781800377486

Buhalis, D., & Amaranggana, A. (2015). Smart tourism destinations enhancing tourism experience through personalisation of services. In I. Tussyadiah & A. Inversini (Eds.), *Information and communication technologies in tourism 2015* (pp. 377–389). Springer.

Buonincontri, P., & Micera, R. (2016). The experience co-creation in smart tourism destinations: A multiple case analysis of European destinations. *Information Technology & Tourism*, *16*(3), 285–315. https://doi.org/10.1007/s40558-016-0060-5

Caragliu, A., Del Bo, C., & Nijkamp, P. (2011). Smart cities in Europe. *Journal of Urban Technology*, *18*(2), 65–82. https://doi.org/10.1080/10630732.2011.601117

Chung, N., Lee, H., Kim, J.-Y., & Koo, C. (2018). The role of augmented reality for experience-influenced environments: The case of cultural heritage tourism in Korea. *Journal of Travel Research*, *57*(5), 627–643. https://doi.org/10.1177/0047287517708255

Dictionary. (2012). *Smart*. https://www.dictionary.com/browse/smart

EU (European Union). (2019). *European capital of smart tourism 2019*. European Union.

EU (European Union). (2022). *Leading examples of smart tourism practices in Europe*. European Commission. Retrieved October 18 from https://smart-tourism-capital.ec.europa.eu/leading-examples-smart-tourism-practices-europe_en

González-Reverté, F. (2019). Building sustainable smart destinations: An approach based on the development of Spanish smart tourism plans. *Sustainability*, *11*(23), 6874.

Google. (2023). *Borneo – Google My Maps*. Retrieved February 20 from https://www.google.com/maps/d/u/0/viewer?mid=1lMoRqMH--041nAQbXkQKJrA9P4Q&hl=en&ll=3.794373312753071%2C114.351196&z=7

Grab. (2016). *Grab expands GrabCar services to Malacca and Kota Kinabalu*. https://www.grab.com/my/press/consumers-drivers/grabcar-in-malacca-kk/

Gutierres, D. (2022, December 7). Grab admits fare surges but insists compliance with LTFRB guidelines. *Inquirer*. https://newsinfo.inquirer.net/1702309/grab-admits-fare-surges-but-insists-compliance-with-ltfrb-guidelines#ixzz7sp9PYb6w

Halim, H. S. (2022). Exploring information technology in smart tourism in Indonesia. In A. Hassan (Ed.), *Handbook of technology application in tourism in Asia* (pp. 471–489). Springer Nature Singapore. https://doi.org/10.1007/978-981-16-2210-6_22

Ilkhanizadeh, S., Golabi, M., Hesami, S., & Rjoub, H. (2020). The potential use of drones for tourism in crises: A facility location analysis perspective. *Journal of Risk and Financial Management, 13*(10), 246. https://www.mdpi.com/1911-8074/13/10/246

Kandampully, J. (2007). *Services management: The new paradigm in hospitality.* Pearson Prentice Hall.

Kastenholz, E., Eusébio, C., Figueiredo, E., & Lima, J. (2012). Accessibility as competitive advantage of a tourism destination: The case of Lousã. In K. F. Hyde, C. Ryan, & A. G. Woodside (Eds.), *Field guide to case study research in tourism, hospitality and leisure* (Vol. 6, pp. 369–385). Emerald Group Publishing Limited. https://doi.org/10.1108/S1871-3173(2012)0000006023

Kontogianni, A., & Alepis, E. (2020). Smart tourism: State of the art and literature review for the last six years. *Array, 6,* 100020.

Li, Y., Hu, C., Huang, C., & Duan, L. (2017). The concept of smart tourism in the context of tourism information services. *Tourism Management, 58,* 293–300. https://doi.org/10.1016/j.tourman.2016.03.014

Lopes, R. O., Malik, O. A., Kumpoh, A. A.-Z. A., Keasberry, C., Hong, O. W., Lee, S. C. W., & Liu, Y. (2019). *Exploring digital architectural heritage in Brunei Darussalam: Towards heritage safeguarding, smart tourism, and interactive education.* 2019 IEEE Fifth International Conference on Multimedia Big Data (BigMM).

Mehraliyev, F., Chan, I. C. C., Choi, Y., Koseoglu, M. A., & Law, R. (2020). A state-of-the-art review of smart tourism research. *Journal of Travel & Tourism Marketing, 37*(1), 78–91. https://doi.org/10.1080/10548408.2020.1712309

Mei, X. Y., & Slettli, V. K. (2022). Smart City (SC) initiative and urban development in rural regions of Inland Norway: A link missing? In *Smart cities, citizen welfare, and the implementation of sustainable development goals* (pp. 62–82). IGI Global.

Merkx, C., & Nawijn, J. (2021). Virtual reality tourism experiences: Addiction and isolation. *Tourism Management, 87,* 104394. https://doi.org/10.1016/j.tourman.2021.104394

MIDA (Malaysian Investment Development Authority). (2021). *Smart tourism: Future of tourism in Malaysia.* https://www.mida.gov.my/smart-tourism-future-of-tourism-in-malaysia/

Park, S. Y., Kim, J., & Pan, B. (2021). The influence of Uber on the tourism industry in sub-Saharan Africa. *Journal of Travel Research, 60*(7), 1598–1611. https://doi.org/10.1177/0047287520951638

Pasquinelli, C., & Trunfio, M. (2020). Reframing urban overtourism through the smart- city lens. *Cities, 102,* 102729. https://doi.org/10.1016/j.cities.2020.102729

Porter, M. E., & Heppelmann, J. E. (2014). How smart, connected products are transforming competition. *Harvard Business Review, 92*(11), 64–88.

Sabah Tourism. (2020). *Sabah: Visitors arrival by Nationality 2020.* https://www.sabahtourism.com/assets/uploads/visitor-2020.pdf

Sabah Tourism. (2022). *Sabah tourism.* https://www.sabahtourism.com/

Simlai, T., & Sandbrook, C. (2021). Digital surveillance technologies in conservation and their social implications. In S. Wich & A. Piel (Eds.), *Conservation technology* (pp. 239–249). Oxford University Press.

The State Government of Sabah. (2022). *Smart Sabah.* Sabah Chief Minister's Office Retrieved February 10 from https://www.smartsabahcorporation.com/

Tribe, J., & Mkono, M. (2017). Not such smart tourism? The concept of e-lienation. *Annals of Tourism Research, 66,* 105–115. https://doi.org/10.1016/j.annals.2017.07.001

UASLogic. (2016). *Using drones for tourism.* Retrieved February 10 from https://www.uaslogic.com/drones-for-tourism.html

Wall, G. (2020). From carrying capacity to overtourism: A perspective article. *Tourism Review*, *75*(1), 212–215. https://doi.org/10.1108/TR-08-2019-0356

Wang, D., Li, X., & Li, Y. (2013). China's "smart tourism destination" initiative: A taste of the service-dominant logic. *Journal of Destination Marketing & Management*, *2*(2), 59–61. https://doi.org/10.1016/j.jdmm.2013.05.004

Wang, D., Xiang, Z., & Fesenmaier, D. R. (2016). Smartphone use in everyday life and travel. *Journal of Travel Research*, *55*(1), 52–63. https://doi.org/10.1177/0047287514535847

13 The Role of Instagram for More Sustainable Tourism Experiences

Monica A. Breiby, Sofie Kjendlie Selvaag, Hogne Øian, Merethe Lerfald, Birgitta Ericsson, and Windy Kester Moe

Introduction

There is an increasing focus on tourism research on sustainability and regenerative tourism for more resilient destinations (e.g., Becken & Kaur, 2021). The literature has turned its attention to the concept of sustainable experiences as a means of obtaining competitive advantages for tourist destinations and enabling sustainable development (Kastenholz et al., 2016). A sustainable experience in tourism can be defined as an experience that raises deep, meaningful emotions and memories that may encourage tourists' contribution toward destination sustainability (Breiby et al., 2020). Hence, it is imperative for destination management and marketing organisations (DMMOs) to find ways of including tourists as active contributors in the processes of branding and designing destinations (Cabiddu et al., 2014). Social media can be useful in such a way, therefore analyses of the use of social media and its influence on tourist behaviour have until now been most common.

It is widely recognised that travel decision-making has changed profoundly due to the Internet and the use of social media. Associated interactive and global technological tools provide new means of travel information in terms of searching, sharing, and experiencing places. Individuals can produce content information about travelling by themselves that is available to everybody. This collaborative phenomenon is called user-generated content (UGC), which has a growing influence on all stages of travel, pre-, during-, and post-trip (Iglesias-Sánchez et al., 2020; Marine-Roig & Clavé, 2015). There is a growing range of social media platforms relying on UGC, but 'Instagram' is still among the most popular ones. This is a visual platform based on users posting and sharing photos, videos, and stories. The popularity of Instagram may also be linked back to the tourist 'gaze' (Urry, 1990) and tourists' search for visual stimuli.

Increased use of social media has resulted in more self-objectivising tourism as tourists visit spectacular attractions with the main goal of taking selfies (Canavan, 2017; Lyu, 2016). Visitors exploring a destination to a greater extent may cause sustainability problems, such as giving more uneven and low economic impacts, increasing pollution, and negative impacts on nature resulting from crowding (e.g., the destinations of Trolltunga, Besseggen, and Lofoten in Norway) (Gössling et al., 2018). On the other hand, the UGC from digital platforms can be used in branding

DOI: 10.4324/9781003335924-17

and experience design processes to increase tourists' and residents' perceived experience value and their sustainable behaviour (e.g., by purchasing local food, guided hiking tours, and other local products and services).

It has been argued that collaboration is the basic idea behind sharing of images, whereby people use images to learn something together in one of several ways. Notably, as scholars increasingly work with Instagram as a digitised research tool, it is important not only to consider the analysis *of photos* uploaded by users to Instagram (Harper, 2012). Equally, we suggest how the application of Instagram may be used to mobilise and create alternative spaces of visual tourism *collaboration with others*, by possibly unravelling a series of variations in expressions, interpretations, and engagements within an area. We also highlight *analyses by others*, by inviting people to be part of a voyage of discovery to a destination (#ourmjosa). Thus, the aim of this chapter is twofold. First, we explore how UGC can be revealed by using different tools, techniques, and methods for analysing Instagram pictures. Second, we ask how these new insights can contribute to more sustainable experiences.

Using a lowland lake-based destination in South-Eastern Norway as the case for the empirical study, we conducted an experiment using Instagram. With the aim of mobilising and obtaining UGC from the perspectives of tourists, second homeowners, and residents, we created a hashtag exclusively for this research purpose. Both a traditional content analysis and an additional collaborative workshop with students were facilitated to explore the potential of inviting others into the processes of analysing and interpreting Instagram pictures. The next section presents a review of key concepts related to sustainable experiences, UGC from Instagram, and visual tourism collaboration. Then the methodology and context of the study are presented. Finally, we compare and discuss the results from the different methods.

Literature Review

Sharing Sustainable Experiences on Social Media

Consumer behaviour has arguably undergone three recent shifts; from material purchases to immaterial experiences, from signalling wealth and status through consumption to signalling self-identity, and to state consumption visibility because of the rise of social media (Bronner and de Hoog, 2019). Social media allows users to construct a self-image and identity to communicate with the wider online community. There is now substantial literature on how users are motivated to use the platforms for self-construction (see Cohen et al., 2022). Sharing travel experiences on social media has become ubiquitous, and doing so may gratify social needs, for self-expression and communication (Liu et al., 2019). At the same time, the Internet has become an increasingly visual medium, wherein individuals tend toward images rather than textual descriptions to express themselves, as in the case of Instagram. Instagram affords 'a style of "you could be here with me photography ..." that invites the viewer to imagine themselves in the frame' (Zappavigna, 2016, p. 272).

The social visibility of travel consumption has been significantly enhanced in the era of social media (So et al., 2018). This contrasts with the past when postcards were the primary way of communicating holiday experiences (Bronner and de Hoog, 2019). It has been argued that holidays are in principle socially visible and are at least partially chosen for the role they can play in signalling identity and values. Users can share luxury, highly exclusive, and extremely expensive travel experiences (see e.g. Lai et al., 2020). But they can also share cheaper and more sustainable travel experiences to visualise their values and care for the environment. It is worth drawing attention to how users can place stress on the aspects that destinations would want to emphasise to differentiate themselves as sustainable destination. Sustainable destinations are a priority in European policies, but 'to attract the attention of tourists they require a holistic management perspective, a long-term process, and stakeholders' involvement' (Iglesias-Sánchez et al., 2020, p. 3). Sustainability is nowadays considered to be one of the most strategic elements in the differentiation between destinations (Iglesias-Sánchez et al., 2020). A sustainable experience in tourism can be defined as an experience that raises deep, meaningful emotions and memories that may encourage tourists' contribution toward destination sustainability (e.g., longer stays, shorter travel distances, and pro-environmental behaviour). This may be fostered by the tourist's interaction with the natural and cultural environment, and contextual activities (Breiby et al., 2020).

Taylor (2020) points to the power of user-generated social media content in influencing others' evaluation and selection of travel destinations. As such, the vicarious consumption of travel has become critical to the travel industry because of its leading to the patronage of destinations (Marder et al., 2019). Shared experiences on social media can thus provide a window into changes in tourism behaviour and travel desires. For example, Conti and Cassel (2020) and Conti and Lexhagen (2020) investigated the intersections between social media and nature-based tourism experiences by looking at Instagram pictures. These studies illustrated how social media can relate to and shape tourism spatiality, tourist identities, and place-making by exploring the role of user-generated online photography content in creating experience value in nature-based tourism. Despite this, Instagram has to date been used timidly by tourism researchers and its exploitation as a visual data source has been limited (Chen et al., 2023) and a limited number of studies have explored the destination images created by DMMOs and how these images correspond with the images by the visitors (Egger et al., 2022). Hence, it is imperative for DMMOs to find ways of including tourists as active contributors in the processes of branding and designing destinations (Cabiddu et al., 2014). One way of doing this is by obtaining UGC with the travellers on Instagram. The rise of social media has led to the co-creation of destinations' images by, among others, the DMMOs on the supply-side and the visitors on the demand-side (Chu, 2020), and according to Thevenot (2007), this has empowered the visitors.

- Thought point: How has the increased use of social media changed the behaviour of tourists and the choice of a destination?

User-Generated Content from Instagram

Social media has radically changed the way people travel. Tourists become potentially interested in destinations at a worldwide level (Iglesias-Sánchez et al., 2020). Associated interactive and global technological tools provide new means of travel information, in terms of searching, sharing, and enjoying trips. Social media is a push factor to promote destinations and its impact on branding has been highlighted. In this framework, individuals can produce content information about their travels that is available to everybody and made searchable by the hashtag (Nautiyal et al., 2022). This collaborative phenomenon is called UGC, which has a growing influence on all stages of travel, pre-, during-, and post-trip (Iglesias-Sánchez et al., 2020; Marine-Roig & Clavé, 2015).

It is worth drawing attention to how UGC can place stress on the aspects that destinations would want to differentiate themselves as s sustainable destination. Tourists play a key role because their perceptions and experiences also influence the destination's image. Hence, UGC should be analysed because sustainability has been transforming and redefining tourism in recent years. Through social media, UGC can contribute to co-creation and reinforce the links between tourist regions and their positioning as sustainable destinations. Economic, social, and environmental dimensions are key tools for positioning, differentiating, and promoting a tourist destination (Hernández et al., 2016). Given that co-creation is a practice of collaborative product development by firms and consumers, it can contribute to a destination's image of feelings, contents, etc. by actors associated with the region: tourists, companies, the local community, etc. 'The experience is the brand. The brand is co-created and evolves with experiences' (Prahalad & Ramaswamy, 2004).

Since its launch in 2010, Instagram has quickly risen in prominence among millennials to become one of the world's most popular social media platforms with more than 1 billion users globally (Cohen et al., 2022). In brief, Instagram is a free visual social media platform based on users posting and sharing content in the form of photos, videos, and stories. Instagram imagery can be supplemented and categorised by adding hashtags and geo-tag locations to describe contexts, emotions, and opinions. Hashtags are a form of user-generated tagging used on microblogging sites such as Instagram. It is also possible to add hearts as likes and commentary fields, creating opportunities for engagement with and among users.

Users search for unique experiences, and they are informed of opportunities for this by reviews uploaded by others on Instagram. According to Iglesas-Sánchez et al. (2020, p.4) 'Written, visual, audio-visual, or mixed posts are in constant demand …' and 'An understanding of how and why users feel motivated to generate content and, consequently, promote the attractiveness of destinations requires further exploration'. Iglesas-Sánchez et al. (2020) further refer to how Seraj (2012) highlights three components that trigger activity in social media: intellectual value stemming from co-creation, the social value from social ties established in communities, and cultural value, which justifies image sharing in the decision-making process. Thus, Instagram has become a strategic support for advertising, promotion, marketing, and providing information. DMMOs should not miss the chance to utilise UGC. The relative novelty of Instagram makes it necessary for scholars to examine its potential. To date, studies in this area have mainly drawn on Trip Advisor. The process of promotion through Instagram is complex and different from that of other social media. Thus, a study focusing on Instagram using different methods and analysis for UGC from tourists contributes to this field.

Analyses of Instagram show that its users visually and statically (virtually a snapshot) document a range of consumption activities frequently associated with fashion, cars, food, holidays, and landscapes, often through staged and manipulated 'selfies'. These are photos they have taken of themselves, usually with a smartphone (Lyu, 2016). Furthermore, we suggest that the features of the Instagram application facilitate for dynamic use, which provides opportunities for mobilising and creating alternative spaces of visual tourism *collaboration with others*. This, in turn, may result in the unravelling of a series of variations in expressions, interpretations, and engagements with and within an area (Harper, 2012). To sum up, the literature review underlines that it is worth drawing attention to how UGC can influence the development of sustainable experiences at a tourism destination (Iglesias-Sánchez et al., 2020). Instagram and its exploitation as a visual data source has until recently been limited (Chen et al., 2023). Hence, the aim of this chapter is twofold. First, we explore how UGC can be revealed by using different tools, techniques, and methods for analysing Instagram pictures. Second, we ask how these new insights can contribute to more sustainable experiences.

- Thought point: How can UGC from social media contribute to more sustainable travel?

Case, Materials, and Methods

In a case study from a tourism destination in South-Eastern Norway, Mjøsa – a lowland lake-based destination, we conducted an Instagram experiment. The destination was included in the research project 'Sustainable experiences in tourism'. The case is justified by the representativeness of the tourism sector in terms of sustainable tourism development (social, environmental, and economic). The destination Mjøsa extends across rich cultural and natural landscapes, including cultural heritage surrounded by three towns with sizeable trade and service sectors, and significant volumes of realised and potential all-year tourism. Moreover, this rural region has a long history of domestic tourism. In the summer months of June–August 2017 for instance, the total number of commercial guest nights at hotels and cabins was 1.5 million (Statistics Norway, 2018) of which 70 per cent was generated by Norwegians and 30 per cent by international visitors (June–August).

It is important to acknowledge that analysing social media content requires serious consideration of privacy issues and ethical use. The data is generated by non-professional 'producers' who have submitted information that includes personal information as web content. This information is then often used by scholars for other purposes than the users originally intended (see, e.g., Kirilenko & Stepchenkova, 2014). Therefore, we created a unique hashtag exclusively for this research purpose and informed about that on Instagram. We then highlighted *analyses with others*, by inviting people to be part of a voyage of discovery to one specific destination (#ourmjosa). This included tourists, second homeowners, and residents, who are all classified as Instagram users in this study.

We used the prefix 'our' instead of 'my' so the user could choose a picture e.g., from a special place the user wanted to share with others and to invite Instagram users to participate in a co-creation of the experience of Mjøsa. All images were posted with their written content and the linked comments were analysed. A total of 469 Instagram posts were collected and saved into a Microsoft Word document for deeper analysis. The posts were then screened by the researchers to remove irrelevant posts. From this, several posts were removed during the data cleaning process for the following reasons: duplicates, videos, advertisement posts, and posts that contained unmeaningful information. As a result, 432 Instagram posts were used in the data analysis, which included both photos and captioned texts with emojis. The experiment lasted from April 2018 until December 2018 to encompass several seasons. The main reason for the chosen period was to include tourists whose presence is significant in the summer season, second-homeowners primarily present on holidays and weekends, and local residents present all year. According to the research aim, the user-generated pictures are analysed from two points of view: a traditional content analysis and a visual collaboration with students.

Content Analysis

According to Weber (1990), content analysis is useful for evaluating social media postings, as it allows scholars to draw inferences from text and/or visual information through a set of procedures. Content analysis is often used for photographs, as it makes it possible to study manifest content through the observable features of the images as well as latent content, examining additional items embedded in the message. The design of the evaluation sheet for content analysis was based on a validated work in the context of sustainable experiences (Breiby et al., 2020). This includes different sustainable experience dimensions such as (1) interaction with the natural environment, e.g., being close to the lake and experiencing a new landscape, (2) interaction with the cultural environment, e.g., farms with local food and beverage, old traditional buildings, (3) views and reflections, e.g., nice view to the lake, learn something new, and (4) contextual activities, e.g., paddling and swimming and different seasons during the year (see Table 13.1). It also includes different seasons such as spring, summer, autumn, and winter.

Visual Tourism Collaboration

A collaborative workshop was facilitated with students, to explore the potential of inviting others into the processes of analysing and interpreting Instagram photos. This may be potentially useful as a professional tool in a process of refining and sharpening the content substance. Hence, we advance the understanding of how different methods can be used to facilitate visual tourism collaboration and possibly contribute to new opportunities and expressions of sustainable tourism experiences. Within 3 hours, third-year BA students (six students) evoked a series

Table 13.1 General stats of the management of content by @ourmjosa: Sustainable experiences and seasons

Different seasons		*Sustainable experiences' dimensions (per cent)*				*Total*
	Post N	*Interaction with the natural environment*	*Interaction with the cultural environment*	*Views and reflections*	*Contextual activities*	
Spring (April–May)	80	24	11	25	40	100
Summer (June–August)	214	7	12	25	55	100
Autumn (September–October)	56	30	11	25	34	100
Winter (November–December)	82	9	28	40	23	100
Total	432					

of latent potentials around lake Mjøsa. They identified ways to understand and use Instagram 'stories' as invitations and engagement of locals and tourists for sustainable tourism development.

The students assisted the lecturer to arrange the room and laying out the printed Instagram stories (pictures and texts). Then the students walked around in silence for ten minutes to reflect on potential connections across the materials. Thereafter, they discussed and suggested possible common features suitable for separating experiences/emotions/'stories', such as different angles (watching Mjøsa from different angles), colours, and time of the day and season. Finally, the students decided that seasons best captured the stories from the connected materials. They organised the materials in four workstations after the dates noted: spring (April–May), summer (June–August), autumn (September–October), and winter (November–December). The lecturer walked from group to group and gave assistance in getting started or encouragement if required. At other points, the students needed one to challenge and question, or listen and acknowledge. Then they combined the four workstations and each of the students interpreted what they saw and gave the others feedback.

Results and Discussion

How Can Different Tools, Techniques, and Methods for Analysing Instagram Pictures Be Used to Co-Generate Content?

Content Analysis

Table 13.1 presents the results from the content analyses regarding different seasons and sustainable experience dimensions. 'Contextual activities' are the major experience, especially in summertime (55 pct), but also in spring and autumn. In the wintertime, not only 'Views and reflections' seem to dominate experiences, but also 'Interaction with the cultural environment' is highlighted in many of the pictures during winter. In addition to 'Contextual activities', both 'Views and reflections' and 'Interaction with the natural environment' score relatively high in the spring and autumn. These results also seem to confirm the validity of the framework of sustainable experience dimensions (Breiby et al., 2020) for the content analysis of Instagram posts in such an experience context.

It should be noted, though, that the themes are not mutually exclusive. For example, the pictures and stories regarding 'Interaction with the natural environment' and 'Views and reflections' are sometimes overlapping.

Further analyses of the Instagram posts were divided into different emotions or feelings, which reveal that emotions are not so easy to differentiate from each other just judged by these photos. The results indicate that 'joy or happiness' and 'calm or serenity' are central in every experience reported and in all four seasons. Examples are pictures of sunrises and sunsets over lake Mjøsa, different sceneries of lights all year combined with activities close to the lake (e.g., kayaking, swimming). These are good examples of how the user invites the viewer to imagine themselves in the frame (Zappavigna, 2016). The Instagram posts also illustrate how nature and activities in nature give the users experience values (Conti & Lexhagen, 2020). The results indicate that the users experienced deep and meaningful emotions and memories, which can be identified as in line with sustainable experiences (Breiby et al., 2020). These may be used in future processes of branding and designing the destination (Cabiddu et al., 2014).

It is notable that selfies appear only rarely in this Instagram experiment with the hashtag #ourmjosa. Pictures, including people, mostly illustrate family members or friends doing activities such as cycling, wandering, or just relaxing nearby the lake. On the one hand, this may indicate that the users are affected by the research purpose by illustrating a special place or activity they want to share with others, and not #mymjosa. It may also reflect that this destination does not have spectacular attractions and typical selfie-tourism today (see Canavan, 2017).

Visual Tourism Collaboration

Each student group constructed specific themes from the Instagram stories (both pictures and text) from Mjøsa. After the students' presentation of their findings, they engaged in substantial discussions of their different interpretations and added observations for reflection. For instance, why are there almost no people in the autumn pictures? Is it because nature is being experienced differently during autumn compared to, e.g., the summer season? Is autumn experienced as a time for rest for both nature and humans? During the spring presentation, a student said he had found a recurrent theme that did not make sense to him, apparently, something happens when it storms or there is flooding because people share these stories, e.g., a bench under water. Another student, coming from Western Norway and the windier seaside used her background to explain that people have the urge to experience nature when it demonstrates its powers in such ways, hence generating an

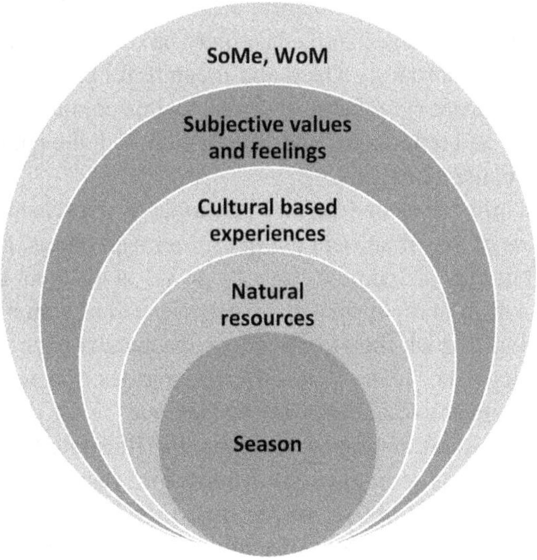

Figure 13.1 The effect of subjective experiences from different seasons

Source: Authors' own work

alternative way of understanding and engaging with nature. This might indicate that when people experience nature in these instances, they have the propensity of transforming it into a spectacular attraction worth visiting and sharing on social media (Lyi, 2016)

Recognising that nature is the premise of all the tourist activities depicted in the photos, the students come to realise how their own understandings had become 'dynamic instead of static'. After presenting their findings and receiving inspiration from other students, they suggest that all seasons work from the premises of nature. From this, distinct activities, and ways of engaging with nature, emerge. In turn, such engagements enable people to experience a stronger emotional appreciation of values other than material ones. This may be seen in relation to intellectual, social, and cultural values, which justifies image sharing in the decision-making process (Seraj, 2012). Figure 13.1 illustrates the effect of subjective experiences from different seasons and how natural and cultural resources contribute to sharing in social media and word of mouth.

How Can New Insights Contribute to More Sustainable Experiences?

The experiment's duality added new research findings of importance for the sustainability of tourists' experiences and behaviour as well as the destination, both individually and collectively. One main finding in the experiment was the great importance of landscape and nature as the premise of all activities. 'Contextual activities' were important in all four seasons according to the hashtag #ourmjosa, revealed by the content analysis *interpreted by others*. Pictures of sunrises and sunsets over lake Mjøsa, different 'natural artistic lights' all year round combined with activities closely connected to the lake may be used for branding the destination (e.g., kayaking, swimming). Deep and meaningful emotions aroused by this experience dimension are 'joy/happiness' and 'calm/serenity'. Experiences characterised by 'Views and reflections' and 'Interaction with the natural environment' are evident in this content analysis.

In addition, a broader knowledge of sustainable experiences was achieved through the process of visual tourism *collaboration with* others. Nature is not only calm and serene but may also demonstrate its power at different times of the year. When it does, it will in many instances be experienced as something both 'forceful' and 'threatening', which transforms into a spectacular experience worth sharing on social media (Lyi, 2016). The different seasons, the natural and cultural resources, and the subjective feelings and values may result in the willingness to share pictures from the destination on social media (illustrated in Figure 13.1).

These findings indicate some possible implications regarding processes on destination design and branding. First, *longer stays* may be achieved by focusing on 'Contextual activities' in all four seasons which will reinforce emotions like 'joy/happiness' and 'calm/serenity'. Second, different activities and ways of engaging with nature are influenced by the culture and history of the place/destination. This may lay the ground for offering *guided tours* based on locally adapted social and environmental values to enable participants to get a deeper sense of place understanding. In addition, this seems to reflect the experiences in line with 'Views and reflections' and 'Interaction with the natural environment'.

The new insights from the study may be used in future processes of branding and designing the destination (see Cabiddu et al., 2014). First, to achieve a more sustainable destination, Instagram photos can provide the DMMO with information regarding the ways in which different visitors perceive the destination, and what kind of services they value during the different seasons. Second, this kind of knowledge is valuable for the pre-visit, visit, and post-visit phases of the tourists' experiences (Iglesias-Sánchez et al., 2020. For example, designing sustainable experiences for different seasons can be important for the aim of distributing the visitation throughout spring and autumn as the shoulder season, which in turn can contribute to lower the rate of seasonal activity among the various tourist businesses. The focus on #ourmjosa instead of #mymjosa as a sense of community may result in a common identity, strengthen the will to take care of a place, and be proud of it.

Conclusion and Implications for Research and Practice

The research results have been brought about using different tools, techniques, and methods for using the sharing of experiences on Instagram as a window into changes in tourism behaviour and travel desire to achieve knowledge that can contribute to the co-creation of more unique sustainable experiences. The tourism literature has underlined that it is worth drawing attention to how UGC can influence the development of sustainable experiences at a tourism destination (Iglesias-Sánchez et al., 2020) and that Instagram and its exploitation as a visual data source have been limited (Chen et al., 2023). An Instagram-experiment mobilised UGC and the subsequent content analyses include both different sustainable experience dimensions, the effects of different seasons during the year, and various emotions related to the tourists' experiences. The visual tourism collaboration also indicates that the different seasons, the natural and cultural resources, the tourists' feelings, and values may result in the willingness to share pictures from the destination on social media (see Figure 13.1).

The main results demonstrate the significance of certain aspects of the contextuality of tourism activities. Being a pivotal context to most activities tourists engage with in Norway, landscapes and nature tend to bring about deep and meaningful emotions and memories that may be defined in line with sustainable experiences. Second, the distinct seasonal variations that characterise the Nordic climate represent important contexts for these emotion and memory processes. We argue that these findings may be used in future processes of branding and designing the destination (see Cabiddu et al., 2014), even for tourists' engagement with social and cultural tourist attractions. Third, we conclude that it is imperative for DMMOs to find ways of including tourists as active contributors in the development processes. One effective way of doing this for more sustainable experiences is by co-create UGC with the travellers on Instagram, thus gaining knowledge of the pre-visit, visit and post-visit phases of the tourists' experiences (Iglesias-Sánchez et al., 2020).

In this study, we have revealed some weaknesses of Instagram as a research tool. Different users may see different pictures on their phones related to their search stories, persons they follow, and algorithms on Instagram. For further research, it might also be relevant to the question: Is it so that some persons are more likely to share their pictures on Instagram than others? Do Instagram users share positive moments rather than negative ones? How is the connection between the image from the users' Instagram pictures and the image of the DMMO used in their marketing of the destination?

We will thank the Instagram users for sharing pictures and the students for participating in the analyses.

Further Questions

- How can other social media platforms contribute to the co-creation of sustainable experiences?
- How can a comparative study from different tourist destinations change the experiences shared on Instagram?
- How are the results in this study conflicting or in line with results found by using more traditional methods such as interviews and survey questionnaires?

Further Readings

Arts, I., Fischer, A., Duckett, D., & Van Der Wal, R. (2021). Information technology and the optimisation of experience – The role of mobile devices and social media in human-nature interactions. *Geoforum*, *122*, 55–62. https://doi.org/10.1016/j.geoforum.2021.03.009

Calcagni, F., Amorim Maia, A. T., Connolly, J. J. T., & Langemeyer, J. (2019). Digital co-construction of relational values: Understanding the role of social media for sustainability. *Sustainability Science*, *14*(5), 1309–1321.

da Mota, V. T., & Pickering, C. (2020). Using social media to assess nature-based tourism: Current research and future trends. *Journal of Outdoor Recreation and Tourism, 30*, 100295.

Eugenio, C., & Farsari, I. (2022). *Disconnection in nature-based tourism experiences: An actor-network theory approach.* https://doi.org/10.1080/11745398.2022.2150665

Wilkins, E. J., Wood, S. A., & Smith, J. W. (2021). Uses and limitations of social media to inform visitor use management in parks and protected areas: A systematic review. *Environmental Management, 67*(1), 120–132.

References

Becken, S., & Kaur, J. (2021). Anchoring 'tourism value' within a regenerative tourism paradigm – A government perspective. *Journal of Sustainable Tourism.* https://doi.org/10.1080/09669582.2021.1990305

Breiby, M. A., Duedahl, E., Øian, H., & Ericsson, B. (2020). Exploring sustainable experiences in tourism. *Scandinavian Journal of Hospitality and Tourism, 20*(4), 335–351. https://doi.org/10.1080/15022250.2020.1748706

Bronner, F., & de Hoog, R., (2019). Comparing conspicuous consumption across different experiential products: Culture and leisure. *International Journal of Market Research, 61*(4), 430–446. https://doi.org/10.1177/1470785318799898

Cabiddu, F., Carlo, M., & Piccoli, G. (2014). Social media affordances: Enabling customer engagement. *Annals of Tourism Research, 48*, 175–192.

Canavan, B. (2017). Narcissism normalisation: Tourism influences and sustainability implications. *Journal of Sustainable Tourism, 25*(9), 1322–1337.

Chen, Y., Sherren, K., Smit, M., & Lee, K. Y. (2023). Using social media images as data in social science research. *New Media & Society, 25*(4), 849–871.

Chu, S. (2020). *Social media tools in experiential internship learning.* Springer.

Cohen, S., Liu, H., Hanna, P., Hopkins, D., Higham, J., & Gössling, S. (2022). The rich kids of Instagram: Luxury travel, transport modes, and desire. *Journal of Travel Research, 61*(7), 1479–1494.

Conti, E., & Cassel, S. H. (2020). Liminality in nature-based tourism experiences as mediated through social media. *Tourism Geographies, 22*(2), 413–432.

Conti, E., & Lexhagen, M. (2020). Instagramming nature-based tourism experiences: An etnographic study of online photography and value creation. *Tourism Management Perspectives*, 34, 100650. https://doi.org/10.1016/j.tmp.2020.100650

Egger, R, Gumus, O, & Kaiumova, E., Mükisch, R., & Surkic, V. (2022). Destination Image of DMO and UGC on Instagram: A Machine-Learning Approach. In: J. L. Stienmetz, B. Ferrer-Rosell, & D. Massimo (Eds.), *Information and Communication Technologies in Tourism 2022*. ENTER 2022. Springer. https://doi.org/10.1007/978-3-030-94751-4_31

Gössling, S., Scott, D., & Hall, C. M. (2018). Global trends in length of stay: Implications for destination management and climate change. *Journal of Sustainable Tourism, 26*(12), 2087–2101.

Harper, D. (2012). *Visual sociology.* Taylor & Francis Group.

Hernández, M. R., Santana Talavera, A., & Parra López, E. (2016). Effects of co-creation in a tourism destination brand image through twitter. *Journal of Tourism, Heritage & Services Marketing (JTHSM), 2*(1), 3–10.

Iglesias-Sánchez, P. P., Correia, M. B., Jambrino-Maldonado, C., & Heras-Pedrosa, C. (2020). Instagram as a co-creation space for tourist destination image-building:

Algarve and Costa del Sol case studies. *Sutainability*, 12, 2793. https://doi.org/10.3390/su12072793

Kastenholz, E., Carneiro, M. J., & Eusébio, C. (2016). *Meeting challenges for rural tourism through co-creation of sustainable tourist experiences*. Cambridge Scholars Publisher.

Kirilenko, A. P., & Stepchenkova, S. O. (2014). Public microblogging in climate change: One year of Twitter worldwide. *Global Environmental Change*, 26, 171–182. https://doi.org/10.1016/j.gloenvcha.2014.02.008

Lai, I. K., Lu, D., & Liu, Y. (2020). Experience economy in ethnic cuisine: A case of Chengdu cuisine. *British Food Journal, 122*(6), 1801–1817.

Liu, H., Wu, L., & Li, X. (2019). Social media envy: How experience sharing on social networking sites drives millennials' aspirational tourism consumption. *Journal of travel research, 58*(3), 355–369.

Lyu, S. O. (2016). Travel selfies on social media as objectified self-presentation. *Tourism Management, 54*, 185–195.

Marder, B., Archer-Brown, C., Colliander, J., & Lambert, A. (2019). Vacation posts on Facebook: A model for incidental vicarious travel consumption. *Journal of Travel Research, 58*(6), 1014–1033.

Nautiyal, R., Albrecht, J. N., & Carr, A. (2022). Can destination image be ascertained from social media? An examination of Twitter hashtags. *Tourism and Hospitality Research*. https://doi.org/10.1177/14673584221119380

Prahalad, C. K., & Ramaswamy, V. (2004). Co-creation experiences: The next practice in value creation. *Journal of Interactive Marketing, 18*, 5–14.

Seraj, M. (2012). We create, we connect, we respect, therefore we are: Intellectual, social, and cultural value in online communities. *Journal of Interactive Marketing, 26*(4), 209–222.

So, K. K. F., Wu, L., Xiong, L., & King, C. (2018). Brand management in the era of social media: Social visibility of consumption and customer brand identification. *Journal of Travel Research, 57*(6), 727–742.

Statistics Norway (2018), Kommersielle gjestedøgn i Mjøsaregionen, [Commercial guest nights in the Mjøsa region], accessed 5 October 2019 at http://www.statistikknett.no

Taylor, D. G. (2020). Putting the "self" in selfies: How narcissism, envy and self-promotion motivate sharing of travel photos through social media. *Journal of Travel & Tourism Marketing, 37*(1), 64–77.

Thevenot, G. (2007). Blogging as a social media. *Tourism and Hospitality Research, 7*(3–4), 282–289.

Urry, J. (1990). *The tourist gaze. Leisure and travel in contemporary societies*. Sage Publications.

Weber, R. P. (1990). *Basic content analysis*. Sage.

Zappavigna, M. (2016). Social media photography: Construing subjectivity in Instagram images. *Visual Communication, 15*(3), 271–292. https://doi.org/10.1177/147035721664322

14 Towards a Sustainable Tourism Experience

Analysing the Zero-emission Tourist Routes in Natural Parks

Rocío González-Sánchez, María Torrejón-Ramos, Sonia Medina-Salgado, and Sara Alonso-Muñoz

Introduction

Tourism activity has positive aspects, including economic, employment, and cultural, but it also has negative aspects on the environment, the living conditions of residents, and heritage (Janusz & Bajdor, 2013). A framework for action is required to protect tourism activity while minimising negative effects. To this end, sustainability plays a fundamental role in the conservation of tourism resources, which are the basis for a tourist destination to be attractive over time. So, sustainability can be seen as applicable to tourism from different perspectives – environmental, economic, social, and cultural. The experiences resulting from the recent health and environmental crises make it necessary to incorporate sustainability into tourist experiences to provide destinations with a competitive advantage (Breiby et al., 2020). Tourists are looking for experiences in the destination that incorporate values beyond personal enjoyment. These include personal or cultural enrichment and minimising the impact on the destination's natural environment or heritage. In the face of rapid and unplanned tourism with a high environmental and social impact on the destination, tourists demand experiences that minimise any negative effects (Menon & Jayawant, 2021).

Technological tools are essential for the development of sustainable tourism experiences. The diversity of tools and the development currently achieved minimises the impact of tourism activities on the environment and enriches the experience. The application of technologies to achieve more sustainable tourism is an innovative approach to the study of the use of technologies for other purposes. In addition, the Sustainable Development Goals belonging to the 2030 Agenda (United Nations, 2015) also incorporates this utility to achieve sustainability objectives in the sector. However, research on the role of technologies in the development of more sustainable tourism experiences is still an underdeveloped field (Azmadi et al., 2022; Neuhofer et al., 2014). This chapter reviews the literature on the enabling role of technological tools to achieve more sustainable tourism experiences. The relationship between both concepts is analysed by considering the most popular technologies and the three dimensions of sustainability; environmental, social, and economic. It then presents a case study of the MOVELETUR project,

DOI: 10.4324/9781003335924-18

which has implemented sustainable routes in Spain and Portugal with the support of technologies that facilitate transportation and communication.

Theoretical Background

What Is Sustainable Tourism?

The concept of sustainability is coined as the economic development that is committed to meeting the needs of future generations, in addition to those of the present generation. Sustainability is a term currently used by practitioners, policymakers, and academics to integrate environmental and social aspects with economic progress (Muñoz-Torres et al., 2018). Sustainability integrates the so-called triple bottom line, considering social and environmental as well as economic concepts and its balance that are interdependent with the three basic pillars: profit, planet, and people (Chen, 2018; Muñoz-Torres et al., 2018). Achieving sustainability at all levels requires a change in thinking and action. It requires the creation of sustainable services and products, new technologies and new sustainable business models. These new business models will have to fulfil not only environmental and social needs, but also institutional and economic requirements (Nasiri et al., 2018). This perspective is also included in the 2030 Agenda for Sustainable Development Goals (SDGs) agreed upon by the United Nations (United Nations, 2015). Concern about sustainability and acceptance of the concept can be traced back to growing evidence of global environmental risks, such as climate change, ozone depletion or loss of biodiversity, among others (Clark & Crutzen, 2005). Sustainable development requires an acceptable supply of energy resources, that is available in the long term and at reasonable costs, and without undesirable social impacts. In addition, responsible energy use must be controlled and pursued, limiting changes to the landscape and nature to pursue a sustainable economy. Organisations should focus on becoming 'less unsustainable', reducing their negative impact on the environment and communities, to become 'more sustainable' organisations, as a measure to create positive impacts while reducing harmful ones (Díaz-Correa & López-Navarro, 2018).

The tourism sector recorded 1.5 billion global travellers, generating employment for 339 million people, and involves 10.40% of the worldwide economic performance (World Travel & Tourism Council, 2019). This industry implies CO_2 emissions and consequently an increase in greenhouse gases. The use of natural resources has high flows and waste consumption. According to Gössling and Peeters (2015), 40% of CO_2 emissions are caused by air travel. The tourism industry supposes an increase in global climate change; thus, the application of sustainability elements in this sector is key (Scott, 2021). Sustainable tourism should consider stakeholders' ethical beliefs, and economic interests. The transition to sustainable tourism development is currently relatively limited (Ivars-Baidal et al., 2021). Hence, tourism destination management and planning are attracting attention with regard to smart tourism destinations (Ivars-Baidal et al., 2019), derived and linked with the smart cities term. Marsal-Llacuna et al. (2015) point out that smart cities include sustainability issues along with the informational and technological aspects, highlighting the fundamental role of Information and Communication Technology (ICT).

- Thought point: How important do you think sustainable tourism is?

The Sustainable Tourism Experience

The quality of tourism services is one of the main sources of competitive advantage for tourism businesses. The development of a competitive and sustainable tourism practice depends on the management of environmental standards, facilities, and safety at tourist attractions (Chen et al., 2017). A tourism experience is currently considered to be the real tourism product (Cuenca & Prat, 2012), and it is most valued because it can enrich tourists' experience (Stamboulis & Skayannis, 2003). Experience towards creating unforgettable memories can attract customers (Pine & Gilmore, 1998). Among the main characteristics of the tourist experience, its complexity, multidimensionality, dynamism, subjectivity, and transience can be highlighted. Factors that positively affect the tourism experience must be identified by suppliers to create value in an increasingly competitive business environment (Kastenholz et al., 2016).

To promote a sustainable tourism experience, it is important to enhance nature-based tourism as this type of tourism can be linked with learning and thus promote healthy attitudes (Wheaton et al., 2015). Also, awareness of sustainable tourism could be enhanced through practices such as transmedia storytelling. Its immersive and participatory nature (Dionisio & Nisi, 2021) can be used as a useful tool for knowledge transfer and the consequent generation of positive social change (Green & Brock, 2000).

- Thought point: Which tourism experience do you remember the most? It was an active or a passive experience?

Regarding a sustainable tourism experience, understanding the needs and sensitivities of visitors and residents is necessary to improve the tourism infrastructure and management of destinations (De Sousa & Kastenholz, 2015). Nowadays tourism activities involve personalisation and interaction based on new tourists' consumption patterns (Qin et al., 2020). Customer intention and behaviour are influenced by experience as a key point from a marketing context (Lee & Jan, 2019). Customer's future behaviour is affected by experiences in the past (Brakus et al., 2009), which relates to customer loyalty and satisfaction, and is essential due to its importance for demand (Ellis & Rossman, 2008). Associated with tourism experiences, it can be an indicator of following responsible behaviour from an environmental point of view. In addition, educational experiences can highly enhance the environmentally responsible behaviour between students and tourists (Lee & Jan, 2015, 2019). From a marketing approach, experiences include the following elements: thinking, sensing, feeling, acting, and relating (Schmitt, 1999).

Technology and Sustainable Tourism

The fast development of new technologies due to the Internet has brought about great changes in all fields. According to World Tourism Organization (UNWTO) (2018), the quality of the tourism experience can be improved through technology and innovation, including Information and Communication Technologies (ICTs) (Lent & Marciniak, 2019). However, there is scarce research on how new technologies can be used for sustainable tourism development (Loureiro & Nascimento, 2021). Literature about how technology affects to keep environmental post-trip behaviour in tourism destinations is also limited (Wheaton et al., 2015). Highlighting that 'prompting' is the most effective when the tourist is prompted, and the action is simple. Simple actions can be taken towards sustainable tourism experience and environmental behaviours through social media, such as Instagram or Twitter, to provide norms, and to promote environmental behaviours by means of education and rewards.

There are three spheres of benefit from using new technologies to construct more sustainable tourism experiences through greener tourism destinations. The environmental sphere, achieving greener processes with less impact on the natural environment. The economic sphere, economising on certain services such as communication and achieve greater development. Finally, the social sphere protects the cultural heritage and the coexistence between tourists and residents (see Figure 14.1).

Sustainable tourism has become particularly relevant in the context of Covid-19, due to the great challenges that the economic and climate crisis poses for the sector (Loureiro & Nascimento, 2021). The impact of the Covid-19 pandemic on traditional tourism has helped the development of virtual tourism technology that provides consumers with sensory information that drives the desire to travel, as well as anticipatory experiences (Yang et al., 2022). In this respect, new technologies can help to face the Covid-19 challenges (Talafubieke et al., 2021). During the pandemic crisis, various tools have been incorporated into the tourism experience. Some of them, such as QR codes, have become popular as they have facilitated various processes and communication of information without physical contact (Azmadi et al., 2022). However, future research will have to study which of all the technologies used during Covid-19 have been incorporated into the routine of businesses and users and, consequently, will continue to be used in the post-crisis period. Some of them will have to provide superior added value to do so. For example, QR codes will be incorporated into an experience if, in addition to accessing certain information, they allow interaction with the experience.

Another example is virtual tourism technology, which can be beneficial for the environment. Some of the reasons include reducing the environmental pollution load of tourist destinations, mitigating carbon emissions, and lessening the impact of human activities on ecosystems. (Yang et al., 2022). Virtual tourism products can also be used to promote economic development in tourism (Talafubieke et al., 2021). The case of virtual reality (VR) is a type of technology in which a 3D space is capable of simulating different sensory feelings (Talafubieke et al., 2021). It also

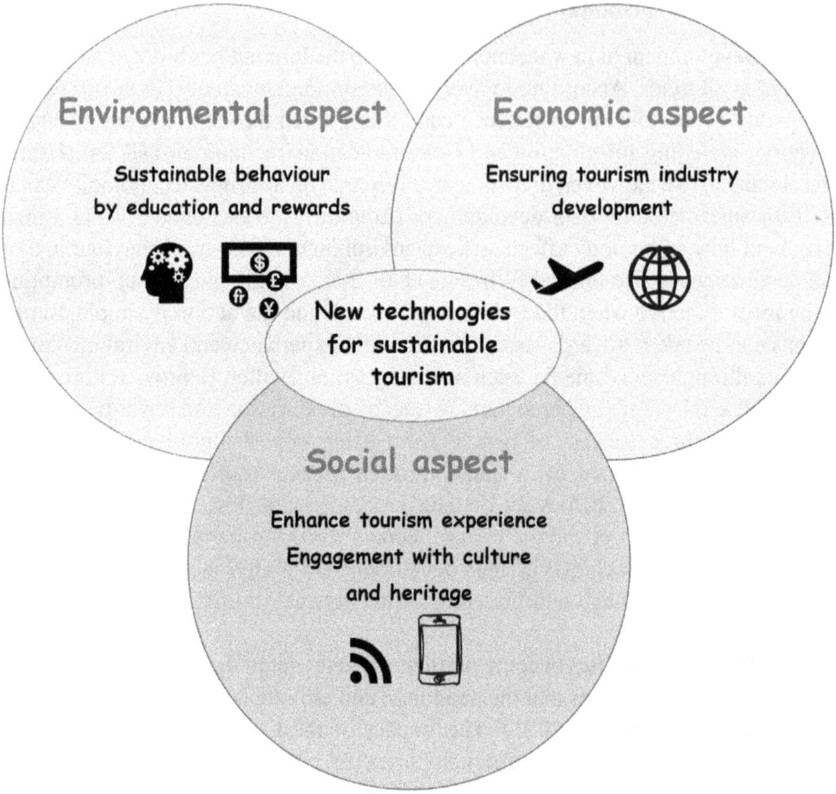

Figure 14.1 Areas for improvement in sustainability with new technologies

Source: Adapted from Tyan et al. (2020)

reinforces the positive emotions of the participants (Beck & Egger, 2018) as well as increases audience share. In tourism, VR offers the option of a closer-to-reality experience. In this way, different values can be conveyed to the visitor, such as participation in conservation behaviours (Hofman et al., 2021). Furthermore, in the analysis of Zhuang et al. (2020), it was shown that other technologies such as artificial intelligence (AI) support sustainable development in tourism. AI-trained data can generate an *ex-ante* estimate of tourist behaviour that can be used to promote environmentally friendly behaviour and contribute to the future of sustainable tourism (Rezapouraghdam et al., 2021).

In addition, according to Jiang et al. (2022), AR offers a revolutionary opportunity to increase engagement with culture and heritage. Other innovative technologies, highlighting Blockchain technology can improve tourism destinations by enhancing payments, and distribution management of assets and inventories in the tourism industry. Blockchain technology can provide rewards based on cryptocurrency systems, which can be associated with sustainable awareness. Visitors who are rewarded for sustainable behaviour are more likely to be willing to undertake environmentally sustainable actions in the future, for instance, to save energy and recycle. Moreover, Blockchain can enhance smart tourism destinations, which help in rewarding sustainable behaviour and improve the tourism experience (Tyan et al., 2020). Smart tourism destinations improve the tourism experience by means of improving customer service and real-time information access (Buhalis & Amaranggana, 2015). Personalised services are provided thanks to smart tourism destinations and real-time data, considering information about tourists before the trip, and with a feedback system for reviewing past experiences. Hence, Blockchain technology plays a key role in providing personalised services in smart tourism destinations (Tyan et al., 2020). In short, innovative tourism development and the reduction of consumer travel costs establish virtual technology as a driving force in the development of sustainable tourism (Yang et al., 2022).

- Thought point: Have you ever been to a smart tourism destination? Which technologies were applied? Do you think that they contribute to sustainable tourism?

Smart Tourism and Sustainability

Using advances in ICTs can mitigate the recognised lack of smart tourism systems, which must be designed with the tourists' vision of sustainable values in consideration (Lim et al., 2017). Multidisciplinarity is an important dimension in building a smart destination. Different stakeholders, both public and private, must be identified as interested actors to anticipate the issues, outcomes, and resources that will transform a destination (Ben Letaifa, 2015). Smart tourism destination improves resource management effectiveness, enhances the tourism experience, and ensures sustainability (Buhalis & Amaranggana, 2013). It rises thanks to ICTs underscored Internet of Things (IoT), end-used internet service systems and cloud computing (Zhang et al., 2012). Smart tourism destination depends on the ICTs' utilisation, based on tourists' needs, seeking for better tourism management and tourism service quality promotion using real-time data from tourists. Such destinations are associated with the co-creation of pleasure value according to the technology available in the place, also considering the tourism destination and organisations' benefits (Boes et al., 2015). The use of ICT aids in sustainable tourism development due to enabling sustainability implementation (Ratten et al., 2019).

A smart destination also focuses its efforts on using technology to develop sustainable mobility. In those countries such as OECD countries that have already started to switch from fossil fuels to renewable energy sources, the impact on greenhouse gas emissions is not significant (Banga et al., 2022). The use of clean energy vehicles through the incorporation of technological tools represents an important added value when it comes to achieving the status of a 'sustainable tourist destination'. Add value according to the mobility tourism experience is analysed by Signorile et al. (2018). New mobility models based on new technologies focus on ICTs that allow sustainable transport services, combining on-demand private and public transport use. Tyan et al. (2020) argue that from a sustainable point of view, technologies applied by smart tourism destinations promote sustainable behaviours. Rewarding and incentives can modify tourists' environmental behaviours and attitudes (Negrusa et al., 2015).

Case Study of the MOVELETUR Project

The MOVELETUR project, 'Sustainable tourism and electric mobility in natural areas,' aims to create a model of sustainable tourism in natural areas. It is a cross-border partnership between Portuguese and Spanish organisations to develop e-mobility on tourist routes (European Commission, 2018). To this end, it has set up a network of green tourist itineraries (see Table 14.1). The enabling tool is the use of new technology both in mobility and in the dissemination of information. This project has attracted international interest and UNESCO is using this project to replicate it as a model for other biosphere reserves.

For this connection between sustainability and technology to work, three fundamental foundations must be developed. Firstly, the promotion of cooperation between public and private entities, and financial and infrastructural support from public entities. At the infrastructure level, recharging points have been fundamental in the development of these green routes. With 16 recharging points for car batteries strategically placed along the route, travellers have enough electricity to avoid shortages. To complement this infrastructure, accommodation and scenic and cultural stops are included. It is essential that the traveller has sufficient infrastructural elements to achieve a complete level of immersion in the experience, in which their most important needs are covered. Secondly, the use of some of these technologies requires the processing of large amounts of data, much of which is protected, including additional legislative and ethical aspects (Kibert et al., 2012). For this reason, some regulations must be adapted to this new reality. Thirdly and no less important, the awareness of tourists through training campaigns or economic incentives or by making more polluting options more expensive.

Technology contributes to environmental sustainability through three fundamental aspects, mobility using green transport, cars, and electric bicycles. This project aims to attract environmentally aware travellers and allows them to visit

Table 14.1 Project technical specification table

Itineraries	*Area of operation*	*Partners*	*Budget*
18 e-bicycle itineraries 14 e-cars itineraries 1 e-car cross-border route through seven Natura 2000 areas in Spain and Portugal	Seven protected natural areas of the Spanish-Portuguese Raya	Natural Heritage Foundation of Castilla y León (coordinating partner), Diputación de Ávila (APEA), EREN, the Association ADIRBA, the Municipality of Braganza, the Instituto Politecnico de Castelo Branco (IPCB), and the Regional Energy and Environment Agency	908,829.13 euros with a 75% financial contribution from the European Regional Development Fund (ERDF)

Source: Adapted from Patrimonio Natural de Castilla and León (2022)

environments of high ethnographic value and restricted access because they are natural parks. The use of electric cars eliminates the impact of mobility on noise and air pollution (with an annual reduction of more than 1.5 tonnes of CO_2), allowing the tourist to experience contact with nature to the full, both the air quality and the proximity to wild animals, as they are not frightened by the noise of vehicles. The second use of technology relates to communication and awareness-raising. For this purpose, various social networks such as Facebook or Twitter are used to communicate both the service and the benefits of clean mobility at destinations. In addition, communication and marketing work is carried out through short videos that are posted on the networks. The third use was through the most widespread technological tool, the smartphone. Thus, a mobile application was developed that allowed travellers to design their own routes. So, travellers can customise routes according to their interests or typologies. Figure 14.2 depicts the constraints or background, the technologies employed, and the main benefits of the project.

The social and economic impact translates into the involvement of residents and local tourism agents. Residents have benefited from a lower negative impact of tourism activity, despite the reactivation of tourism. This reactivation has led to an increase in the activity of local businesses.

Based on this project, the implementation of sustainable routes with bicycles and electric vehicles in green spaces has been analysed. A network of tourist itineraries on the border of Castilla and León (Spain) and the central and northern regions of Portugal has been designed that offers 33 alternatives for discovering natural areas, 8 of them to be done in electric cars and the rest in other vehicles

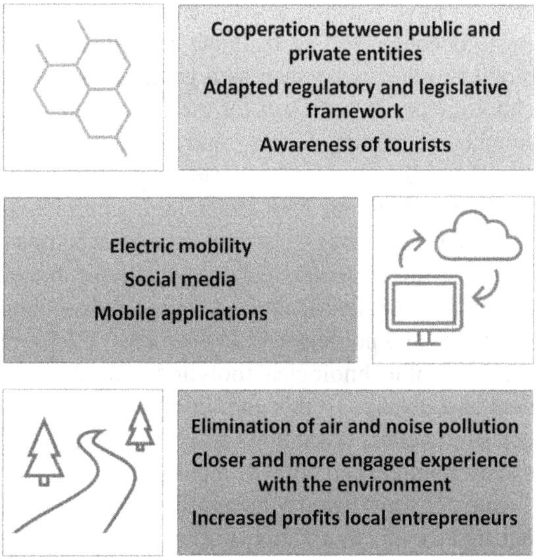

Cooperation between public and private entities
Adapted regulatory and legislative framework
Awareness of tourists
Electric mobility
Social media
Mobile applications
Elimination of air and noise pollution
Closer and more engaged experience with the environment
Increased profits local entrepreneurs

Figure 14.2 Project background, tools, and benefits

Source: Authors' own work

without CO_2 emissions. For this purpose, the infrastructure has been built to enable the recharging of the electric mobile elements. In addition, the android mobile technology allows the consultation of the information of the different routes. The use of technologies to achieve a tourist experience that is more committed and integrated with nature is completed with the use of social networks that favour communication and publicity of the project.

Conclusion

Tourism is intrinsically linked to the concept of experience, so understanding how tourists experience is fundamental to the study of tourism consumption (Sharpley & Stone, 2011). Achieving a balanced interaction that allows the development of tourist experiences without environmental damage is fundamental to the development of the tourist experience. So, sustainability must be a framework for any tourism experience. Breiby et al. (2020, p. 348) define sustainable experience in tourism as 'an experience that elicits deep and meaningful emotions and memories that can foster tourists' contribution to the sustainability of the destination'. This study focuses on the environmental sustainability of the tourism experience. Ensuring that a tourist can have a tourism experience with zero impact on the environment in which it takes place would favour both the experience itself and the environment or heritage in which it takes place. Recent studies have considered the importance of sustainable tourism experiences, claiming that environmental awareness can lead to changes in tourists' travel behaviour.

After reviewing the literature and analysing the case of the project, we can conclude that technologies have reached a sufficient variety, level of development, and cost reduction to become tools to facilitate sustainable tourism experiences. However, technology should not be seen as a goal, but as an enabler. The mere possession of technology is not sufficient for the development of sustainability if it is not accompanied by economic, cultural, and regulatory measures. Sustainable mobility allows tourists to develop their experience without generating a negative ecological footprint on environment. New technologies are a key tool for achieving more sustainable tourism experiences, but they must be accompanied by other elements. (1) The incorporation of certain technological tools in a tourist destination requires infrastructures with a significant cost. This requires cooperation between public and private entities and pooling certain resources. (2) Tourists play a fundamental role in the success of technological tools and, if used correctly, can generate greater commitment and loyalty. To this end, information and training campaigns are needed to increase travellers' awareness and skills. Finally, (3) we are moving in a more complex environment and with the management of a large amount of data and information, which is why it would be advisable to establish new regulations and update current legislation. In addition to the elements that must accompany the implementation of these new technologies so that the experience is developed within a framework of sustainability, the choice of the technologies to be used and their utilities for our type of traveller is fundamental.

Further Questions

- Can you think of a real tourist destination and propose a more sustainable development of its activities, through the application of new technologies?
- What changes are necessary beyond technological transformation?
- What contextual factors do you consider most relevant in implementing technological tools for more sustainable tourism experiences? How can these factors be promoted?

Further Readings

Gössling, S. (2017). Tourism, information technologies and sustainability: An exploratory review. *Journal of Sustainable Tourism*, 25 (7), 1024–1041. https://doi.org/10.1080/09669582.2015.1122017

Jeong, M., & Shin, H. H. (2020). Tourists' experiences with smart tourism technology at smart destinations and their behavior intentions. *Journal of Travel Research*, 59 (8), 1464–1477. https://doi.org/10.1177/0047287519883034

Neuhofer, B., & Buhalis, D. (2017) Service-dominant logic in the social media landscape: New perspectives on experience and value co-creation. In: Sigala, M. and Gretzel, U. (eds.) *Advances in social media for travel, tourism and hospitality: New perspectives, practice and cases*, Routledge, pp. 13–25.

Stankov, U., & Gretzel, U. (2020). Tourism 4.0 technologies and tourist experiences: A human-centered design perspective. *Information Technology & Tourism*, 22, 477–488. https://doi.org/10.1007/s40558-020-00186-y

Tussyadiah, I. P., & Fesenmaier, D. R. (2009). Mediating tourist experiences. Access to places via shared videos. *Annals of Tourism Research*, 36 (1), 24–40, http://doi.org/10.1016/j.annals.2008.10.001

Zeynep, A. Gedikoglu, Sheila J. Backman, Joseph P. Mazer, Kenneth F., & Backman, F.A. (2020). Conceptual framework to understand online destination images, Handbook of *r*esearch on *s*ocial *m*edia *a*pplications for the *t*ourism and *h*ospitality *s*ector, (114–135). http://doi.org/10.4018/978-1-7998-1947-9.ch008

References

Azmadi, A. S. A., ABD Hamid, M., & Hanafiah, M. H. (2022). Rise of the QE code application adoption: Towards a conceptual post-Covid-19 smart sustainable tourism framework. *International Journal of Social Science Research, 4*(1), 478–488. https://myjms.mohe.gov.my/index.php/ijssr/article/view/17985

Banga, C., Deka, A., Kilic, H., Ozturen, A., & Ozdeser, H. (2022). The role of clean energy in the development of sustainable tourism: Does renewable energy use help mitigate environmental pollution? A panel data analysis. *Environmental Sciences and Pollution Research*, 29, 59363–59373. https://doi.org/10.1007/s11356-022-19991-5

Beck, J., & Egger, R. (2018). Emotionalise me: Self-reporting and arousal measurements in virtual tourism environments. *In Information and communication technologies in tourism.* Springer, 3–15.

Ben Letaifa, S. (2015). How to strategize smart cities: Revealing the SMART model. *Journal of Business Research, 68*(7), 1414–1419. https://doi.org/10.1016/j.jbusres.2015.01.024

Boes, K., Buhalis, D., & Inversini, A. (2015). Conceptualising smart tourism destination dimensions. In *Information and communication technologies in tourism*; Springer, 391–403. https://doi.org/10.1007/978-3-319-14343-9_29

Brakus, J. J., Schmitt, B. H., & Zarantonello, L. (2009). Brand experience: What is it? How is it measured? Does it affect loyalty? *Journal of Marketing*, *73*(3), 52–68.

Breiby, M. A., Duedahl, E., Øian, H., & Ericsson, B. (2020). Exploring sustainable experiences in tourism. *Scandinavian Journal of Hospitality and Tourism*, *20*(4), 335–351. https://doi.org/10.1080/15022250.2020.1748706

Buhalis, D., & Amaranggana, A. (2013). Smart tourism destinations. In Z. Xiang, & I. Tussyadiah (Eds.), *Information and communication technologies in tourism 2014* (pp. 553–564). Springer.

Buhalis, D., & Amaranggana, A. (2015). Smart tourism destinations enhancing tourism experience through personalisation of services. In I. Tussyadiah, & A. Inversini, (Eds.), *Information and communication technologies in tourism* (pp. 377–389). Springer. http://dx.doi.org/10.1007/978-3-319-14343-9_28

Chen, C. W. (2018). Guidance on the conceptual design of sustainable product–service systems. *Sustainability*, *10*, 2452. http://dx.doi.org/10.3390/su10072452

Chen, L., Ng, E., Huang, S.-C., & Fang, W. T. (2017). A self-evaluation system of quality planning for tourist attractions in Taiwan: An integrated AHP-Delphi approach from career professionals. *Sustainability*, *9*, 1751. http://dx.doi.org/10.3390/su9101751

Clark, W. C., Crutzen, P. J. & Schellnhuber, H. J. (2005). Science for global sustainability: Toward a new paradigm. *KSG Work. Pap.*, 120, 1–28. https://dx.doi.org/10.2139/ssrn.702501

Cuenca, M., & Prat, A. (2012). Ocio experiencial: antecedentes y características. *Arbor. Ciencia, Pensamiento y Cultura*, *188*(756), 265–281.

De Sousa, A. J. G., & Kastenholz, E. (2015). Wind farms and the rural tourism experience – Problem or possible productive integration? The views of visitors and residents of a Portuguese village. *Journal of Sustainable Tourism*, *23*(8–9), 1235–1256. http://dx.doi.org/10.1080/09669582.2015.1008499.

Díaz-Correa, J. E., & López-Navarro, M. A. (2018). Managing sustainable hybrid organisations: A case study in the agricultural sector. *Sustainability*, *10*, 3010. https://doi.org/10.3390/su10093010

Dionisio, M., & Nisi, V. (2021). Leveraging Transmedia storytelling to engage tourists in the understanding of the destination's local heritage. *Multimedia Tools Applications*, *80*, 34813–34841. https://doi.org/10.1007/s11042-021-10949-2

Ellis, G. D., & Rossman, J. R. (2008). Creating value for participants through experience staging: Parks, recreation, and tourism in the experience industry. *Journal of Park and Recreation Administration*, *26*(4), 1–20.

European Commission (2018). MOVELETUR Sustainable Tourism & Electric Mobility [ES] https://www.managenergy.eu/node/568. Accessed January 10, 2022

Gössling, S., & Peeters, P. (2015). Assessing tourism's global environmental impact 1900–2050. *Journal of Sustainable Tourism*, *23*(5), 639–659. http://doi.org/10.1080/09669582.2015.1008500

Green, M. C., & Brock, T. C. (2000). The role of transportation in the persuasiveness of public narratives. *Journal of Personality and Social Psychology*, *79*(5), 701–721. https://doi.org/10.1037/0022-3514.79.5.701

Hofman, K., Walters, G., & Hughes, K. (2021). The effectiveness of virtual vs real-life marine tourism experiences in encouraging conservation behaviour. *Journal of Sustainable Tourism*, *30*(4), 742–766. https://doi.org/10.1080/09669582.2021.1884690

Ivars-Baidal, J. A., Celdrán-Bernabeu, M., Jose-Norberto, M., & Perles-Ivars, A. (2019). Smart destinations and the evolution of ICTs: A new scenario for destination management? *Current Issues in Tourism*, *22*(13), 1581–1600. https://doi.org/10.1080/13683500.2017.1388771

Ivars-Baidal, J. A., Vera-Rebollo, J. F., Perles-Ribes, J., Femenia-Serra, F., & Celdrán-Bernabeu, M. A. (2021). Sustainable tourism indicators: what's new within the smart city/destination approach? *Journal of Sustainable Tourism*, https://doi.org/10.1080/09669582.2021.1876075

Janusz, G. K., & Bajdor, P. (2013). Towards to sustainable tourism framework, activities and dimensions. *Procedia Economics and Finance*, *6*, 523–552.

Jiang, S., Moyle, B., Yung, R., Tao, L., & Scott, N. (2022). Augmented reality and the enhancement of memorable tourism experiences at heritage sites. *Current Issues in Tourism*, http://dx.doi.org/10.1080/13683500.2022.2026303

Kastenholz, E., Maria João Carneiro, M. J., & Eusébio, C. (2016). Diverse socializing patterns in rural tourist experiences – A segmentation analysis. *Current Issues in Tourism*, *22*(4), 729–748. https://doi.org/10.1080/13683500.2015.1087477

Kibert, C. J., Thiele, L., Peterson, A., & Monroe, M. (2012). *The ethics of sustainability*. Portal Rio.

Lee, T. H., & Jan, F. H. (2015). The effects of recreation experience, environmental attitude, and biospheric value on environmentally responsible behavior of nature-based tourists. *Environmental Management*, *56*, 193–208.

Lee, T. H., & Jan, F. H. (2019). The low-carbon tourism experience: A multidimensional scale development. *Journal of Hospitality and Tourism Research*, 10, 1–29. http://doi.org/10.1177/1096348019849675

Lent, B., & Marciniak, M., (2019). Enhancing tourism potential by using gamification techniques and augmented reality in mobile games. *Vision 2025: Education excellence and management of innovations through sustainable economic competitive advantage*. 11210–11221.

Lim, C., Mostafa, N., & Park, J. (2017) Digital omotenashi: Toward a smart tourism design systems. *Sustainability*, *9*, 2175. https://doi.org/10.3390/su9122175

Loureiro, S. M. C., & Nascimento, J. (2021) Shaping a view on the influence of technologies on sustainable tourism. *Sustainability*, *13*, 12691. https://doi.org/10.3390/su132212691

Marsal-Llacuna, M. L., Colomer-Llinàs, J., & Meléndez-Frigola, J. (2015). Lessons in urban monitoring taken from sustainable and livable cities to better address the smart cities initiative. *Technological Forecasting and Social Change*, *90*, 611–622. https://doi.org/10.1016/j.techfore.2014.01.012

Menon, A., & Jayawant, S. (2021). Designing sustainable tourism experiences for the tourists of tomorrow. In A. Chakrabarti, R. Poovaiah, P. Bokil, V. Kant (Eds.), *Design for tomorrow—Volume 2. Smart innovation, systems and technologies*, vol 222. Springer. https://doi.org/10.1007/978-981-16-0119-4_66

Muñoz-Torres, M. J., Fernández-Izquierdo, M., Rivera-Lirio, J. M., Ferrero-Ferrero, I., Escrig-Olmedo, E., Gisbert-Navarro, J. V., & Marullo, M. C. (2018) An assessment tool to integrate sustainability principles into the global supply chain. *Sustainability*, *10*, 535. https://doi.org/10.3390/su10020535

Nasiri, M., Rantala, T., Saunila, M., Ukko, J., & Rantanen, H. (2018). Transition towards sustainable solutions: Product, service, technology, and business model. *Sustainability*, *10*, 358. https://doi.org/10.3390/su10020358

Negrusa, A. L., Toader, V., Sofică, A., Tutunea, M. F., & Rus, R. V. (2015). Exploring gamification techniques and applications for sustainable tourism. *Sustainability*, *7*, 11160–11189. http://dx.doi.org/10.3390/su70811160

Neuhofer, B., Buhalis, D., & Ladkin, A. (2014). A typology of technology enhanced experiences, *International Journal of Tourism Research*, 16, 340–350. https://doi.org/10.1002/jtr.1958

Patrimonio Natural de Castilla y León (2022). Proyecto MOVELETUR, 'Turismo sostenible y movilidad eléctrica en espacios naturales'. https://patrimonionatural.org/proyectos/interreg-moveletur [Accessed 16 January 2022]

Pine, B. J., & Gilmore, J. H. (1998). Welcome to the experience economy. *Harvard Business Review*, *76*, 97–105.

Qin, Y., Huang, Y., Luo, S., & Miao, Y. (2020). Research on sustainable development of forest park tourism based on ASEB grid analysis. *IOP Conference Series: Earth and Environmental Science*, *585*. http://dx.doi.org/10.1088/1755-1315/585/1/012060

Ratten, V., Braga, V., Álvarez-García, J., & Del Río, M. D. L. C. (2019). *Tourism innovation: Technology, sustainability and creativity*.: Routledge.

Rezapouraghdam, H., Akhshik, A., & Ramkissoon, H. (2021). Application of machine learning to predict visitors' green behavior in marine protected areas: Evidence from Cyprus. *Journal of Sustainable Tourism*, http://dx.doi.org/10.1080/09669582.2021.1887878

Schmitt, B. (1999). Experiential marketing. *Journal of Marketing Management*, *15*, 53–67.

Scott, D. (2021). Sustainable tourism and the grand challenge of climate change. *Sustainability*, *13*(4), 1966. https://doi.org/10.3390/su13041966

Sharpley, R., & Stone, P. R. (2011). *Tourist experience: Contemporary perspectives*. Routledge.

Signorile, P., Larosa, V., & Spiru, A. (2018). Mobility as a service: A new model for sustainable mobility in tourism. *Worldwide Hospitality and Tourism Themes*, *10*(2), 185–200. https://doi.org/10.1108/WHATT-12-2017-0083

Stamboulis, Y., & Skayannis, P. (2003). Innovation strategies and technology for experience-based tourism. *Tourism Management*, 24, 35–43. https://doi.org/10.1016/S0261-5177(02)00047-X

Talafubieke, M., Mai, S., & Xialifuhan, N. (2021). Evaluation of the virtual economic effect of tourism product emotional marketing based on virtual reality. *Frontiers in Psychology*, 12. http://dx.doi.org/10.3389/fpsyg.2021.759268

Tyan, I., Yagüe, M. I., & Guevara-Plaza, A. (2020). Blockchain technology for smart tourism destinations. *Sustainability*, *12*, 9715. http://dx.doi.org/10.3390/su12229715

United Nations (2015). Resolution adopted by the General Assembly on 25 September 2015. Transforming our World: The 2030 Agenda for Sustainable Development, A/RES/70/1. https://www.un.org/en/development/desa/population/migration/generalassembly/docs/globalcompact/A_RES_70_1_E.pdf [Accessed 6 June 2022]

Wheaton, M., Ardoin, N. M., Hunt, C., Schuh, J. S., Kresse, M., Menke, C., & Durham, W. (2015). Using web and mobile technology to motivate pro-environmental action after a nature-based tourism experience. *Journal of Sustainable Tourism*, 1–22. http://dx.doi.org/10.1080/09669582.2015.1081600

World Tourism Organization – UNWTO (2018). *Community involvement needed in cultural tourism's digital transformation*. Available at https://www.unwto.org/global/press-release/2018-11-13/community-involvement-needed-cultural-tourism-s-digital-transformation-says [Accessed 20 June, 2022]

World Travel & Tourism Council (WTTC). (2019). *Annual report*. Available online: https://www.wttc.org/about/media-centre/press-releases/press-releases/2019/travel-tourism-continues-strong-growth-above-global-gdp/ [Accessed 19 June 2022]

Yang, C., Yan, S., Wang, J., & Xue, Y. (2022). Flow experiences and virtual tourism: The role of technological acceptance and technological readiness. *Sustainability*, *14*, 5361. https://doi.org/10.3390/su14095361

Zhang, L., Li, N., & Liu, M. (2012). On the basic concept of smarter tourism and its theoretical system. *Tourism. Tribune*, *5*, 66–73.

Zhuang, X., Hou, X., Feng, Z., Lin, Z., & Li, J. (2020). Subjective norms, attitudes, and intentions of AR technology used in tourism experience: The moderating effect of millennials. *Leisure Studies*, 1–15. https://doi.org/10.1080/02614367.2020.1843692

15 Conclusion

Future Prospects and the Way Forward

Xiang Ying Mei (Editor)

The experience economy is evolving, together with advancements in technology and changes in tourism behaviour. Therefore, the new exchange of currency and service will be based on companies helping consumers to achieve desired outcomes through experiences. With the constant need for stimulus to gain unique experiences, along with the reliance on technology, it is not surprising that the overall tourism ecosystem also needs to be adapted.

As illustrated in several chapters, changes in tourist behaviour led to the demand for a higher level of experience and these experiences are then shared on social networking sites (SNS). Moreover, the co-creation of value using technology is a way to accomplish such a goal. This also calls for changes in the tourism ecosystem where technology has now taken an important role to facilitate tourists' overall experience when on holiday. Technology may facilitate sustainable experiences formation as digitalisation and sustainability are not relevant not only in the tourism industry but also in the global society. Whether smart tourism and smart tourism destinations will be the norm for destinations, technologies and digitalisation will undoubtedly continue to play even more significant roles in tourism experiences.

What Is Next?

Technology and innovation will continue to develop and there is no concrete factual knowledge of what will be the next innovation that will influence and reshape the tourism experience. The world has already seen technologies such as Augmented Reality (AR) and Virtual Reality (VR) that challenge the need for the physical presence of tourists in order to experience immersion and absorption. Now there is the next level of chatbots that uses artificial intelligence (AI) such as ChatGPT, which opens up further innovation and possibilities that will impact the future experience economy. AI will elevate the possibilities of using robotics and integrating such technologies in every effort of service encounters in existing technologies, including self-service technologies (SSTs) and others. The question is however whether such solutions will impact the tourism industry and tourism experience in a possible manner. As illustrated in several chapters, although some positive outcomes including time and cost reduction and enhanced efficiency may occur, integrating too much technology too fast does not guarantee positive tourist experiences on the

DOI: 10.4324/9781003335924-19

users' side. Furthermore, technologies may be positively received and sought by some user groups while negatively perceived and experienced by others.

As human beings and human needs will continue to progress, so will the need for experiences and types of experiences evolve. Like any development, some types of commodities, products, services, and even experiences will reach the maturity stage. Thus, Pine and Gilmore (2011, 2019) suggested the fifth stage in the progression of economic value frameworks to be *transformation.* As mentioned in the introductory chapter, companies must now guide long-term personal transformation as the memorability and uniqueness of experiences are simply not enough anymore. It is thus suggested that the new economy in the experience economy is transformative experiences. The question is how tourism providers are going to facilitate such a personal transformation to occur through unique and memorable experiences and the role of technology in this process.

With the development of social media and user-generated content (UGC), there is no turning back as travellers who are reliant on eWOM (electronic word-of-mouth) will continue to be even more dependent on such technology and its possibilities. However, as emphasised, UGC and social media are not necessarily all positive for tourism providers such as hotels and other accommodation establishments and even destinations themselves. In recent years, much has been documented on the negative impact of online reviews due to false and untruthful reviews (Mei, 2022). Thus, consumers have become more sceptical and critical about such types of eWOM. Moreover, not everything presented on social media represents reality as pictures can be modified with filters in order to be presented in the best light. This leads to unrealistic expectations and thus disappointing and negative experiences.

The Impact of the Pandemic and Post-COVID

The impact of the pandemic on the world has been evident and tourism is one of the industries in the experience economy that really took a devastating hit. As illustrated in some of the chapters, technology and digital tools have facilitated many business operations due to social distancing and lockdowns. Some of such technologies will also continue to be relevant even post-COVID.

In terms of the tourism industry and experiences in general, during the pandemic, much was focused on the 'new normal' with destinations such as Venice and Barcelona getting used to not receiving massive groups of tourists and the consequences of such. For destination sustainability and sustainable tourism experiences, this was a positive development due to the destructive effect of overtourism over the years. The consequences of the pandemic are still lingering with a lack of staff at airports, airlines, and other services in the world's major airports leading to massive delays and missing connecting flights and luggage for travellers in the past year. This indicates that people's urges and thirst for unique experiences through travel and tourism have not seemed to be quenched. Rather, travellers are seeking to catch up for a lost time due the pandemic. It thus seems that the world is already heading back to the 'old normal'. The challenge now post-COVID is to seek a balance between the economic recovery by welcoming tourists back and considering the locals' needs and quality of life (Krizanovic, 2022). This is not only relevant for the most popular destinations, but any destinations where the tourism industry is a significant economic booster. The question is how technology can contribute to combat overtourism and how smart solutions can be implemented to relieve pressure on resources and infrastructure. Through travel apps in combination with AI and various ticket systems, it is perhaps possible to prevent the industry returning to its devastating pre-COVID stage in destinations challenged with overtourism (Globaldata Travel and Tourism, 2022).

Another development during the pandemic due to closed borders is people's newfound love and appreciation of local and domestic destinations by experiencing slow tourism and the outdoor life in nearby destinations that do not require long-distance travelling or travelling by air. It may also have been emphasised by the urge to seek escape, personal growth, health and well-being, and relationship building (Egger et al., 2020), as a consequence of the fast-pacing world pre-COVID. In line with such development, more people are realising the negative impact of a constant dependency on technology such as physical, mental, and social problems (Jiang & Balaji, 2022). Hence, there is a need for digital-free tourism and tourism spaces where individuals can disconnect from technology (Egger et al., 2020). This leads to the discovery of new destinations and tourism experiences. It will be interesting to see how the balance of technology reliance and abstaining from, or limiting usage of, digital tools can be achieved and whether such development will also continue to shape the future experience economy.

Implications for Future Research and Practices

Future research interests are raised through the chapters and cases, including understanding how tourist behaviour changes in line with digitalisation or how technology has changed consumer behaviour. Other more concrete topics as future research agenda include as follows:

- New use of social media in experience expectation and formation
- Shifts in tourism ecosystem and its impact on tourism experience formation and value co-creation
- New type of destinations, travellers, and tourism experiences to counteract the dependency on technology
- Immersion and transformation of experiences with the aid of technology, digitalisation, and digital tools
- Adapting technology to various types of consumers and those who are technology adverse
- New social trends and demographic that changes travel behaviours
- Customer experience innovation and the role of tourism and hospitality providers
- Sustainable experience formation through digital aids in various economies

References

Egger, I., Lei, S. I., & Wassler, P. (2020). Digital free tourism – An exploratory study of tourist motivations. *Tourism Management*, *79*, 104098. https://doi.org/10.1016/j.tourman.2020.104098

Globaldata Travel and Tourism. (2022). *Smart city solutions are vital to combat overtourism*. https://www.hotelmanagement-network.com/comment/smart-city-combat-overtourism/

Jiang, Y., & Balaji, M. S. (2022). Getting unwired: What drives travellers to take a digital detox holiday? *Tourism Recreation Research*, *47*(5–6), 453–469. https://doi.org/10.1080/02508281.2021.1889801

Krizanovic, P. (2022). *Barcelona looks for balance when welcoming post-covid tourism*. https://skift.com/2022/06/24/barcelona-looks-for-balance-when-welcoming-post-covid-tourism/

Mei, X. Y. (2022). The impact of negative online reviews (NORs) on hospitality micro enterprise (ME) owners. *Anatolia*, 1–3. https://doi.org/10.1080/13032917.2022.2119592

Pine, B. J., & Gilmore, J. H. (2011). *The experience economy: Updated edition*. Harvard Business Press.

Pine, B. J., & Gilmore, J. H. (2019). *The experience economy, with a new preface by the authors: Competing for customer time, attention, and money*. Harvard Business Press.

Index

Note: *Italicized* and **bold** pages refer to figures and tables respectively, and page numbers followed by "n" refer to notes.

For Product Safety Concerns and Information please contact our EU representative GPSR@taylorandfrancis.com
Taylor & Francis Verlag GmbH, Kaufingerstraße 24, 80331 München, Germany

www.ingramcontent.com/pod-product-compliance
Lightning Source LLC
Chambersburg PA
CBHW060254220326
41598CB00027B/4101
* 9 7 8 1 0 3 2 3 7 2 1 8 1 *